COLLIER QUICK AND EASY SERIES

ELECTRONICS

IMPROVE PRACTICAL OR VOCATIONAL SKILLS
SUPPLEMENT YOUR FORMAL EDUCATION
GET MORE FUN OUT OF HOBBIES

This Collier guide is designed to offer concise, authoritative information in a clear, readable manner. Carefully prepared with the latest, up-to-the-minute material, it is also valuable as a source for permanent reference. Titles in The Quick and Easy series include—

AMERICAN HISTORY
Robert Sobel, Ph.D.

ARITHMETIC
Simon Dresner

BOOKKEEPING
Morton D. Bluestone, M.A.

BOWLING
Hal and Jean Vermes

CARPENTRY
Clarence Herisko

CHESS
Richard Roberts

DRIVING
Edward A. McInroy, M.A.

ECONOMICS FOR BUSINESSMEN AND INVESTORS
George G. Dawson, Ph.D., and Russell H. McClain, Ph.D.

EFFECTIVE BUSINESS CORRESPONDENCE
Abraham Ellenbogen

EFFECTIVE SPEAKING
Bernice Loren

ELECTRONICS
Jesse Dilson

COMPLETE GUIDE TO GOOD MANNERS IN BUSINESS AND SOCIAL LIFE
Dorothy Sara

FAMILY CAMPING
William P. Luce

GOLF
Robert Scharff

HI FI AND STEREO
Richard Roberts

HOME IMPROVEMENT AND MAINTENANCE
Martin Sara

HOME NURSING CARE
Lucille Gidsey, R.N., and Dorothy Sara

HUNTING
Robert Scharff

INSURANCE
Martin Cornwall

LAW
Jesse Raphael, LL.B.

MAGIC
Hal G. Vermes

MAKING HOME MOVIES
Bob Knight

MOTOR BOATING
Robert Scharff

PHYSICAL FITNESS
Justus Schifferes, Ph.D.

PLAYING THE GUITAR
Frederick M. Noad

RAPID READING
Myron Q. Herrick, The Reading Laboratory, Inc.

RUNNING A MEETING
Jack T. Parker

SELLING PERSON-TO-PERSON
Hal G. Vermes

SEWING
Dorothy Stepat De Van

SKIING WITH CONTROL
Rick Shambroom and Betty Slater

TENNIS
Robert Scharff

TV WRITING
George Lowther

WATER SKIING
Glen E. Anderson

WORLD HISTORY
Edwin Dunbaugh, Ph.D.

COLLIER QUICK AND EASY SERIES

ELECTRONICS

JESSE DILSON, B.S.

JESSE DILSON, B.S.
SENIOR MEMBER, INSTITUTE OF ELECTRICAL AND ELECTRONICS ENGINEERS

COLLIER BOOKS, NEW YORK
COLLIER-MACMILLAN LTD., LONDON

Originally published under the title
*The Collier Quick and
Easy Guide to Electronics*

Library of Congress Catalog Card Number: 62-16972

First Edition 1962
Second Printing 1966

The Macmillan Company
Collier-Macmillan Canada Ltd., Toronto, Ontario

Printed in the United States of America

FOREWORD

THIS BOOK has been written for people who want a simple introduction to a possible career in electronics, and for those others who realize that in a technology-dominated world the inhabitants ought to know more about science.

There is nothing mysterious about any science, and certainly none about electronics. Unlike the biologist, for example, who must take the subjects of his study as he finds them, the electronics engineer *creates* the subjects of his. Radio, television, radar, computers were not discovered; they were invented. They were conceived in logic and from logical beginnings. If the reader will think logically as he reads these pages, he will find that the mysteries will vanish, and that electronics can indeed be self-taught.

A useful feature of this book is the glossary which concludes each chapter. The glossary fulfills a double function: it serves, in effect, as a summary of the material of the chapter; it also helps clarify the material by bringing into sharper focus the meaning of its technical terms. All these terms and their definitions are assembled in an appendix to provide the reader with a built-in electronics dictionary.

JESSE DILSON

NOTE

IN THE following pages, frequent use is made of such expressions as "a-c voltage" and "d-c voltage," where a-c stands for alternating current and d-c for direct current.

Strictly speaking, such language is rather foolish; an electrical quantity is either current or voltage, not both. But the use of these terms is so deeply rooted in the professional lives of engineers and technicians alike, that it is equally foolish to avoid using them. The terms may be unscientific, but their meaning is clear.

JD

CONTENTS

Chapter One

THE ELECTRON

SHORTLY AFTER Thomas Edison invented his incandescent lamp, he performed an experiment with it which helped bring the electron to the attention of the world. Into the glass bulb of the lamp he sealed a metal plate wired in series with a battery and an ammeter. Then he turned on the current to light up the lamp filament, and observed some strange results: when the positive pole of the battery was connected to the metal plate inside the bulb, the ammeter showed that an electric current was flowing through the series circuit; but when the battery connections were reversed, the ammeter registered zero.

Reasoning from the basic electrical law that like charges repel and opposite charges attract, Edison was able to interpret clearly the results of his experiment. Current could flow through the circuit because electrified particles crossed the gap between the two electrodes in the lamp. These particles could only have been urged across the gap by the force of attraction of the plate when it was positive. They must therefore have been negatively charged. With the reversal of the battery connections, the plate in the bulb was given a negative potential; it then repelled the negative particles to halt their movement from the filament, and current ceased to flow.

Later experimenters confirmed this explanation of the

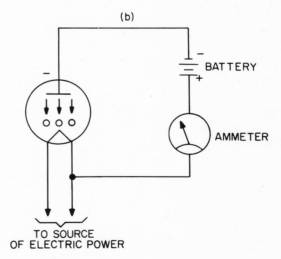

Fig. 1.1. *The Edison Effect:* In (a), electrons from the filament are attracted to the positive plate, and the ammeter needle indicates current flow in the circuit. In (b) the electrons are repelled by the negative plate, and the ammeter needle indicates zero current.

"Edison effect" and further discovered that these invisible particles of negative electricity—which they termed *electrons*—are so tiny as to have only 1/1800 the mass of the lightest atom, the atom of hydrogen.

Thermionic Emission

The modern theory of heat helps us understand where the electrons in Edison's lamp came from in the first place. According to this theory, the atoms of a hot object are in constant vibration; the higher the temperature of the object, the greater the energy of vibration of its atoms.

Atomic theory provides the final clue. The atom consists of a nucleus around which electrons continuously circle, much as the planets of the solar system circle around the sun. In the heavier atoms, like those in the metal filament of the electric light bulb, the outermost of these electrons are so distant from the nucleus that they can be shaken free of the atom if only the atom vibrates strongly enough. The intense heat of the brilliantly burning filament provides more than enough energy for that.

This method of producing electrons through heat is called *thermionic emission*. The cloud of free electrons around the incandescent filament of an electric light bulb serves no purpose whatever, but the electrons emitted from the hot element of the electron tube make a good. many modern miracles possible.

Ionization

The glass bulb of an electric light is supposed to enclose a complete vacuum, but the pump that can totally evacuate a bulb has yet to be devised. Some traces of air, at least a few molecules, are sure to remain. If one of these molecules should get in the way of a speeding electron, the force of the impact is likely to drive one or more of the electrons out of an atom in the molecule. Since the atom is electrically neutral to begin with, the loss of an electron will endow it with a positive charge. Such a charged atom is called an *ion,* and the process which creates it is known as ionization.

It may also happen that an atom of gas may capture an oncoming electron without losing any of its own. Having thus been given an extra negative charge, the atom becomes a negative ion. Aside from electron collisions, ionization can take place through other means. Powerful radiation like X-rays or the mysterious cosmic rays emanating from outer space can act as ionizing agents.

Under certain conditions, ionization can be very useful in electronics. In fact, as one of the following chapters will show, small amounts of gas are deliberately introduced into some types of electron tubes to insure that extensive ionization will occur.

GLOSSARY

Ammeter. An instrument for measuring electric current.

Atom. Smallest unit of a chemical element.

Electrode. A metal body capable of having an electric charge.

Electron. A subatomic particle of negative charge.

Filament. The hot wire in a vacuum tube.

Ion. An atom with an electric charge.

Molecule. A group of atoms.

Nucleus. The center of the atom.

Plate. The electrode in a vacuum tube which collects electrons.

Potential. Degree of electrification of a body.

Chapter Two

THE FIRST ELECTRON TUBE

THE INCANDESCENT LAMP which Edison used to demonstrate the effect named for him was not merely a scientific curiosity. As his successors were quick to discover, the lamp with its sealed-in plate could function as a *rectifier*—a device for converting alternating voltage into direct current. Modern electronic engineers know that the rectifier, because it can change a-c into d-c, is valuable in at least one type of circuit, the *power supply*.

The power supply is a necessity in almost every type of electronic equipment. Whether the equipment contains vacuum tubes or transistors, it must have a dependable source of d-c voltage to feed those tubes and transistors and keep them working properly. That source of d-c voltage is as urgently needed in the table-top home radio receiver as it is in gigantic radar installations. Most homes in the United States are supplied with 60 cycle a-c power; military installations are equipped with a-c generators furnishing 60 or 400 cycle power. Before either of these power sources can be used to operate the simple radio receiver or the complex radar system, they must first be converted to d-c by well-designed power supplies. This chapter will show how the modern power supply circuit is put together and how it works.

The Diode Rectifier

The modern vacuum tube rectifier differs from Edison's experimental lamp only in some minor details. Connections to the filament and the plate are now brought out to metal prongs at the base of the tube; the filament is usually coated with barium and strontium oxides, materials which emit electrons in generous quantities when heated; and the tube is sturdier and more compact than

its ancestor. But the two essential electrodes, the filament and plate, still remain. Because of its two electrodes, the modern rectifier is known as a *diode*.

The Edison effect experiment can be repeated in a slightly different way to show how the diode performs its rectifying function. The first change, of course, is to substitute a modern diode for the Edison lamp with its sealed-in plate; the second, to replace the battery with an a-c generator. Since the generator goes first through a positive and then a negative voltage phase, its use relieves the experimenter of the need for changing the battery connections. Assuming that the needle of the ammeter is capable of following the variations of the current which will then flow, what will the ammeter indicate?

Without actually performing the experiment, we can easily predict its results. As the generator goes into its positive phase, the plate of the diode becomes increasingly positive. A steadily increasing flow of electrons will then be attracted to the plate and the ammeter will show an increasing current. As the generator voltage falls to zero, the current through the circuit will similarly drop. During the time the generator goes through the negative part of its cycle, the plate of the diode repels the electrons emitted by the filament, and the ammeter shows zero current flow for that interval. Thus, although the voltage of the generator has changed its direction, the flow of current through the diode and its series circuit has been restricted to a single direction.

If we make another change in this diode circuit and replace the ammeter with a resistor, we find that the voltage drop across the resistor varies in the same way as the current flowing through it. That voltage will rise and fall with the current, but will not change its polarity

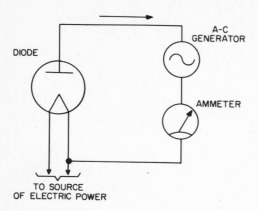

Fig. 2.1. *Edison Effect, Second Version:* The battery is replaced by an a-c generator. Current flows in the direction of the arrow when the generator terminal connected to the plate is positive; no current flows when the plate-connected pole is negative.

because the current creating it does not change direction. A voltage like this, which varies in quantity but not in polarity, is called a *pulsating d-c* voltage. When we take the final step of filling the gaps between the pulsations in the voltage across the resistor, we will have succeeded in designing a circuit to convert the alternating voltage of the a-c generator into a d-c voltage—a voltage which maintains its polarity and is fairly constant in quantity.

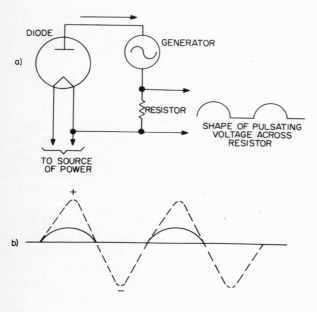

Fig. 2.2. *Edison Effect, Third Version:* The schematic diagram of the circuit is shown in (a), with a resistor now replacing the ammeter. Diagram (b) indicates how the pulsating voltage across the resistor is generated: dotted line represents positive and negative variations of generator voltage; solid line represents current flow through resistor.

The Filter

A device which smooths those pulsations into a fairly steady voltage is the *filter*. At least one element of the electrical filter is the *choke,* a coil of wire wound around an iron core. The choke, being made of an unbroken conductor, can carry current, but it tends to oppose changes in that current, much as a heavy piece of furniture tends to resist efforts to move it. Through this electrical obstinacy, the choke is useful in helping to smooth out the pulsations of the current through the resistor.

But the choke alone cannot carry out the filtering process successfully. It needs the help of one or more *capacitors*. Basically, the capacitor consists of two metal plates separated by a non-conducting material called the dielectric. This construction enables the capacitor to absorb an electric charge and hold it for some time. In

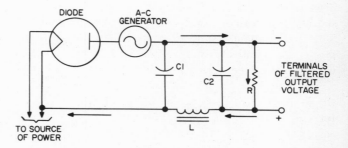

Fig. 2.3. *The Filter Added:* The filter is composed of a choke (L) and two capacitors (C_1, C_2). Electronic current flow is indicated by the arrows; the point at which electronic current enters a resistor is always negative.

effect, the device works like a mechanical shock absorber; just as a shock absorber shields a vehicle from holes and bumps in the road, the capacitor helps keep the voltage across the resistor at a constant level.

The Half-Wave Power Supply

What we now have, in our circuit of the diode, the resistor, the filter, and the a-c generator, is a fairly simple arrangement known as the *half-wave power supply*. This circuit, or a slight variation, is used in the ac-dc type of table-top home radio receiver where the a-c generator is the 60 cycle power main terminating in the home wall socket. Other than that, there is no really important difference between the ac-dc power supply and the circuit just described. For anything bigger than the ac-dc radio receiver, however, this half-wave power supply is hardly satisfactory. One of its handicaps is that the d-c voltage it develops is not high enough; another that it is somewhat inefficient.

A remedy for the first defect is to multiply the voltage

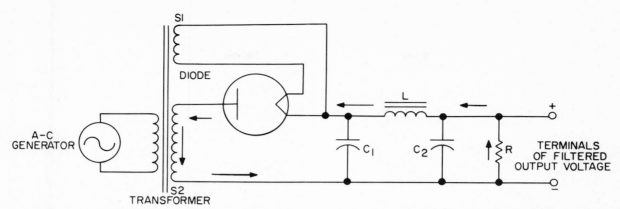

Fig. 2.4. *The Half-Wave Power Supply:* The stepped-up voltage of the large secondary winding (S_2) is applied to the diode plate. The small step-down secondary winding (S_1) supplies power to the diode filament. Arrows show direction of current flow.

of the a-c generator by connecting a *step-up transformer* between the generator and the diode rectifier. The step-up transformer consists of two separate coils of wire wound about a single iron core. Its primary winding, a comparatively small number of turns of heavy wire, is connected across the terminals of a wall plug which, plugged into the wall outlet, takes the place of the a-c generator. The secondary winding, with many turns of finer wire, is connected to the diode. Since the secondary has several times the number of turns of the primary, the a-c voltage delivered to the diode is a multiple of the voltage of the power mains. The d-c voltage output of the power supply is therefore increased.

Besides raising the voltage produced by the circuit, the transformer offers another advantage. If it is equipped with another secondary winding, one with just a few turns of wire, it can produce a small a-c voltage sufficient to keep the filament of the diode rectifier hot. This method of connecting the *stepped-down* a-c voltage to the heater terminals of the rectifier tube is a common feature of the modern power supply.

The Full-Wave Power Supply

While the transformer increases the d-c output of the half-wave power supply, it does little to improve its efficiency. Since only a single diode is used, the power supply can function properly during the positive half of the input a-c voltage cycle; it is idle for the negative half. Therefore the name "half-wave" is given to the circuit, and hence its inefficiency. The half-wave power supply operates like the factory worker who tries to do his job with only one hand.

The power supply is enormously improved when it is converted from a half-wave to a *full-wave* circuit. This is done by adding a second diode and tapping the center

of the step-up transformer secondary winding to provide a return path for the currents of the two diodes.

The second diode is wired into the circuit in substantially the same way as the first. Where the plate of the first diode is connected to one terminal of the transformer step-up secondary, the plate of its companion is connected to the opposite terminal. Electrons flow in the first diode when, during one phase of the a-c voltage across the secondary, the plate of that diode is positive. In that same interval the plate of the second diode is negative and the second diode cannot conduct. Upon reversal of the a-c phase, the action of the circuit seesaws: now the plate of the second diode becomes positive and current begins to flow through it; the plate of the first diode turns negative and current through it is blocked. Our factory worker is now using both hands.

Modern Power Supplies

The full-wave circuit is the most common type of power supply used in electronic equipment. While the power supply in a television receiver is fairly simple when compared to the ones used in bigger installations, the full-wave rectification, with similar filtering, prevails in most equipments.

Tube manufacturers have helped power supply design engineers by fabricating a *duo-diode rectifier*. This device has two diodes conveniently combined in a single tube. Each of the two plates in the tube is connected separately to a prong at its base. Although schematic diagrams usually represent the tube as having a single filament, there are actually two filaments, connected in series, each surrounded by a plate. The terminals of this filament series arrangement are wired to a third and fourth base prong.

Additional economies in space and price have been achieved by capacitor manufacturers. The capacitors

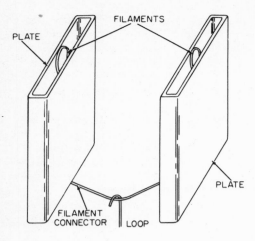

Fig. 2.5. *Construction of Duo-Diode Rectifier:* **The two filaments are connected in series, with the connecting wire frequently clamped against vibration by a loop, as shown. Each of the terminals at either end of the filaments is soldered to a prong at the base of the tube.**

in the filter of the modern power supply are usually of the electrolytic type, which operate through electrochemical action. Thanks to the chemistry of the electrolytic, its dielectric is an exceedingly thin film of nonconducting material. It is therefore possible to pack a large electrical capacitance into comparatively little space. A peculiarity of this type of capacitor is that its terminal wires are marked with a plus or a minus sign to indicate polarity. The technician replacing a faulty electrolytic capacitor in a power supply must be careful to connect the plus terminal of the capacitor to the

positive terminal of the supply; if he is not, something is likely to burn out.

The resistor in the power supply also deserves a note. Since it usually carries heavy currents, it is bound to get fairly hot and must be ruggedly constructed. Often, it is tapped—or "bled"—at several points along its length to provide d-c voltages at various levels; hence the term "bleeder."

The power supply, like most electronic equipment, is usually built on a metal chassis. To save lengths of wire between mutually connecting wire terminals in the unit—the negative connections of the electrolytics, for example—equipment manufacturers simply solder the proper terminals to the handiest point on the chassis. Since it is fabricated of a single metal sheet, the chassis can be depended upon to conduct electric currents well. This practice is not by any means confined to the manufacture of power supplies; it is followed in building many types of electronic devices.

GLOSSARY

Bleeder resistor.   The resistor connected between the positive and negative terminals of a power supply.
Capacitor.   An electronic component consisting of two metal plates separated by a nonconductor.
Chassis.   The metal base on which most electronic equipment is built.
Choke.   An electrical component usually consisting of a coil of wire wound around an iron core.
Component.   A part in an electrical circuit.

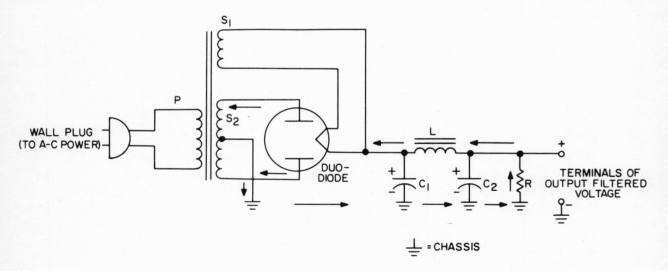

Fig. 2.6. *The Full-Wave Power Supply:* **Arrows show the direction of d-c current flow. When the top diode plate is positive, current is drawn from filament to plate which flows through the center tap of the high-voltage secondary** (S₂) **and chassis. When the a-c voltage at the top diode plate turns negative, the voltage at the bottom plate becomes positive and draws current. Capacitors C₁ and C₂ are electrolytics; R is the bleeder.**

Current. The flow of electrons through a circuit.

Cycle. A complete positive and negative alternation of a-c voltage.

Dielectric. The non-conducting element in a capacitor.

Diode. A vacuum tube with two active electrodes.

Duo-diode. A vacuum tube containing a double diode.

Electrolytic. A type of capacitor with permanent polarity markings.

Filter. A circuit consisting of a choke and one or more capacitors.

Full-wave power supply. A power supply using two diodes which draw current during both the positive and negative half-cycles of the input a-c voltage.

Half-wave power supply. A power supply using a single diode which draws current during one phase of the input alternating voltage.

Oxide. A chemical coating usually applied to the electron-producing element in an electronic tube.

Power supply. An electronic circuit which converts an input a-c voltage into an output d-c voltage.

Primary. The input winding of a transformer.

Pulsating d-c. An electric current which flows in a single direction and varies in intensity.

Resistor. A component which opposes the flow of a-c and d-c current.

Schematic. A drawing using conventional symbols which shows the connection of components in a circuit.

Secondary. The output winding of a transformer.

Step-down transformer. A component consisting of two coupled coils in which the output voltage is less than the input voltage.

Step-up transformer. A component consisting of two coupled coils in which the output voltage is greater than the input voltage.

Voltage. Electromotive force; the electrical force required to push current through a circuit.

Chapter Three

AM DETECTION

IF THE DIODE, working at the power frequencies of 60 and 400 cycles per second, is so extremely useful in the power supply, it can be equally useful in the *detector*— a circuit which operates at the much higher radio frequencies. The detector is essential not only in the home radio receiver, but in every electronic system in which electromagnetic waves are transmitted across large distances.

The function of the detector, briefly, is to extract meaningful content from a transmitted signal. How it performs this function can best be discovered by examining one type of transmission, the amplitude-modulated or AM signal.

Amplitude Modulation

The business of a radio station is to transmit sound, in some form, by electrical means. The first step in this process is to convert the sound into an electrical signal. This is done by a *microphone,* which transforms the sound waves into correspondingly varying voltage, and by an *audio amplifier* which strengthens that voltage. If both the microphone and amplifier are high-fidelity devices, the electrical wave-form put out by the amplifier will be undistorted—that is, it will correspond very closely to the sound waves creating it.

Some means must be used to transmit this audio signal to the antennas of home radio receivers. Any attempt to transmit the audio signal directly would be doomed to failure under ordinary conditions. An average audio signal has a frequency of 5,000 cycles per second. To transmit a signal of this frequency efficiently would require an antenna twenty miles high! The next best method is to impress the audio signal on a second

signal of much higher frequency known as the *carrier*. With its high frequency, the carrier can be efficiently transmitted using much smaller components.

One method of impressing the audio signal on the carrier is that known as *amplitude modulation*. In this method, the peaks of the carrier wave are elongated or shortened in accordance with the variations of the sound to be transmitted. If an intense sound should strike the microphone in the studio, there will be a marked difference between the heights of the elongated and shortened carrier wave peaks; if the sound at the microphone is weak, the peaks of the carrier wave will be more nearly equal. The word "peak" is the common equivalent of the engineering term "amplitude"; modulation is the act of changing. Hence, amplitude modulation is the act of changing the peaks of the carrier signal in the same way that the audio signal varies.

Pictorially, the audio signal can be represented by

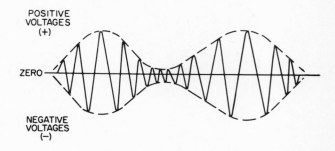

POSITIVE VOLTAGES (+)

ZERO

NEGATIVE VOLTAGES (−)

Fig. 3.1. *Representation of the AM Signal:* The horizontal line represents zero signal voltage; distances above the line correspond to positive voltages, those below the line to negative voltages. Solid lines indicate the carrier, dotted lines the audio signal.

a continuous curve touching the peaks of the carrier wave. The negative peaks of the carrier are modulated in the same way as the positive peaks. Consequently, a representation of the audio signal by one curve tangent to the positive peaks of the carrier, and another curve tangent to the negative peaks, will show *two* audio signals, one the mirror image of the other. These two audio signals are completely opposite in phase, one of them rising at the same moment the other is falling.

This is the way the carrier arrives at the antenna of the AM radio receiver. The audio signal is the meaningful signal, it represents the sound the listener wants to hear. If the detector circuit in the receiver extracts both audio signals from the modulated carrier, the two signals will oppose each other, and nothing will be heard from the receiver's loudspeaker. It is then necessary to make use of only the positive half-cycles of the modulated carrier and to ignore the negative half-cycles. This operation, as we have seen in the preceding chapter, is one which the diode is suited to perform.

The Detector Circuit

The detector circuit is made up of the secondary winding of a transformer, a diode, and a resistor, connected in series. A small capacitor shunts the resistor. Except for one detail—the construction of the transformer—the circuit closely resembles that of the half-wave power supply, (see Chapter 2). Because it is required to handle low power frequencies of 60 or 400 cycles per second, a transformer should have a compact iron core to operate efficiently. However for the comparatively high frequency voltages of the AM carrier, the transformer with an air or powdered iron core is best.

When the alternating voltage of the AM carrier is applied to the primary of the detector circuit transformer, a voltage of the same frequency appears across the terminals of the secondary winding. On positive half-cycles of this signal, the plate of the diode is positive, and current flows through the series circuit; on negative half-cycles, no current is drawn. If there were no shunting capacitor, the voltage developed across the resistor in the circuit would then consist of a series of pulses of various heights corresponding to the positive half-cycles of the carrier. However, the "shock-absorbing" ability of the capacitor prevents the voltage across the resistor from dropping all the way to zero between pulses. Instead, it guarantees a gradual transition of the voltage from one pulse peak to the next, so that the voltage across the resistor will have substantially the same shape as the audio signal. The capacitor, in effect, has *bypassed* the high frequency carrier wave away from the resistor, leaving only the much lower frequency audio voltage to appear across it. This resistor, incidentally, is often called the load resistor of the detector circuit since it carries the end-product, or load, of the circuit's work.

The Detector Diode

In the AM radio receiver, the audio voltage developed across the detector load resistor is amplified to proper strength, and is then applied to a loudspeaker where it is translated into audible sound. The detector diode is therefore in a sensitive position. Any electrical disturbance it generates will come through the loudspeaker as noise.

If the diode in the detector circuit is a simple fila-

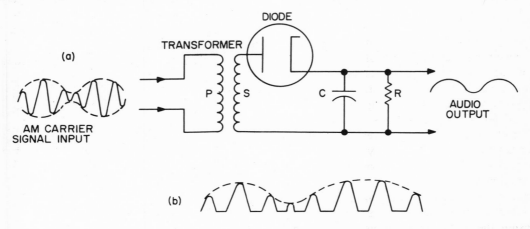

Fig. 3.2. *The Detector Circuit:* (a) Current is drawn in the diode on positive half-cycles of the AM carrier signal. The absence of parallel lines between the primary (P) and the secondary windings (S) indicates that the transformer is air-cored. R and C are the load resistor and shunt capacitor respectively. The heater of the cathode-plate diode is not shown; (b) The appearance of the load voltage if the shunt capacitors were absent. The dotted curve shows the voltage when the capacitor is included.

ment-plate type, it will produce an audio signal; but it is also likely to contaminate that signal with a 60 cycle voltage. This undesirable voltage will be heard at the loudspeaker as a low-pitched, annoying hum. The trouble can be traced to the filament of the diode. When a 60 cycle current is passed through a filament for heating purposes, a 60 cycle voltage appears across its terminals. This voltage is communicated to the plate through the electron stream, and shows up across the detector load resistor. To eliminate the hum problem, it is necessary to deprive the filament of its job of producing electrons, and reduce it to the role of merely supplying heat. In most modern tubes—the exception is the duo-diode power supply rectifier discussed in the preceding chapter—the electron-producing element is the *cathode*, a small, usually cylindrical metal piece which surrounds but does not touch the filament. The cathode is painted with an electron-rich oxide coating, and supplies quantities of electrons for the operation of the tube when it is heated by the filament.

As for the filament itself, it is no longer part of the detector—or whatever circuit the tube is designed to service; in fact, it is often omitted altogether from schematic drawings. In recognition of its simple single function, engineers often refer to it as the *heater*. The tube is still called a diode even though it actually contains three electrodes, because only the cathode and plate are active in the circuit work.

A Simple AM Radio Receiver

In a sense, the detector circuit is the most important circuit in the AM radio receiver, while all the other circuits are fancy trimmings. This, of course, is an exaggeration, but it is possible to build a receiver with barely more than the detector circuit. The receiver may be found wanting in some respects, but it will work!

The first step is to rig up some device to catch the modulated carrier signals transmitted by a local AM station. This device is called the *antenna*. For the sim-

ple receiver we propose, the antenna should consist of a good, long string of wire, insulated from its supports. One terminal of the primary winding in the transformer of the detector circuit is now wired to the antenna; the other terminal of the primary is connected to something—a radiator pipe, for example—which is in good electrical contact with the earth. When this is done, the circuit between the antenna of the AM transmitter, the antenna of the receiver, and the ground between the two will be completed, and an alternating AM carrier current will flow through the primary winding of the detector transformer.

The detector circuit will then do its work, and an audio voltage will appear across the load resistor. To convert the audio voltage into sound, a pair of headphones connected between the resistor terminals is necessary. A loudspeaker cannot be used simply because the output of an unaided detector circuit lacks the power to move the diaphragm of the speaker. The listener can now use the headphones and hear the transmission of the local station.

The Resonant Circuit

If there is more than one AM station in the listener's area, however, he will find that his crude receiver picks up the transmissions of all stations simultaneously. His headphones will vibrate with a jumble of music, political discussions, and commercials. What he needs is a station selector, something which will permit him to choose just one transmitter at a time.

The station selector he can use is a *variable capacitor*—or *condenser,* as capacitors are sometimes called. The variable capacitor consists of two sets of meshed metal plates, one of which can be rotated within the other. By wiring the variable capacitor across the secondary terminals of the detector transformer, the listener creates a *resonant circuit* consisting of the secondary winding of the transformer and the capacitor. For any one setting of the variable capacitor rotor plates, the coil and capacitor combination will resonate best to the transmission of a particular station.

The phenomenon of *resonance* is one which occurs almost everywhere in nature. It occurs in sound just as in electricity. Resonance in sound can be shown by a simple experiment: if a note is sung near the strings in a piano—the experimenter must keep one foot on the loud pedal to hold the dampers off the strings—the string which normally produces that note will vibrate in sympathy, and the experimenter will hear that same note "played." In this experiment, only the string of the proper length and thickness to produce that tone will vibrate; the others will remain practically inaudible.

The same sort of sympathetic vibration occurs in our

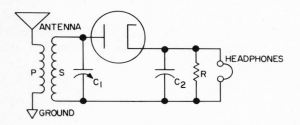

Fig. 3.3. *The Crude Receiver:* The variable capacitor C_1 and the secondary (S) of the transformer are the resonant circuit. C_2 is the shunt capacitor of the detector circuit. The diode heater, not shown, is connected to an a-c voltage source.

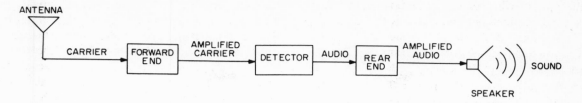

Fig. 3.4. *Simplified Block Diagram of the Radio Receiver:* The forward end selects and amplifies the carrier; the detector extracts the audio signal; the audio amplifier strengthens the audio signal; the speaker translates the audio signal into sound. NOTE: Block diagrams like these are a simple and convenient way of indicating the important sections of electronic equipment, and the progress of signals from one section to the next. These diagrams frequently omit the power supply, which is always understood to be present.

simple radio receiver: the resonant circuit of coil and capacitor corresponds to the vibrating piano string, and the transmission of the AM station corresponds to the experimenter's voice. When the rotor plates of the variable capacitor are set so that the resonant frequency of the coil and capacitor combination equals the carrier frequency of the station, the voltage across the terminals of the combination will be at a *maximum* for that frequency. That voltage will be applied to the plate of the detector diode, and the headphones of the crude receiver will hear only the audio signal of the carrier to which the resonant circuit is tuned.

R-F and Audio Amplifiers

Obviously, this one-tube receiver has its defects. For one thing, it has trouble distinguishing between two stations with neighboring carrier frequencies; in technical terms, its *selectivity* is poor. For another, its use of headphones allows only one listener to hear the transmitted program.

Redesigning the detector circuit will do little toward improving the selectivity of this simple receiver. The best solution is to insert several circuits between the antenna and the detector. At least one of these circuits should be a radio frequency amplifier, which multiplies the tuned-in carrier voltage. In strengthening the signal of the chosen station, the r-f amplifier weakens the transmissions of interfering ones in comparison. By the same token, the r-f amplifier intensifies the feeble reception of distant stations to improve the sensitivity of the receiver.

The problem of allowing many people to hear the broadcast simultaneously is solved by using a loudspeaker. But "driving" a speaker requires much more audio power than the detector alone can supply. The answer, then, is to install an audio amplifier at the detector output to bring the audio signal up to sufficient strength. Circuits between the antenna and the detector might be termed the forward end of the receiver, and the audio amplifier the rear end.

Radio and Television

While the basic principles of FM (frequency modulated) radio differ radically from those of AM radio, the receivers in both systems are essentially the same. Each is equipped with an antenna to pick up the transmitted signal, a forward end to amplify the signal, a detector to extract the audio from the modulated carrier, an audio amplifier to strengthen the audio signal and finally a speaker to convert the electrical audio energy into sound.

With a few simple changes, the same essential set-up can be applied to the television receiver. Because television also transmits pictures in addition to sound, its transmitters must therefore generate two carrier signals. One of these carriers conveys the signal to the receiver which, in the end, will be heard. This signal is called the audio signal ("audio" is Latin for "I hear"). It is

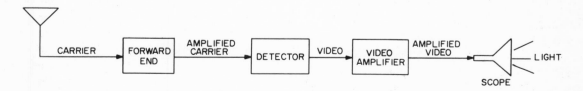

Fig. 3.5. *Simplified Block Diagram of the TV and Radar Receivers:* This block diagram is characteristic of the video channel in TV and radar receivers. It corresponds to the basic block diagram of the radio set.

extracted from its carrier, amplified, and applied to a loudspeaker in generally the same fashion as that just described for radio. The second carrier is impressed with a *video* (Latin for "I see") signal which, in the end, will be seen. The carrier of the video signal goes through the same basic process in the receiver as the sound carrier: it is first amplified; then, in a circuit almost exactly like the one described in this chapter, is discarded in favor of the signal it carries. The device which finally converts the amplified video signal into a picture with light and dark elements is the giant tube which, to the layman is the "picture" tube, and to the television engineer, the *kinescope*.

Radar

Many radar devices combine a transmitter and a receiver into a single unit using the same antenna. The transmitter emits high frequency radio waves in short, repeated bursts which are in effect the carrier of the radar transmitter. If some object—a ship, an airplane, even a bird—is in the vicinity of the transmitter, that body reflects those bursts back to the radar antenna, as if the radar transmitter were a searchlight and the object the reflector of its beams. The returning bursts are then amplified in the forward end of the radar receiver and, in a detector circuit, are discarded in favor of the pulse modulations they carry. The pulses are amplified in the rear end of the receiver and are finally brought to a "scope" to be translated into light. By viewing and interpreting these pulses as they appear on the screen of the scope, the radar operator can get the information he wants—the direction in which the object caught in the radar's beam lies, and its distance from the radar station. Hence the name radar, formed from the initial letters of "RAdio Direction And Range."

GLOSSARY

Air core transformer. A transformer of two or more windings around a hollow non-magnetic form.

Amplitude. The peak of an a-c current or voltage wave.

Amplitude modulation. A system of radio transmission in which the amplitude of a carrier is varied in accordance with a meaningful signal.

Antenna. A metal structure or wire which picks up or transmits electromagnetic energy through space.

Audio. An electric signal corresponding to sound.

Audio amplifier. An electronic device to strengthen the audio signal.

Bypass capacitor. A capacitor which routes a-c current around another component.

Carrier. A high frequency signal upon which a meaningful signal is impressed.

Cathode. The element in a vacuum tube which emits electrons.

Condenser. Common term for a capacitor.

Detector. A circuit which extracts the meaningful (audio or video) signal from the carrier.

Distortion. Variation in the output signal of an amplifier as compared with the input signal.

Frequency. The number of cycles per second of an a-c voltage.

Frequency modulation. A system of radio transmission in which the frequency of a carrier is varied in accordance with a meaningful signal.

Headphones. Head telephone receivers; a headset.

Heater. The filament in a vacuum tube.

High Fidelity. A system which reproduces sound with a minimum of distortion.

Insulation. A nonconducting material.

Kilocycle. One thousand cycles.

Load. A component developing a useful voltage.

Microphone. A device which converts sound into an audio signal.

Powdered iron core. A coil or transformer core containing powdered iron.

Pulse. A voltage which rises and falls abruptly.

R-f. Radio frequency; the frequency of a received carrier signal.

Rear end. The receiver circuits following the detector.

Resonance. Sympathetic electrical vibration of a circuit to a signal.

Resonant circuit. A circuit in resonance.

Selectivity. The ability of a receiver to choose a particular carrier.

Speaker. A device which converts electrical signals into sound.

Speaker diaphragm. The vibrating element of a speaker.

Station selector. The receiver device which chooses a particular carrier.

Variable capacitor. A capacitor consisting of two intermeshing sets of metal plates.

Video carrier. The carrier of a video signal.

Video signal. An electrical signal corresponding to light.

Chapter Four

GROWTH OF THE ELECTRON TUBE

IN ANY SYSTEM of communication by electrical means, amplification is essential. This is especially true of electronic systems in which a transmitter and receiver are involved. At the transmitter, amplification of the radiated signal is required if the signal is to be received at some fairly distant point. The portion of the transmitter's signal energy picked up by the receiver antenna is so small that it is of little use unless it is somehow strengthened. The long range communication so commonplace today would be impossible if no means were available for amplifying the transmitted and received signals.

While the invention of the diode provided communication engineers with a powerful tool, it left the problem of amplification unsolved. The solution came in 1907, when the American inventor Lee de Forest patented the triode. De Forest's work provided the break-through and into the breach he made poured a multitude of inventions which have brought electronics to its present stage of vigorous growth.

The Triode

The contribution made by de Forest was the conversion of the diode to a triode by inserting a third electrode between the electron-producing element and the plate. Originally, the extra electrode was made of several spaced parallel wires; and because of its resemblance to the familir gridiron, was termed the *grid*. It still retains that name, but in modern tubes it is usually a helix of very thin wire wound around, although not in contact with the tube cathode. Actually, most modern triodes contain four elements, the fourth being the necessary but relatively unimportant heater.

The grid of the triode is placed so that its distance from the cathode is much less than its distance from the plate. Now it is a basic physical principle that the force exerted by one body on another is intensified if the bodies are brought closer together. Since the grid is much nearer to the cathode than the plate, it follows that a small voltage applied to the grid will exert a much more forceful control over the electrons coming from the cathode than an equal voltage applied to the plate. While the grid cannot mechanically impede the movement of electrons from cathode to plate—to the

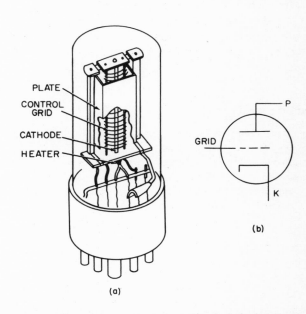

PLATE
CONTROL GRID
CATHODE
HEATER

P
GRID
K

(b)

(a)

Fig. 4.1. *The Triode:* The construction of the tube is shown in (a), its schematic symbol in (b). In (b), the heater is not indicated.

infinitely tiny electron the spaces between the grid wires are enormous—it can and does control that movement by the force of its electric field. It is the word "control" that is important in the preceding sentence; the triode can work as an amplifier because a small voltage placed on its *grid* exerts as strong a controlling influence on the electron stream as does a much larger voltage on its plate.

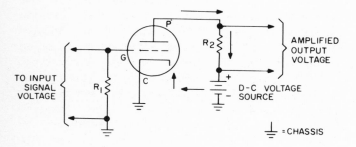

Fig. 4.2. *Basic Triode Amplifier Circuit:* **The signal to be amplified is connected between grid and cathode, across the grid load resistor R₁. Amplified version of the input signal is developed across the plate load resistor R₂. The direction of electron flow is shown by the arrows. Common connection between the negative terminal of the d-c voltage source, the cathode, and one terminal of R₁ is made through chassis.**

In the normal operation of the triode as an amplifier, therefore, the signal to be amplified is applied to the grid of the triode. The plate of the tube is connected through a load—generally a resistor, but sometimes a transformer winding—to the positive terminal of a power supply (Chapter 2). Thus given a positive potential, the plate attracts a stream of electrons from the cathode to itself. The varying voltage of the signal on the grid, at the same time, exerts its control over the electron stream. The result is that the varying voltage created across the load by the current passing through it is several times the signal voltage at the grid. Hence the circuit is an amplifier: its output signal voltage is much larger than the input voltage.

Bias

In a simple circuit of the type just described, amplification will occur; but distortion is also likely to take place. The input signal is usually an alternating voltage. In its positive phase, it gives the grid a positive potential, and some of the electrons leaving the cathode are attracted to the grid wires. If the input signal is strong enough, an appreciable number of electrons will be attracted to the grid, and a current will flow through the grid load resistor. Since the point at which elec-

tronic current enters a resistor is negative, the grid will be given a small negative voltage at the moment the input signal voltage is rising to a positive peak. The net effect is to depress the positive peak of the signal the circuit is amplifying; the wave of the signal will be sheared sharply where it should be rising smoothly. This *distorted* version of the signal being amplified will then appear in the voltage across the plate load resistor. Obviously, distortion in a circuit like the audio amplifier should be avoided at all costs.

The cure for this type of distortion is to apply to the grid, in addition to its input signal, a small negative d-c voltage. The purpose of this bias voltage, as it is called, is to keep the grid from becoming positive even when the input signal voltage is at its maximum positive point. Thus, if the bias voltage is −4, a signal voltage having a peak of 3 volts cannot drive the grid positive.

A, B, and C Voltages

Radio receivers, in the days before power-line operation, were equipped with three sets of batteries known as A, B, and C. The A battery was the voltage source for keeping the tube heaters lit; the B battery, of considerably higher voltage, was the plate circuit battery for the triodes then in use throughout the receiver; and the C battery was one of small voltage supplying bias to the triode grids. Nowadays, thanks to easily available a-c power lines and the invaluable power supply, battery-operated sets are more or less a thing of the past. But the custom of the A, B, C nomenclature still remains. Although the voltage for the heaters of receiver tubes is now usually derived from a small secondary winding of the power supply transformer, it is still occasionally called the A voltage. The B voltage designation is much more common. Its source is the receiver power supply. The C term is very rarely used now, and the old C battery is practically a museum piece. In the modern receiver, grid bias voltage is not usually obtained from the power supply, as might be expected, but through a very ingenious device known as *cathode biasing.*

Cathode Biasing

The d-c voltage in the plate circuit of the triode keeps the plate of the tube at a high positive voltage even with no input signal at the grid. Consequently, a certain amount of d-c current is always flowing from cathode to plate, through the load resistor, through the power supply, through the chassis, and back to the cathode to complete the circuit. Ordinarily, this current would go to waste; it really has no function when the amplifier circuit is not operating on an input signal. But if a

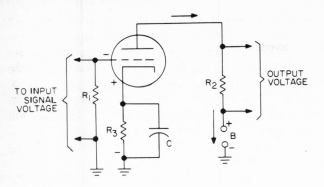

Fig. 4.3. *Cathode Biasing:* R₃ is the biasing resistor and C the cathode bypass capacitor. Polarity markings indicate the potentials resulting from the action of the cathode bias circuit. The B voltage is obtained from the receiver power supply; the plate current of the triode (arrow) passes through the power supply on its way to chassis.

resistor shunted by a capacitor is installed between the cathode of the tube and chassis, the plate current performs the very valuable function of supplying the grid of that tube with its bias.

The current flowing through the plate circuit must pass through the cathode resistor on its return to the tube cathode. With no signal on the grid, this current is an unvarying d-c, and the voltage it creates across the cathode resistor is similarly unchanging. The point at which the current enters the resistor is negative. This negative voltage is, however, connected to the grid through chassis and the grid load resistor. Hence the grid takes on this negative d-c voltage and is biased.

If there should be a signal voltage on the grid, the plate current flow will still be in one direction, but its intensity will vary to correspond with the variations of the grid signal. This is where the capacitor shunting the cathode resistor comes into play; it bypasses the variations in the current around the resistor. The d-c part of the current, on the other hand, cannot get through the capacitor and must flow through the resistance path. Consequently, the voltage across the resistor retains its unvarying character, and provides the grid with bias. Its shunting capacitor is often called the *cathode bypass* in recognition of its work.

Cutoff

The grid controls the flow of electron current in the triode in much the same way as a faucet controls the flow of water from a tap. Just as it is possible to tighten a faucet to the point where the stream of water is completely cut off, it is possible to apply so negative a voltage to the triode grid as to repel all electrons back to the cathode and cut off the plate current stream. The

voltage at which the grid is just negative enough to halt plate current entirely is known as the cutoff voltage, or more simply, *cutoff*. If the grid should be driven even more negative than cutoff, no change in the situation will occur; there will still be an absence of plate current.

In this latter fact lies a second possible cause of distortion. If a strong signal is applied to the grid, the negative swings of its voltage added to the negative bias may drive the grid into and beyond cutoff. Since no corresponding plate current can flow for grid voltages more negative than the cutoff value, there can be no output signal for some part of the signal voltage cycle. The wave shape of the output signal then loses its resemblance to the input signal—that is, distortion takes place. An analogous situation occurs when a mechanical stop is fixed alongside a swinging pendulum. As long as the pendulum restricts the extremes of its motion to a point just short of the stop, its swings will not be interfered with; if it should attempt to expand its motion beyond that point, its swings will be cut short and its regular motion distorted.

Saturation

Generally, the plate current in the triode increases as the grid voltage rises. But a point can be reached at which further rises in grid voltage cannot force corresponding increases in plate current. At that point, the plate current is said to be *saturated*. Thus, there is a value of grid voltage which, when exceeded, will not attract any additional electrons to the plate.

If the signal applied to the grid of an amplifier should swing so strongly positive as to go beyond this value, there will be no corresponding increase in the plate current. As a result, the output voltage does not reflect these input voltage peaks, and is consequently a distorted version of the input signal.

The types of distortion discussed here can all be lumped under the heading of *amplitude distortion,* principally because they affect the peaks or amplitude of the signal the circuit is intended to strengthen. In general, amplitude distortion is caused by *overdriving;* that is, by forcing the amplifier circuit to handle signals beyond its normal capacity.

Amplifier Classes

In electronics, as in life generally, the advantages of a particular method are usually accompanied by certain disadvantages. The type of amplifier predominantly used in audio and r-f circuits is, as we have seen, useful because it produces an undistorted output; but, since plate current flows even with no signal applied to the grid, the circuit is inefficient. Such an amplifier is termed *Class A*. According to the established definition, a class A amplifier is one in which the grid bias and signal voltages are such that plate current flows at all times.

There are other types of amplifier which are more efficient than the class A type, and whose tendencies to distortion are compensated for in one way or another. One such is the *Class B amplifier*. In this type, the bias voltage applied to the grid is approximately equal to the cutoff value. Hence very little plate current flows except when a signal voltage is applied to the grid; then, only the positive half-cycles of the a-c signal voltage are reproduced in the output of the amplifier.

In between the class A and class B variety is the *Class AB* amplifier. Plate current in this type flows for more than half the cycle of the input signal voltage but less than the entire cycle.

Finally, there is the *Class C* amplifier, in which the grid is biased so negatively as to be beyond cutoff. With no signal on the grid, definitely no plate current can flow; when a signal is put on grid, plate current flows for less than half the signal voltage cycle. Class C amplifiers are most efficient because plate current consists for the most part of powerful and useful pulses. Consequently, they are used a good deal in transmitters of all types.

One final note is needed to round out this system of amplifier classification: If grid current flows for any part of the input signal cycle, a figure 2 is written after the class letter; if no grid current flows, a figure 1 is used. This method of letter-and-number amplifier classification appears so frequently in electronic literature that it must find a place in any good book on the subject.

The Duo-Diode Triode

The triode, as it is used in many modern radio receivers, is yet another example of the aid tube manufacturers give designers trying to achieve economies in price and bulk. In these sets, the first stage after the detector is a triode audio amplifier circuit. Recognizing this fact, the tube manufacturers fabricate a two-in-one tube which performs the functions of both detector and first audio amplifier, and is known as a duo-diode triode. As the name implies, the tube contains two diodes and a triode, all within a single envelope. One heater and cathode serves as the electron-supplying combination for the diode and triode sections.

In the usual design, the two diode plates are connected together outside the tube to function as the common plate of a single diode. As in the detector circuit of the preceding chapter, the jointly acting plates are connected to the secondary winding of a transformer with the cathode of the tube connected through the chassis to the load resistor. Here, however, the resistor is equipped with a sliding tap which is joined through a capacitor to the grid of the triode section of the tube. By rotating the tap over the circular-shaped resistance element, the operator of the receiver can adjust the volume of the sound coming from the speaker. For example, if the tap is set near the chassis end of the load resistor, only a weak audio voltage is fed to the triode grid for amplification. Naturally, then, the sound generated by the receiver speaker is low in volume. But if the tap is adjusted toward the opposite end of the resistor, the audio voltage it picks off the load resistor is stronger, and the speaker output

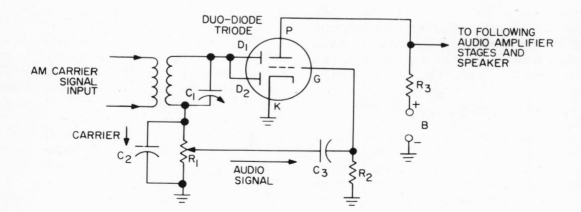

Fig. 4.4. *Combination Detector and First Audio Stage:* The two diode plates (D_1, D_2) are tied together to serve with the cathode (K) as a single diode. R_1 is the detector load resistor and volume control, shunted by C_2. The audio signal is coupled from the detector to the triode grid by C_3. R_2 and R_3 are the grid and plate load resistors respectively. The tuning capacitor is C_1.

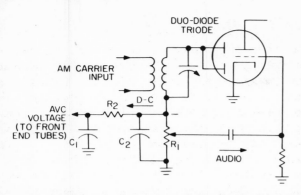

DUO-DIODE
TRIODE

AM CARRIER
INPUT

AVC
VOLTAGE
(TO FRONT
END TUBES)

R₂

D-C

C₁

C₂

R₁

AUDIO

Fig. 4.5. *Automatic Volume Control Circuit:* Audio component of detector load resistor (R_1) is filtered out by R_2 and C_1. The remaining d-c voltage is fed to the grids of the tubes in the receiver front end. The d-c voltage is proportional to the strength of the input carrier signal and is negative. For simplicity, the plate circuit of the tube is omitted.

is amplified. This tap and the resistance element over which it slides is the familiar volume control of home radio receivers. It is adjusted by a shaft projecting through the front panel of the radio.

A word might be said about the function of the capacitor between the volume control tap and the grid of the triode. The current flowing through the detector load resistor—and therefore the voltage picked off by the volume control tap—is made up of both an a-c audio component and a d-c component. This d-c component arises from the rectifying action of the diode, which restricts current flow to one direction. Now a capacitor, as we have seen earlier in this chapter, will allow the passage of a-c but represents a broken circuit to d-c. It therefore offers a path to the audio signal for reaching the triode grid. The d-c voltage developed across the detector load, however, is kept from getting to the grid. Hence the function of the capacitor is to bring the audio signal from the detector output to the amplifier input, and at the same time isolate the triode from the effect of the d-c voltage. A capacitor introduced between circuits for this purpose is called a *coupling* condenser.

Automatic Volume Control

The d-c voltage developed across the detector load resistor is unwanted in the triode audio amplifier, but it can be used to advantage in other circuits of the receiver. The system in which it is prepared for that use is known as the automatic volume control circuit, abbreviated *avc*.

The intensity of the current flowing through the detector circuit is proportional to the strength of the carrier signal applied to the circuit. Consequently, the d-c voltage appearing across the detector load resistor is

larger for a stronger input carrier, and smaller for a weaker input. This characteristic of the d-c voltage can be put to work; but the voltage must first be filtered for its accompanying audio signal by a resistor-capacitance circuit. What emerges from the filter is a negative d-c voltage proportional to the strength of the signal input to the detector.

This avc voltage is used to good effect when applied to the grids of the tube amplifiers in the forward end of the receiver. The voltage automatically adjusts the amplifying ability of these tubes by increasing their sensitivity when it is less negative and decreasing their sensitivity when more negative. If, for example, an especially strong carrier signal arrives at the detector diode plates, the avc voltage developed is highly negative. When applied back to the grids of the amplifying tubes of the forward end, the voltage decreases the sensitivity of the tubes and reduces the signal to more easily handled proportions.

The avc system has a second beneficial effect: it helps reduce distortion. As we have seen, distortion is the result of overdriving amplifiers. By reducing a strong carrier to a manageable level, the avc system helps prevent distortion attributable to that cause. Still a third argument for avc is its ability to reduce noise. When a station is tuned in correctly, the strength of its carrier is at a maximum, the avc voltage is highly negative, and the amplification at the forward end diminishes. The level of the signal is reduced, but so is the noise. Since the station's signal is usually more intense than the noise signal, the station's transmissions come through the speaker clearly against an almost completely noiseless background. This explains why, on many receivers, the noise between stations is more pronounced than when a station is turned in.

Automatic Gain Control

A system very much like avc is *automatic gain control* —abbreviated *agc*—an arrangement used in radar receivers and in the video sections of the television set. Since radar and television produce light rather than sound as an end product, the "gain" controlled by agc is the amplification of the tubes handling a video as against an audio signal. In both these electronic equipments, an overly strong video carrier can cause a reversal of light values, with normally white areas turned dark and dark areas white, so that the reproduced picture has the appearance of a photograph negative. This is a situation the agc system can help correct. Also, by reducing distortion, the agc cooperates in achieving a more accurate picture. Finally, agc is a valuable ally in eliminating *snow,* the visual evidence of electrical noise.

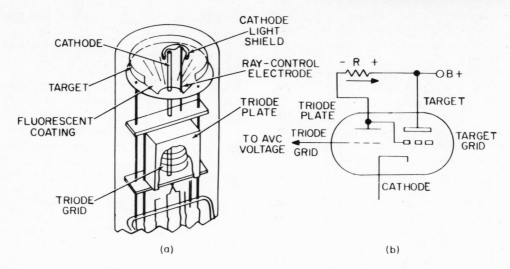

Fig. 4.6. *The Magic Eye:* **Construction of the tube is shown in (a). Circuit of tube is shown schematically in (b). When arc is at maximum negative, low plate current flows to triode plate, left-hand terminal of resistor (R) is at high positive potential, and target grid admits strong electron flow for maximum target illumination (minimum shadow). Arrow shows direction of triode plate current.**

The Magic Eye

Since the avc or agc voltage is a maximum only when the carrier signal is tuned in properly, it can be used to stimulate a special kind of tuning indicator known, rather romantically, as the *"magic eye" tube.*

The tube contains a triode and a target section. Electrons from the single cathode flow to the plate through the gaps between the controlling grid wires, in normal triode fashion, in the triode section of the tube. In the target section, however, the electrons strike a fluorescent plate, known as the target, which glows under their impact. This target electron stream is controlled by a grid-like electrode. When the target grid is positive, its attraction accelerates the electrons into setting almost all of the circular target aglow; when it is less positive—relatively more negative—it reduces the intensity of the stream to cause the appearance of a shadow angle on the target. Part of the secret of the magic eye's operation is the fact that the target grid is permanently connected to the plate of the triode section.

In the circuit arrangement of the tube, the avc voltage is applied to the triode grid. The plate of the triode is connected through a resistor to the target. This last, in turn, is wired directly to the B+ of the receiver's power supply. Now, if the tuning dial of the receiver is not accurately set to a desired station, the avc voltage fed to the triode grid is not as strongly negative as it should be. A fairly large plate current will then flow through the resistor to B+, and the voltage at the plate of the triode will drop to become relatively negative.

Obtaining this negative potential through its internal connection to the triode plate, the target grid reduces the intensity of the electron stream it controls, and a large shadow angle appears in the fluorescent target.

When the receiver is correctly tuned, the avc voltage is at its maximum negative. The plate current in the triode section of the magic eye then diminishes, and the target grid becomes highly positive. With an increased intensity of electron flow to the target, more of its area is illuminated, and the shadow angle narrows. Thus, by adjusting the dial of his receiver for minimum shadow angle on the magic eye, the operator can tune in his station at maximum signal strength.

GLOSSARY

A voltage.   The voltage applied to the terminals of a tube heater.

Amplitude distortion.   Distortion in which the peaks of a signal are altered.

Agc.   Automatic gain control; an electronic system in radar and the visual section of television receivers which controls the amplification of forward end tubes.

Avc.   Automatic volume control; an electronic system in radio receivers which controls the amplification of forward end tubes.

B voltage.   A positive d-c voltage applied to the plate of a tube through the plate load.

Bias.   A negative d-c voltage applied to the control grid of a tube through the grid load.

C voltage. A former term for bias voltage.

Cathode biasing. A method of obtaining bias by the insertion of a resistor shunted by a capacitor in the cathode circuit of a tube.

Class A. Operation of an amplifier tube in which plate current flows for a complete cycle of the input grid voltage.

Class AB. Operation of an amplifier tube in which plate current flows for more than half but less than the full cycle of input grid voltage.

Class B. Operation of an amplifier tube in which plate current flows for approximately half the cycle of input grid voltage.

Class C. Operation of an amplifier tube in which plate current flows for less than half the cycle of input voltage.

Coupling capacitor. A capacitor used between circuits to allow a-c signal voltage to pass from one circuit to another while blocking the passage of d-c.

Cutoff. The condition in a tube in which the grid is so negative as to halt the flow of electrons to the plate.

Grid. A thin wire mesh between cathode and plate in a triode.

"Magic eye" tube. A vacuum tube used as tuning indicator which is controlled by avc voltage.

Overdriving. Applying an excessive signal to an amplifier tube.

Saturation. The condition in a triode in which maximum current flows from cathode to plate.

"Snow." The flaky appearance of a television picture indicating high noise level.

Triode. A tube containing three active electrodes.

Chapter Five

MODERN VACUUM TUBES

WHILE THE triode performs satisfactorily in an audio amplifier circuit, it is much more troublesome when operated as an r-f amplifier. The receiver using it in this function shows a tendency to break into appalling howls. If this trouble is analyzed, it is found that the triode r-f circuit *oscillates;* the circuit acts as a miniature transmitter, radiating a high frequency signal to other circuits in the receiver.

The essential cause of this oscillation is the capacitance that exists between the plate and grid of the triode. Both of these structures are metallic, and they are separated from each other by the near-vacuum within the tube. In effect, they form a capacitance which couples the output of the amplifier back into the input. This feedback of energy tends to *aid* the input signal to such an extent that the circuit receives more energy than it loses, and "spills over" into oscillation.

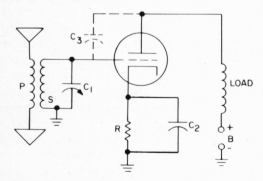

Fig. 5.1. *Typical Triode R-F Amplifier.* The carrier signal is transferred from the primary winding (P) to the secondary (S) of the input transformer. C_1 is the tuning capacitor; R and C_2 are the cathode bias resistor and shunting capacitor. The interelectrode capacitance (C_3) between plate and grid inside the triode is indicated by dotted lines. Feed back of energy from plate to grid occurs through this virtual capacitor.

No such parallel condition takes place in a triode audio amplifier. The audio signal rarely has a frequency higher than 10 kilocycles—10,000 cycles per second. A signal of so comparatively low a frequency is poorly coupled through a capacitance as small as that between the triode grid and plate. The frequency to which an r-f amplifier is normally tuned, however, may be in the neighborhood of 1000 kc—one hundred times the frequency of audio. Thus the small interelectrode capacitance of plate and grid denies passage to audio frequencies while rather freely permitting the passage of r-f.

The Screen Grid Tube

In the early days of radio, when the triode was the only amplifier available, all sorts of circuit variations were tried to rid the r-f stage of its unwanted oscillation. Some of these were fairly successful, although they required delicate adjustment. But the heart of the problem was not attacked until the invention of the screen grid tube.

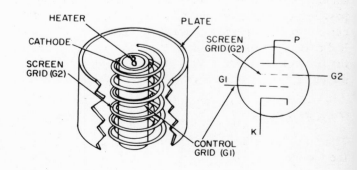

Fig. 5.2. *Construction of the Tetrode*

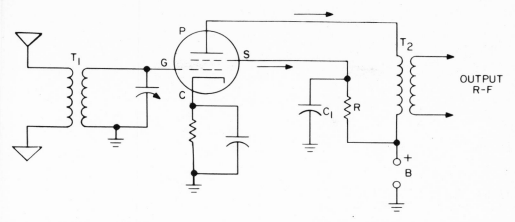

Fig. 5.3. *The Tetrode as R-F Amplifier.* **Electrons attracted to the screen grid (S) flow down the screen-dropping resistor (R), thus lowering the B+ voltage at the screen. C_1 is the screen by-pass capacitor. Most of the tube electrons flow** **through the plate circuit, and the voltage across the load— the primary of the second transformer (T_2)—is the amplified r-f signal.**

The screen grid, for which the tube was named, is a fourth electrode of finely meshed wires inserted between the grid and plate as an electrostatic shield between the two elements. But if the screen grid is directly connected to ground—as it should be to act as a shield—the electric field of the plate is shut off from the cathode, and the plate loses its ability to attract the electrons the cathode emits. In the circuit connections of the tetrode, therefore, the screen grid is connected to ground. through a capacitor, and is directly wired to a positive d-c source of almost as high a potential as that given to the plate. Since r-f can pass easily through the capacitor to ground, the screen grid fulfills its shielding function. At the same time, the screen's positive potential attracts electrons from the cathode, and these make their way to the plate through the openings in the screen's mesh.

The screen grid can be given its high positive potential by connecting it through a resistor to the positive terminal of the power supply. A portion of the electron stream in the tube is attracted to the screen wires, and passes through the resistor. The voltage drop across the resistor lowers the potential of the screen to a level somewhat below that of the plate. With the screen by-pass capacitor diverting the r-f component of the screen current to chassis, the voltage drop across the resistor is d-c. Because the function of the resistor is to depress the d-c voltage applied from the power supply to the screen grid, it is designated the *screen-dropping* resistor.

The Pentode

Thus the triode, a three-element tube, developed into the tetrode, a four-element tube. But the arrival of the tetrode did not mean the end of vacuum tube evolution. Hardly had experimentation with the new tube

begun when it was found that it was not the ideal solution to the r-f amplifier problem.

The tetrode owed its loss of popularity—it is almost obsolete nowadays—to a phenomenon known as *secondary emission*. If an electron is driven with strong impact against a metal object, it will knock one or more secondary electrons out of the metal. Secondary emission of this sort is not likely to occur in triodes; any secondary electrons emitted by the plate when it is struck by a primary electron from the cathode will be repelled back to the plate by the normally negative grid. In the tetrode, however, the electrode nearest the plate is the screen, and the screen is provided with a normally high positive potential. Thus secondary emission is a likely occurrence in the tetrode.

Suppose a strong r-f signal is applied to the control grid of the tetrode amplifier. On the positive-going swings of this signal, a strong current of electrons will flow from cathode to plate. The point at which this current enters the plate load becomes negative, driving the d-c voltage applied to the plate to a reduced level. The voltage of the screen, however, is just about constant since its bypass capacitor renders it immune from signal variations. For input signal peaks, therefore, the screen can be more positive than the plate. Secondary electrons emitted by the plate will then be attracted from the plate to the more positive screen, in a direction *opposite* to the plate current flow. Consequently, at the moment that the input signal swings to strong peaks, the net cathode-to-plate current flow is weak. The signal voltage across the plate load is then low when it should be high, and the output signal is distorted.

Obviously, the cure for this condition is to prevent the secondary electrons from flying to the screen. This was done by inserting a third grid between the plate and

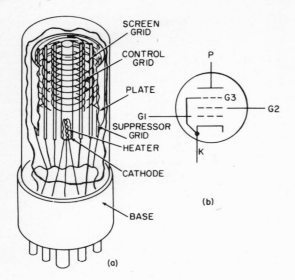

Fig. 5.4. *Construction of the Pentode*

screen, and connecting that grid either internally or externally to the tube cathode. Since the new electrode has a much lower voltage than the plate and is therefore comparatively negative, it repels secondary electrons back to the plate where they belong. Because its function is to suppress secondary emission, this third grid is called the *suppressor;* the tube containing it is the modern *pentode,* a word coined from the combination of the prefix "penta," meaning "five," and the final three letters of "electrode." Since the tube contains five active electrodes—a cathode, three grids, and a plate— the term is apt.

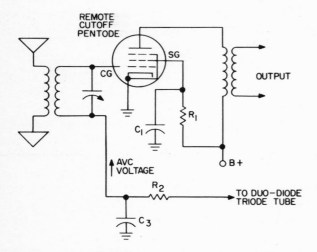

Fig. 5.5. *R-F Amplifier with AVC:* R$_2$ and C$_3$ are the audio filter of the avc circuit (see avc schematic, Chapter 4). The avc voltage is fed to the control grid (CG) of the remote cutoff pentode through the secondary of the input transformer. In this type of tube, the suppressor grid is connected internally to the cathode.

The Remote Cutoff Pentode

The pentode was the answer the young electronics industry was waiting for, and with its development, further progress was rapid. But even the new tube could be improved. It could be made so that quite a heavily negative voltage would have to be applied to the control grid before the plate current would be cut off.

The discussion of cutoff in the preceding chapter demonstrated that an amplifier can easily be overdriven if only a small negative grid voltage is sufficient to bring the tube into the cutoff condition. To provide a tube which would allow stronger signals to be handled without at the same time introducing distortion, engineers devised the *remote cutoff* pentode. This tube owes its name to the fact that its cutoff point is pushed back, so to speak, to a remote, highly negative value. And it achieves its aim through an ingeniously constructed control grid.

As in many tubes, the control grid of the remote cutoff pentode is a helix. But it differs from grids of other tubes in the spacing between the coiled turns. At the extreme ends, the turns are fairly close together; towards the middle of the helix, the turns are further apart. If a voltage sufficiently negative to send other tubes into cutoff were applied to this grid, the tight windings towards the terminals of the helix would repel electrons from the nearest portions of the cathode, but the widely wound middle of the helix would still permit electrons from the cathode's center to come through. To shut off plate current completely in such a tube, a grid voltage more negative than usual is necessary.

In effect, the remote cutoff tube combines several amplifier tubes into one. If the grid is given a highly negative bias, short of cutoff, the amplifying ability of the tube is relatively small. If the grid is biased less negative, the amplifying ability of the tube is increased. Hence the amplification of an r-f circuit containing the remote cutoff pentode can be changed by changing the grid bias of the tube. This knack of the remote cutoff tube for adjusting its amplification automatically at the command of a variable bias, renders it suitable for use in a receiver using avc (Chapter 4). The remote cutoff pentode is also known as the *variable mu* tube; the Greek letter *mu* is the engineer's symbol for a tube's ability to amplify.

The Beam Power Tube

Although the pentode has displaced the tetrode for most applications, one modified form of the tetrode is still fairly popular in home receivers. This is the beam power tube, so called because it concentrates its elec-

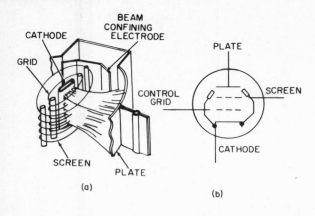

Fig. 5.6.   *The Beam Power Tube:* **Details of construction (a) and schematic symbol (b).**

trons into beams and because it is used as a power rather than a voltage amplifier.

The beam power tube is built in a rather unique way. One unusual characteristic is that the control grid and screen grid are both helixes, with the windings of one directly behind the windings of the other. Thus the electrons are propelled from cathode to plate in concentrated beams in the interstices of the coinciding grid helixes. The beam effect is enhanced by the second unusual feature—a set of two beam-forming structures internally connected to the cathode. Since this connection gives these structures a negative potential compared to the highly positive screen, they exert a repelling force on the electrons to squeeze them into an even greater concentration. The focus of the electron beam is just ahead of the plate. In the face of this highly concentrated negative charge only a short distance from it, the plate cannot emit secondary electrons. Thus the tube forces its own electron stream to work as a virtual suppressor.

The beam power tube is one of a class of vacuum tubes known as power amplifiers, which are generally situated in an audio amplifier just ahead of the speaker. The tube is valuable because it delivers large quantities of current and, therefore, the large quantities of audio power needed to drive the speaker adequately. But we shall see more of this in a future chapter (Chapter 10).

Combination Vacuum Tubes

Electronic equipments nowadays are so complex, both in circuitry and function, that they are necessarily bulky. An important problem the designers of these devices continually wrestle with is the problem of packaging—how to cram a maximum of components into a minimum of space.

In the preceding chapters, at least one contribution of tube manufacturers to the solution of the problem of packaging was discussed. There are many others. The tube manuals published by these manufacturers offer many different combinations of diodes, triodes, and pentodes—the basic vacuum tube units in service today—within a single miniature glass envelope. Just one of these tiny tubes can supplant three simpler types by performing all three functions simultaneously.

The 6T8 miniature is a good example. When plugged into its socket in the chassis of a home radio receiver, this tube stands a bit less than two inches high and is barely an inch in diameter. Yet it works simultaneously in three different directions: it is an AM detector, an FM detector, and a first audio amplifier. The tube manual refers to it as a "triple diode—high-mu triode," which is to say that it contains three diodes and a high amplifier triode. All of these operate with two cathodes supplying the necessary electrons. These two cathodes, each working with a diode plate, make up the FM detector—a circuit to be discussed in a later chapter. One of these cathodes can simultaneously be used with the remaining diode plate and the triode grid-plate section to fulfill the functions of an AM detector and first audio stage respectively—a circuit shown in the preceding chapter. In about one and a half cubic inches, the 6T8 handles all the activity that would otherwise have to be performed by four or possibly five tubes.

Using the Tube Manual

When radio was young, each tube manufacturer went his own way without much regard either to his competitors, his consumers, or the infant industry itself.

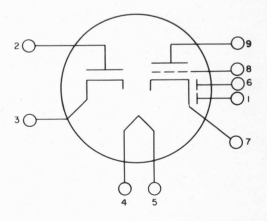

Fig. 5.7.   *A Combination AM-FM Receiver Vacuum Tube:* **(a) Schematic of the miniature 6T8 type with a nine-pin (noval) base. Two of the diode units (1,7;2,3) are used as a duo-diode FM detector; the remaining diode (6,7) can be used as AM detector; the triode (7,8,9) serves as first audio amplifier.**

Things are very much different today. Tubes are no longer "radio tubes," fit only for use in a puzzling music-box with erratic tendencies. They are now "electron tubes" charged with grave responsibilities in communications, navigation, and national defense. Their manufacturers have become equally respectable; where each designated his various products by a private numbering system, all now adhere to a uniform method of nomenclature. The technician who looks up the characteristics of a particular tube in the manual of one manufacturer can be certain that another company's tube with the same designation will show identical characteristics.

Modern tubes are usually typed by an initial number, one or two letters, and a final number. In almost all cases, the first number is an approximation of the voltage normally applied to the heater terminals. The 6T8, discussed in the preceding section, should thus be given a 6.3 heater voltage in normal operation. The letter or letters following the first number is a code which may indicate the function of the tube, and the final number is a rough measure of the number of electrodes in it.

This system has its value. A technician called upon to do a quick repair job on an equipment with a burnt-out 12AT6 knows, without even consulting the tube manual, that he had better not try a 6AT6 in its place even though the identity of the letters and final number in the designations indicate that the tubes are practically twins. If he is audacious enough to make the attempt, he will find that the replacement tube will meet the same fate as its predecessor. Obviously, a heater designed for 6 volt operation cannot tolerate the 12 volts applied to its socket terminals.

But if he must find a quick replacement for, say, a damaged 6K6 tube, he might consider a 6V6 for the job. Before he actually makes the replacement, though, he must check with the tube manual to see if the base

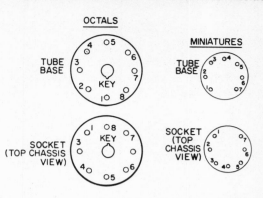

Fig. 5.9. *Octal and Miniature Bases and Sockets:* This diagram shows how the base pins and socket holes are counted. The miniature base shown is a heptal or seven prong type.

connections of the replacement tube are identical with those of the original. If he makes the replacement without taking this precaution, he is apt to find that the voltages delivered to the tube socket are not reaching the correct electrodes inside the tube's envelope. As it happens, the 6V6 is a practical replacement for the 6K6; the tube manual shows that their characteristics are pretty much the same.

Octal and Miniature Tubes

Two types of tubes are generally found in military and commercial electronic gear: one of these is the larger, sturdier-looking *octal* type, so called because it is equipped with eight base pins; the other is the more fragile *miniature*. The latter are far more prevalent.

The pins in the octal tube base are arranged in a circle around a cylindrical extension of the tube's insulating base material. On this cylinder, and running along its length, is a projection known as the *key*. The pins are numbered consecutively, counting clockwise from the key. Thus in the 6K6, an octal type, the plate connection is made to the third pin counting clockwise from the key. One caution, however: pin 3 of the tube *base* does not match pin-hole 3 of the tube *socket* counted clockwise from the key slot. The reason for that, of course, is that the count of the pins at the tube is made looking *up* at the base of the tube, while the count of the pin-holes in the socket is made looking *down* at the socket. If this clockwise count of the socket holes is to be made accurately, it must be made looking at the underside of the socket—that is, from beneath the chassis. This is usually the technician's-eye-view of the equipment he is working on anyway.

Miniature tubes are furnished with more slender base pins. Moreover, they have no key. But at one point in the circumference of the base, two of the con-

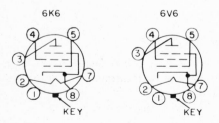

Fig. 5.8. *A Good Replacement:* Since both tubes have the same base connections, the same function, the same heater voltage, and use the same type of socket, one is a safe substitute for the other. Pin 6 is missing in both drawings; in some octal types, unconnected pins are omitted by the manufacturer.

secutive pins are spaced wider apart than the others. Looking at the base of the tube, the count is made clockwise with the wide-spaced pin at the left counting as number 1. Most of the miniatures have a seven-pronged base; a tube like the 6T8, discussed above, has so many electrodes crammed into it that it needs two extra base pins. Such a tube naturally demands a special socket. The same caution noted above for counting pins of octal tubes applies also to miniatures.

Transmitter Tubes

The vacuum tubes used in transmitters are basically much like the receiver tubes discussed so far. Diodes, triodes, pentodes—in some cases, even tetrodes—find a place in the transmitter just as they do in other electronic equipments. The essential difference is the extremely large amount of power that the tubes in the transmitter must handle.

Unlike the receiver, which deals only with the small carrier signal its antenna picks up—a signal usually measured in millionths of a volt—the transmitter must generate its own carrier with sufficient power to be dispersed over thousands of square miles in the vicinity of its antenna.

The device which generates the carrier is, inevitably, the vacuum tube. An AM transmitter in the broadcast band may emit a carrier of 1,000 kilocycles per second. If that signal had to be produced by a mechanical generator like those in a-c power stations, the armature of that generator would have to rotate at the terrific speed of one million revolutions per second, an impossible pace. Yet, frequencies in the order of 1,000 kilocycles are considered low in modern electronic communications systems. The best available means of producing the high frequency signals used in these systems is the vacuum tube.

The first of the series of stages in the transmitter is the master oscillator. We have seen, earlier in this chapter, how unwanted oscillations are produced when a triode functions as an r-f amplifier. This same ability of the triode to generate a signal is desirable in the transmitter, and is put to use for the generation of the transmitter's carrier. The output of the master oscillator is then amplified in a series of r-f stages, and before it is put on the antenna, is given a last boost in amplitude by the "final"—a huge r-f power amplifier.

In discussing the tubes used in transmitters, the rectifiers in the transmitter power supply cannot be overlooked. The master oscillator, and various amplifier tubes used throughout the transmitter require enormous amounts of d-c power. This power is furnished by the transmitter's power supply. While transmitter power supplies, if electronic, generally follow the lines described in Chapter 2, the rectifiers they employ are usually mercury vapor rather than vacuum tube diodes. These tubes can, because of their gas content, conduct extremely heavy currents and are therefore capable of supplying the power demanded.

As for the other tubes in the transmitter, these vary in size depending on the uses to which the transmitter is put. A powerful AM transmitter designed for overseas broadcasts may contain tubes standing as high as a man of average size. These tubes, usually in the transmitter final, handle such great amounts of r-f power that keeping them safe from the heat they generate is a problem. In the larger transmitters, the heat is carried off by water circulating in jackets surrounding the tubes; in the smaller stations, the tubes are air-cooled by a system of blowers.

FM, television, and radar installations operate on frequencies far above those of the AM broadcast band transmitters. At these high frequencies, the range of the station is limited to line-of-sight by the very nature of such high frequency waves. Since FM and television broadcast installations are held to this relatively small range, their power need not be too high, and their tubes are correspondingly small. The basic electronic principle that higher frequencies require smaller components is a second factor in keeping FM and television transmitter tubes from being bulky.

However, radar is a special case. In the giant "early warning" installations which guard our northern approaches, for example, the antennas are raised to great heights to extend the line-of-sight limitation. Larger and more powerful tubes are therefore necessary to cover the added range. Furthermore, radar detection and tracking of aircraft depends on the reflection of the transmitted carrier beam by the aircraft body, and in the process, a good portion of the energy in the beam is lost. If the radar receiver is to get enough of the reflected energy to show up clearly on its scope, the radiated beam must be a powerful one.

GLOSSARY

Beam power tube. A power amplifier in which the electron stream is concentrated to form a virtual suppressor.

Bug. A high-speed telegraph key.

Camera tube. The tube in a television camera which converts the lights and darks of a picture into the picture signal.

Electrostatic shield. A metal mesh used to screen one device from the electric field of another.

Feedback. The transfer of energy from the output of a circuit back to its input.

Final. The last amplifying stage of a transmitter.

Interelectrode capacitance. The effective capacitance between electrodes in a vacuum tube.

International Code. The system used in radio telegraphy in which a group of dots and dashes stands for a letter of the alphabet.

Line-of-sight. As far as the eye can see; the range of very high frequency signals.

Mercury vapor tube. A tube containing a small pool of mercury.

Master oscillator. The carrier-generating stage of the transmitter.

Miniature tube. A small glass tube generally used in receivers.

Octal tube. A tube with a standard eight-pin base.

Pentode. A tube containing five active elements.

Power amplifier. A tube or circuit designed to amplify both voltage and current.

Remote cutoff pentode. A type of pentode in which an unusually high negative grid voltage is required to drive the tube into cutoff.

Screen. The electrode just beyond the control grid in a tetrode or pentode.

Secondary emission. Electrons knocked out of a metal by incident primary electrons.

Suppressor. The grid between screen and plate in the pentode.

Tetrode. A tube containing four active elements.

Variable-mu tube. Same as the remote cutoff pentode.

Chapter Six

SPECIAL ELECTRON TUBES

DIODES, TRIODES, and pentodes are so useful, and therefore so commonplace in electronic gadgetry, that it would seem that they are the only electron tubes worthy of account. There are many others, of course, which are not perhaps as versatile as the tubes already discussed, but are extremely useful in certain special applications. Some of these special tubes are evacuated as much as modern technology allows; others, like the mercury rectifier, are deliberately spiked with a gas of some kind.

The Photocell

A special type of vacuum tube not usually found in communications equipment is the photocell. As its name implies—the prefix "photo" is a combining form meaning "light"—the photocell reacts to light falling upon it. Actually, the term "photocell" is a telescoping of the longer but more descriptive term "photoelectric cell"; it is a device which converts light energy into electrical energy.

The common variety of photocell is a diode containing a cathode and an anode. The cathode, usually a semicylindrical structure, emits electrons when struck by light just as the cathode in the thermionic diode emits electrons under the influence of heat. A second electrode, corresponding to the plate of the thermionic diode, is required to capture the emitted electrons. This electrode, the anode, is provided with a positive d-c voltage for that purpose.

Because of its faculty for converting the light energy incident upon it into electrical energy, the photocell has many applications. It is an invaluable aid to the photographer, who calls the device which contains it his

exposure meter, a device consisting usually of little more than a photocell connected in series with a battery—for anode voltage—and a miniaturized ammeter. The position of the ammeter needle tells the photographer how much light his subject is reflecting, and he uses that information to calculate the correct exposure. A similar device has been used in television receivers to regulate the brightness of the picture in accordance with the external light in the living room; if the room is brightly lit, the picture brightness is automatically turned up; if the room is dark, the brightness is turned down. The photocell is also the secret behind the mystery of doors which open as they are approached. An invisible beam of light from a source on one side of the entrance to a photocell on the other is interrupted by an advancing solid body, a relay is activated, and the door swings open. In this action there is a double energy conversion: the photocell converts light into electricity, the relay converts electrical into mechanical energy.

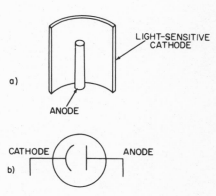

Fig. 6.1. *The Photocell:* **(a) Structure; (b) Schematic.**

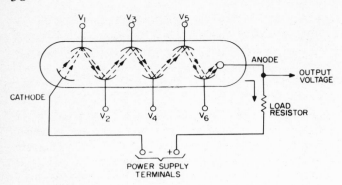

Fig. 6.2. *The Electron Multiplier:* V₁ to V₆ are progressively increased d-c voltages applied to plates 1 through 6. Arrows show the direction of the electron stream.

Electron Multipliers

The effectiveness of the light-to-electricity energy conversion of the photocell can be tremendously increased through the principle of secondary emission. This is the principle on which the *electron multiplier* tube operates. The tube contains a single photosensitive cathode, a series of plates to which progressively larger d-c voltages are applied, plus a final collecting anode. When light strikes the cathode, emitted electrons are attracted at high speed to the first positive plate. Each of these primary electrons may, on striking the plate, dislodge

two or more secondary electrons. The secondary electrons, in turn, are attracted to the second plate, which is provided with a positive d-c potential larger than the first. Striking the second plate at high speed, the electrons' impact brings on a multiplied stream of secondary electrons. These new electrons are then attracted to the third plate with its higher potential step, causing a strong secondary emission, and so on. The electron stream emerging from the last plate is finally collected by the anode before flowing through a load resistor.

The Image Orthicon

The modern television camera tube, known as the *image orthicon,* is a striking example of how the photocell with an electron multiplier is put to use. Thanks to the efficiency lent to the image orthicon by the multiplier, the days of acute discomfort of actors under intense, hot studio lights are gone forever.

The image orthicon is a long, evacuated glass tube, enlarged at one end. At the enlarged end of the tube is a photocathode which, like the cathode in the photocell, emits electrons in varying quantity depending on the intensity of light falling on its surface. The camera lens focuses the light reflected by the object on the photocathode, which then emits an electron "image" corresponding to the light and dark elements of the visual image projected by the lens. To insure that the

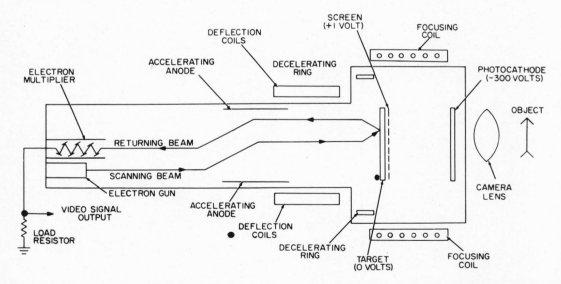

Fig. 6.3. *Cross-Section of the Image Orthicon:* Light from the object is focused by the camera lens on the photo cathode. An electron "image" corresponding to the object travels to the target, dislodging secondary electrons. An image pattern of positive charges appears on the target. The scanning beam loses electrons to the positive image charges in proportion to the strength of the individual

charges. Before the electron beam returns to flow through the load resistor, it is amplified by the electron multiplier. The voltage across the load resistor is therefore a fairly strong video signal, varying with the light and dark elements in the original object. The motion of the scanning beam is controlled by deflection currents flowing through the deflection coils.

electrons will be emitted in the same relative positions as their points of origin on the photocathode, thus preserving the precise correspondence of the electron to the visual image, a focusing coil is placed around the enlarged end of the tube. With a d-c current of constant intensity passed through this coil, a steady magnetic field directed along the axis of the tube is produced. Since a magnetic field can control the path of moving charges, the image electrons are constrained to travel along properly spaced paths.

Some distance back inside the enlarged portion of the tube is a target of semi-insulating glass, set parallel to the photocathode. A fine screen mesh is situated very close to the target and between target and cathode. With potentials of −300 volts applied to the photocathode and zero to the target, the target is 300 volts positive with respect to the photocathode. Consequently, the electrons making up the electron image are attracted to the target, passing through the openings in the screen.

Upon striking the target, these primary electrons eject secondary electrons which are picked up by the screen. A positive potential of about one volt is applied to the screen, not nearly enough to attract many of the electrons coming from the photocathode, but sufficient to pick up and carry off secondary electrons from the target. By losing these secondary electrons, the target surface is covered with varying positive charges corresponding to the light and dark elements in the object "on camera." Since the target material is only partially conductive, its surface charge pattern will remain stationary for a very short time.

At the opposite end of the tube is an electron gun, so called because it shoots a continuous and concentrated beam of electrons. The movement of the beam is controlled by the magnetic fields of two sets of current-carrying coils. One of these fields is directed vertically, at right angles to the tube axis; this field orders the sidewise movement of the beam. The other, directed horizontally at right angles to the tube axis, orders the beam's up and down movement. The currents creating these fields are so varied as to sweep the beam from side to side, and at the same time provide it with a downward motion. In this fashion, the electron beam is forced to scan the target horizontally while moving progressively downwards.

As it moves from point to point over the positive-charge image on the target, the beam gives up enough of its electrons to neutralize the particular positive charge it encounters. Thus partially depleted, it follows a return path in the direction of its origin to meet the first of a series of electron multiplier plates. The multiplier augments the numbers of the electrons, and the strengthened current flows through a load resistor. The voltage across that resistor is the *video signal* since

the current flowing through the resistor varies in accordance with the positive charge pattern on the target —a pattern which represents the object being telecast.

The Electron Gun

The electron gun is so important a component in the image orthicon and related vacuum tubes that it should be further explored. The gun consists of a heater enclosed within an oxide-coated cathode. Around the cathode is the grid, a metal cap pierced by a pinhole. The cathode-emitted electrons are allowed to pass through the pinhole, but the intensity of the electron beam is controlled by a negative voltage applied to the cap. Because this cap exerts the same sort of valve control as does the grid in the ordinary triode, it too is known as the grid, although it is differently shaped. Beyond the grid are two anodes. Both of these are given high positive potentials, the second anode having a higher potential than the first. The effect of these anodes on the electron beam is to speed up the movement of its component electrons.

Having passed the second anode in their progress along the tube, the electrons now meet an accelerating anode, usually a metallic ring painted on the inside of the glass envelope. The extremely high positive potential applied to the accelerating anode provides a final increase in speed to the now fast-moving electrons. This high speed is necessary if the electron beam is to be swung successfully through its movements by the deflection coils. The beam is, in effect, a wire carrying current; the "wire" is surrounded by a magnetic field, and it is the interaction between this magnetic field and those of the deflection coils which pushes the beam through its scanning motions.

Once the beam passes beyond the fields of the deflection coils, its electrons can safely be slowed down. In fact, it is advisable to do so to avoid spoiling the target's charge image with secondary electrons ejected by the impact. This slowing-down process is managed

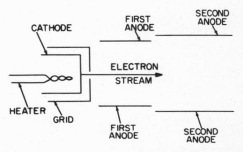

Fig. 6.4. *Cross-Section of the Electron Gun:* The cathode, heated to a high temperature, emits electrons which pass through grid cap pinhole. The electron beam is accelerated by the first and second anodes successively.

by a decelerating ring, a metallic coating on the inside of the glass wall at the wide end of the tube. The decelerating ring is given a positive potential; but its potential is so low, compared to the voltage on the accelerating anode, that the oncoming electrons see it as a relatively negative charge and jam on the brakes, so to speak.

Beam Blanking

The important electrode in the electron gun is the grid. When the image orthicon beam has scanned through one horizontal line of image charges on the target, the current through the horizontally-deflecting set of coils is reversed to pull the beam back to its starting point for scanning the next horizontal line. During this retrace interval, a highly negative voltage is fed to the grid to drive it into cutoff, thus shutting off the beam and preventing it from messing up that portion of the target's charge image in its retrace path. When the beam is back to start a new scan, the cutoff pulse is removed from the grid, the beam is directed at the target again, and the current through the horizontally-deflecting coil set is restored to its original direction. The beam then embarks on its second scanning cycle. In all this time, the vertically-deflecting set of coils is slowly but steadily pushing the scanning beam downwards. The beam is thus forced to cover the vertical length of the target even as it traverses the target's width.

Interlaced Scanning

When the scanning beam has finished its side-swinging run from the top to the bottom of the target, it completes—as television engineers put it—one *field*. At the moment the field is ended, a highly negative blanking

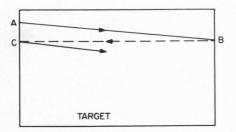

Fig. 6.5. *How the Image Orthicon Target Is Scanned:* The beam begins scanning horizontally and downwards from point A. When it reaches the end of its scan, at B, the beam is cut off and reappears at C to start scanning the next line. The dotted line shows the path of retrace the beam would take if it were not cut off. The dimensions of this drawing are exaggerated for simplicity.

pulse is applied to the electron gun grid, and at approximately the same moment the current in the vertically-deflecting set of coils is reversed. Thus the beam is cut off and yanked back up to the top of the target to begin a new field.

However, the horizontal lines scanned during the first field are not close enough together to give a full picture definition. To fill in these gaps between lines, the beam begins its scanning of the second field at a point halfway between the first and second lines it traced before. The horizontal lines of the second field are thus interlaced between the lines of the first. When the beam reaches the end of this second field, it is again blanked out, and returned to the same point of the target at which the first field began. The completion of the second field marks the end of a *frame*. This system of copying the target image rather sketchily at one moment and then filling in the missing details at the next is known as interlaced scanning.

Some Television Statistics

The remarkable ingenuity of the interlaced scanning system comes sharply into focus when some of the technical statistics of television are examined. One field is scanned in 1/60 of a second. While the video signal obtained for that field does not correspond to a fully detailed picture of the object before the camera, it corresponds to a complete picture in the sense that the picture is the result of scanning the entire height and width dimensions of what the camera lens sees. The television viewer, watching the screen of his set at home, gets a fleeting image of this field. Before that image has a chance to fade from his consciousness, it is succeeded in the next 1/60 of a second by a second image hardly different from the first. Now 1/60 of a second is an extremely short interval; the actors in the televised scene have barely shifted their positions in that time. Consequently the viewer gets a definite impression of continuous, fluid motion on the part of the principals in the scene as one field is rapidly succeeded by the next.

Obviously, if many lines are scanned in the short field interval of 1/60 of a second, the time allowed for scanning a single horizontal line must be extremely short. The standards of the Federal Communications Commission—the governing agency in the United States for radio and television—provide the clue for figuring this time interval. They specify a field of 262½ horizontal lines. Dividing 1/60, the time for one field, by 262½, the number of lines in that field, gives a result of 1/15,750. Thus the time occupied in scanning one horizontal line is the astonishingly brief interval of 1/15,750 of a second.

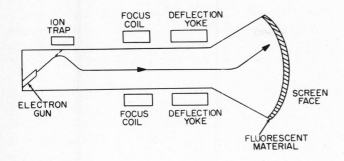

Fig. 6.6. *The TV Receiver Kinescope:* The video signal is applied to the grid (not shown) in the electron gun. The video-modulated beam, swung over the fluorescent material by the deflection yoke, pinpoints the light and dark elements of the televised picture. The electron gun is set at an angle to rid the beam of heavy ions; the ion trap re-directs the electrons to the screen, while the ions in the beam take the direction of the dotted line.

The TV Receiver Kinescope

The kinescope—or, as it is more familiarly known, the picture tube—is to the television receiver what the image orthicon tube is to the television transmitter. However, the kinescope's basic function is exactly the reverse of the image orthicon's. Where the orthicon begins with a visual image and ends with a video signal, the kinescope begins with a video signal and ends with a visual image.

Both tubes contain similar electron guns, similar focusing coils, and similar deflection coils. But in the kinescope, the target for the scanning beam produced by the electron gun is a fluorescent coating on the inner wall of the tube's face. When this coating is struck by the electron beam, it emits energy in the form of light; and the intensity of the light emitted is roughly proportional to the intensity of the electron beam. This suggests that the video signal with which the kinescope begins its picture-painting process should be applied to the electron gun's grid since it is the grid's job to control the intensity of the electron beam. With the video signal thus varying its intensity, the electron beam sketches out the light and shade pattern of the transmitted picture on the television receiver's screen as it scans the tube's fluorescent coating.

There is a type of painting known as pointillism, in which the artist gets his effect by bunching tiny dabs of tint. Viewed up close, such a painting makes no sense; but seen from a distance, the dots coalesce to form definitely recognizable objects. If the pointillist painter were to adopt the scientific method of spotting his dabs of color along a horizontal line at the top of the canvas and follow that policy all the way down to the bottom, then come back and fill the spaces be-

tween the lines with more rows of dots, he would exactly duplicate the action of the television receiver kinescope.

Looking at the deflection yoke in a television receiver gives the impression that the deflection coils in the yoke are wound about the tube axis. If they were, they could not possibly fulfill their function. They are wound in pancake form, around a line at right angles to the long axis of the tube, and are pressed into a curve to fit the tube neck. Thus, as in the image orthicon, their magnetic fields are at right angles to the tube axis. The function of the focus coil is also similar to that of its fellow in the image orthicon: to keep stray electrons from wandering away from their proper path.

A device with which practically all kinescopes are equipped is the ion trap, a permanently magnetized metal piece mounted on a clamp fitting around the neck of the tube just ahead of the electron gun. Along with electrons, the gun emits heavy ions ripped out of the cathode material. These massive ions are not easily deflected; if nothing were done to trap them, they would continually bombard the center of the fluorescent target and burn a hole in it. They are controlled by setting the electron gun in the tube so that it is directed towards the side of the tube neck. The electrons are redirected towards the fluorescent target by the magnetic field of the ion trap, leaving the ions to bang harmlessly against the glass neck of the tube.

Synchronization

In the language of electronics, a device which operates properly only when controlled by signals from a distant source is called, for obvious reasons, a "slave." The kinescope of the television receiver is in the slave category. Its beam is controlled in intensity by the video signal which is developed in the image orthicon, transmitted to the receiver, and applied to the kinescope grid.

But the scanning movement of the kinescope beam must also be controlled from the transmitter. If the beam is to reproduce exactly the image scanned by the transmitter image orthicon, it must move in synchronism with the beam of the latter; the two beams must be focused on the same relative point in their targets at exactly the same moment. Thus, the two beams scan each horizontal line in synchronism. At the end of the line, a highly negative voltage is applied simultaneously to the grids of the two tubes to cut both off, and a *sync pulse* is sent to the receiver commanding it to reverse the current through the horizontally-deflecting set of coils in the kinescope deflection yoke. At the same moment, the current through the image orthicon's horizontally-deflecting coil is reversed, and the beams of both tubes swing back to begin the scan of the next line.

The same sort of thing occurs when both scanning beams have come to the bottom of their targets: the currents in their respective deflection coils are reversed to bring the beams back to the top of their targets and start them scanning a new field.

Aspect Ratio

In the movies, a single frame of a film strip is quite small; but when the film is projected onto the theater screen, that small frame is expanded to respectable dimensions.

The same idea is applicable to the TV system. The target in the image orthicon is small; but the picture which appears on the kinescope screen in the home is much larger. As a matter of fact, the picture can be increased or decreased in both width and height at the whim of the owner of the set. But if the image is not to be distorted, if the men and women portrayed in it are not to be excessively tall or short, fat or thin, the proportions of the picture should be exactly the same as the proportions of the image orthicon target. The ratio of the target's width to its height is as 4 is to 3. Regardless of the actual dimensions of the picture at the receiver, then, the same *aspect ratio* of 4:3 should be preserved.

The parallel drawn here between television and the movies is apt; TV borrowed its aspect ratio from Hollywood.

The Radar Scope

If modern television has taken some of the movies' standards, it has also relied heavily on radar. Urged on by the need, in World War II, for inventing more and better tracking devices than the enemy, electronics engineers made tremendous progress in radar knowledge and techniques. These they applied so successfully to television, that by the time peace was restored, the present system of television was almost completely developed.

Since the two systems are similar in many ways, it is to be expected that the television picture tube would resemble the radar scope. Like the TV tube, the radar scope is equipped with an electron gun, a deflection system, and a fluorescent screen on which an image of light and dark areas is displayed. The type of display depends on the type of equipment used and the information the equipment is designed to acquire.

PPI Scope

A common variety of radar equipment offers the PPI or plan position indicator display, in which a map of the territory surrounding the radar antenna appears on the face of the scope.

The antenna of the PPI radar rotates continuously through a complete circle. As it does so, it emits rapid bursts of high frequency signals which cover a narrow sector of the scanned area. The time interval between the emission of the "main bang" from the antenna and the return of echo pulses is so very short compared with the speed of rotation of the antenna—the signal and its echoes travel with the speed of light—that the antenna can be considered stationary in that interval.

While the antenna is in that relatively stationary position, it receives echoes in the form of a train of pulses. Since objects closest to the antenna reflect the r-f energy directed at them earlier than objects further away, the initial pulses in the train represent solid bodies nearest the antenna. The remainder of the pulses are spaced out in proportion to the remoteness of the objects reflecting them. This pulse train is applied as a video signal to the control grid of the PPI scope.

The center of the display on the circular face of the scope represents the position of the antenna. This is the point struck by the tube's electron beam in its resting position. However, the beam is allowed to rest only for a moment. The instant the antenna emits its main bang of r-f, the electron beam is swung radially outward from the center of the tube face. As it does so, it traces a visible line on the tube's fluorescent screen, a line composed of light and dark gradations corresponding to the pulses fed to the electron gun grid. If the radial deflection of the electron beam sweeps the beam outward from the tube face center at a constant rate, the lights and darks of the traced line will be spaced in the same way as the echo pulses. Thus that line, as seen on the scope screen, will be an accurate picture of the terrain illuminated by the antenna's r-f beam at that moment.

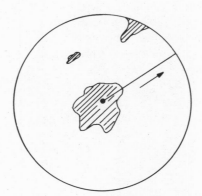

Fig. 6.7. *The PPI Display:* The radial line traced by the electron beam rotates around the tube screen to paint out a map of the radar-swept terrain. The arrow indicates direction of the trace.

When the electron beam has finished its scan out to the limit of the tube screen, a highly negative blanking pulse is put on the grid to blank out the beam, and the beam is quickly snapped back to its resting point at the screen center. By the time the antenna lets loose its next r-f bang, it has rotated some small angle around its axis. When the bang occurs, the electron beam leaves its resting place to begin the sweep of a second radial line, painting a light and dark picture of the echoes from the terrain as it goes; the angle between the second and first scanned lines on the tube face is exactly equal to the angle through which the antenna has turned. As the antenna continues its rotation, the electron beam continues its radial sweeps. Thus by the time the antenna has turned through one whole revolution, the electron beam has painted a map of the whole circle of the surrounding area.

Since the antenna takes several seconds to complete a revolution—a rather long interval as time is reckoned in electronics—the picture traced by the first few sweeps of the electron beam should not be allowed to fade before the rest of the radial lines in the circle have been swept out. If the material of which the tube's fluorescent screen is made has a long *persistence,* all parts of the PPI pattern will remain visible simultaneously. A long persistence screen is one in which the light produced fades out completely only after a long time has elapsed.

PPI Radar Synchronization

In the PPI radar, the slave system prevails just as it does in television. The radar system, however, demands that the electron beam in the radar scope be slaved to the antenna as well as to the transmitter. The trace of the beam from the center of the tube face outward must begin at the instant the antenna delivers its main bang. Also, the rotation of the radial trace around the face of the tube must keep in step with the rotation of the antenna around its mast.

The first slaving operation is guaranteed through coordination between the oscillator of the transmitter and the sweep circuits. At the instant the oscillator delivers its r-f burst to the antenna, a sync pulse is sent to the sweep circuits. The pulse triggers the circuits into delivering a steadily increasing current to the deflection coils, and the magnetic field generated by the current moves the tube's electron beam steadily outward from its resting point at the center of the tube face to the outer rim. Thus the radial movement of the beam is kept slaved to the r-f radiation of the antenna.

If the deflection coils around the neck of the radar scope remain stationary, the radial line traced by the electron beam will also remain stationary. To keep the line rotating around the face of the tube, the deflection coils must be kept revolving around the neck of the tube. Some connection must therefore be made between the coils and the antenna to maintain the slave relationship between the traced line and the antenna. A mechanical connection between the two is not often practical; the antenna is usually so far away from the scope that a whole mess of gears, shafts, and pulleys would be needed to link them together. It is far better to use *synchros*.

A synchro is a small device equipped with a shaft

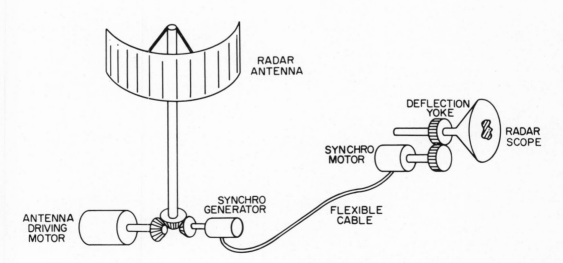

Fig. 6.8. *Slaving Deflection Yoke of Scope to Radar Antenna:* The antenna driving motor rotates the PPI radar antenna and the shaft of the synchro generator. A signal sent along the cable to the synchro motor rotates the radar scope deflection yoke in step with the antenna. Thus the radial trace of the electron beam in the scope turns in synchronism with the antenna's rotation.

and energized by an a-c voltage. In the type of synchro known as the *synchro generator,* rotation of the shaft produces an a-c signal proportional to the angle through which the shaft is turned. The opposite number of this device is the *synchro motor.* If the synchro motor is provided with an a-c signal, its shaft will respond by turning through an angle proportional to the signal. A connection between the output of the synchro generator and the input of the synchro motor through a long flexible cable can establish a mechanical linkage: when the shaft of the synchro generator at one end of the cable is turned through a particular angle, the shaft of the synchro motor at the other end automatically rotates through the same angle.

This system can coordinate the PPI radar antenna and the radar scope deflection coils. The same set of gears used to rotate the antenna also turns the shaft of a synchro generator. The signal output from the generator is brought through a cable to a synchro motor whose shaft is geared to the radar scope deflection yoke. Thus, as the antenna makes its repeated, unwearying round, the deflection yoke revolves with it around the neck of the radar tube.

Electrostatic Deflection, the Oscilloscope

The "writing" tubes discussed so far all employ the method of electromagnetic deflection, in which the electron beam doing the writing is moved over its fluorescent target by the magnetic fields of deflection

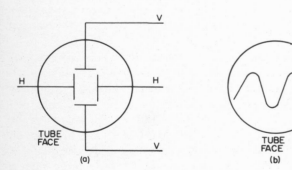

Fig. 6.9. *Electrostatic Deflection Plates:* (a) The horizontally-deflecting plates, labelled H, move the beam horizontally; the vertically-deflecting plates are marked V. This is the view of the plates through the tube face if there were no fluorescent screen. Connections to the plates are usually made through prongs in the tube base; (b) The wave shape of an unknown voltage on the oscilloscope tube face. The sweep circuit voltage on the horizontally-deflecting plates carries the beam steadily across the face of the tube; the unknown voltage, applied to the vertically-deflecting plates simultaneously swings the beam up and down.

coils. There is another type of writing tube, however, which uses an electric field between parallel plates as the beam-deflecting means. Aside from their differences in deflection modes—plus the fact that engineers generally prefer electromagnetic to electrostatic deflection—the two types are practically identical.

Electrostatic deflection works on the basic principle that a force of attraction exists between electrons and a positive charge, and a force of repulsion between electrons and a negative charge. In the writing tube using this principle, there are two sets of parallel plates. One of these sets is oriented in the horizontal plane, the other in the vertical plane. Both sets are placed in the flaring angle of the tube bell so that the open square they form is pierced at its center by the undeflected beam. The beam is thus free to move up and down or sideways in response to voltages applied to the plates. That pair of parallel plates which moves the beam vertically is termed *vertically-deflecting;* the remaining pair moves the beam horizontally, and is called *horizontally-deflecting.* Focusing of the beam is accomplished by purely electric means; the focusing devices are the anodes in the electron gun and a heavily positive anode coating of graphite on the inner glass wall.

Tubes of this type are frequently used in the very versatile device known as the oscilloscope—or oscillograph. The oscilloscope is usually used for viewing the shape of an unknown wave. In this application, the terminals of the unknown voltage are connected to the vertically-deflecting plates. To the horizontally-deflecting plates are connected the output terminals of the *sweep circuit,* an electronic arrangement within the instrument which repeatedly generates a steadily rising and sharply falling voltage. Thus the electron beam in the tube is swung across the face of the tube at an even rate, whips back to its starting point, and recommences the horizontal scan at its even pace. As it makes its repeated horizontal scan under the influence of the sweep circuit, the electron beam is also being deflected vertically by the unknown voltage.

By being waggled up and down at the same time it is moved evenly across the face of the tube, the beam writes the shape of the unknown wave on the fluorescent screen. Since the beam repeatedly traces the same path —it will do so as long as the voltages are maintained on the deflecting plates—the shape of the unknown voltage traced in light on the fluorescent screen will maintain itself unwaveringly for leisurely examination.

Ultra High Frequency Vacuum Tubes

The history of communications through electromagnetic waves is a record of continuous exploration and exploitation of the upper radio frequencies. After the conquest of the low frequency broadcast bands and the higher frequency bands used for transoceanic broadcasting, researchers began work on the range of carrier frequencies known loosely as very high frequency or vhf. This is the range now used in the United States for FM radio and television transmissions.

The development of radar showed that satisfactory operation of the system depends on the use of frequencies even higher than vhf. Here radar engineers took a tip from Nature. Bats are nearly blind, yet in flying about the caves they inhabit, they cleverly manage to evade every obstacle placed in their path. Naturalists know how the bats manage their adroit navigation: in flight, the winged rodents emit sounds of extraordinarily high pitch from time to time. If an obstacle is close to the animal, the echo of its cry is immediately returned; if the obstacle is off at a distance, its reflection of the sound will take longer to reach the bat's acute ears. Furthermore, the bat knows that the *direction* from which the echo comes is the direction in which the obstacle lies.

The bat's secret in locating accurately the solid bodies in his vicinity is the high pitch of the cries he emits. High frequency sounds are much more directional than those of low frequency. If the bat is not consciously aware of this scientific fact, radar engineers are. The oscillators the radar engineer designs for his radar gear are generators of ultra high frequency electromagnetic waves. The engineer knows that by using radiation of such high frequency he is limiting the range of his equipment because of the line-of-sight barrier (Chapter 5); nevertheless, he is willing to make the sacrifice if his equipment gains in accuracy.

Transit Time

When the first investigations of ultra high frequency began, it was discovered that the tubes which were so helpful in equipment using lower frequencies were practically helpless at the higher. One difficulty is *transit time*. The electron in an ordinary triode must have enough time to make its transit through the cathode-grid space before the signal on the grid has made much of a change. If that signal has a frequency in the ultra high range, it will first put the grid at a positive potential to welcome the oncoming electron; the signal's negative phase will arrive so soon thereafter, however, that the grid may become negative enough to repel the electron before it can get there. The time for one complete cycle of uhf is so short—it is measured in small fractions of a millionth of a second—that the electron is apt to be kept hesitating uncertainly between the grid and the cathode and never arrive at the plate of the tube. Obviously, the tube good enough for broadcast band or even vhf equipment is useless or too inefficient for uhf.

Nor is this all. In wiring broadcast band equipment, nothing serious happens if a longer lead between connection points is substituted for a shorter one. But uhf equipment wiring is much more critical. A wire is made of metal, and therefore possesses some inductance, the quality of a coil which lends it the ability to oppose the flow of a varying current (Chapter 2). Because the currents in uhf equipment vary at such a tremendous rate, even a short length of wire has enough inductance to impede current flow. This fact makes necessary two peculiarities in radar oscillator design: first, currents are carried from one part of the oscillator to another by means of hollow tubes, known as *waveguides,* rather than by wires; second, because the wire leads connecting the internal elements in ordinary tubes to the prongs at the base are much too long, special types of tube must be used for the uhf oscillator.

The problem of transit time is reduced in these special types by miniaturization. In these smaller tubes, the electrodes are closer together and the time of flight of an electron to or through them is consequently diminished. As for the problem of long leads, this is controlled by the ingenious design of many of these tubes, in which the associated circuit is so intimately a part of the tube itself that leads are rarely necessary.

The Cavity Resonator

Every oscillator tube must be somehow connected to a resonant device. That device may be a coil and capacitor arrangement like that discussed in Chapter 3; but, whatever its nature, the resonant device is necessary if the energy radiated by the oscillator is to have the particular frequency the circuit designer has planned for it.

At uhf, however, a resonant coil and capacitor circuit is impractical because of the length of leads such a circuit requires, and the tendency of high frequencies to exaggerate the electrical characteristics of coils and capacitors. Uhf engineers have therefore resorted to the *cavity resonator* as their favorite resonating device in radar and other ultra high frequency equipment.

The cavity resonator is basically little more than a hollow metal chamber. Its principle of operation is somewhat like a glass tube partially filled with water. When such a tube is struck, it emits a musical tone whose pitch can be varied by changing the length of the air column either through pouring some of the water out or by putting more water in. In similar fashion, the cavity resonator can be tuned to a particular frequency by adjustment of its dimensions. And, just as the glass tube emits its characteristic tone under the shock of a mechanically applied blow, the cavity resonator emits its characteristic electromagnetic wave frequency under the excitation of a uhf vacuum tube oscillator.

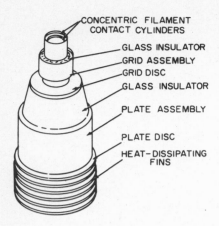

CONCENTRIC FILAMENT
CONTACT CYLINDERS
GLASS INSULATOR
GRID ASSEMBLY
GRID DISC
GLASS INSULATOR
PLATE ASSEMBLY
PLATE DISC
HEAT–DISSIPATING
FINS

Fig. 6.10. *A Type of Lighthouse Tube:* The tube, 2½ inches high and 1¼ inches at its base, is pushed top foremost into the cavity. Terminals inside the cavity make contact with filament cylinders, grid and plate discs, supplying them with necessary voltage. The tube is cooled by circulating air around the heat-dissipating fins.

The cavity resonator thus offers a means of bringing the oscillator tube so close to its resonant "circuit"— the cavity resonator is, in effect, a resonant circuit— that no connecting leads are necessary. The lighthouse type of oscillator tube, for example, is connected to its cavity resonator simply by being shoved into the res- onator's space. The klystron and the magnetron tubes have their cavities built into them.

Lighthouses, Klystrons, and Magnetrons

The *lighthouse* tube, so named because of its appear- ance, is a vacuum tube triode suitable for uhf use. Its three electrodes are set extremely close together to keep transit time short. Electrical contact to the elec- trodes is made through sealed-in metal discs. The tube's

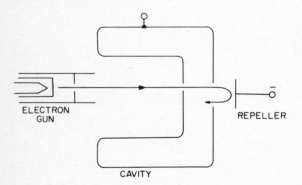

ELECTRON
GUN
REPELLER
CAVITY

Fig. 6.11. *Schematic Diagram of Klystron:* Electrons from the electron gun are accelerated to the highly positive cav- ity. They are reflected in bunched formation by the repeller, and set up oscillations in the cavity.

socket is really the cavity into which the tube is inserted. When the tube is slipped into place, the discs click into contact with their proper connections, and the electrodes are brought into the circuit.

The *klystron,* a second variety of uhf oscillator, is made up of a small electron gun, a cavity resonator, and a repeller electrode arranged in that order. A highly positive voltage is applied to the cavity, and a negative voltage, which can be varied, to the repeller. Electrons from the gun are accelerated towards the cavity and pass through grids to the repeller. Because of the re- peller's negative voltage, the electrons return in bunches to the cavity, which is thus stimulated into resonating. The pulses of electrons fed back to the cavity from the repeller have the same effect in causing the klystron to oscillate as repeated blows on the glass tube men- tioned above have on the contained air column.

We have seen, in the image orthicon and radar scopes described in this chapter, that a magnetic field can cause the path of a moving electron to curve. If the magnetic field is made strong enough, it can force a stream of electrons to curve through a complete circle and thus double back on itself. This method of having electrons go round and round at an extremely rapid pace is the one followed in the uhf oscillator tube known as the *magnetron.* The tube is really a diode, with a cathode to emit electrons, and a plate or anode in the shape of a cavity resonator. The magnetic field is directed at right angles to the electron path, and its strength is such that the electrons just miss the plate in making their circular tour back to the cathode. So rapidly do these electrons whirl around their circle within the cavity that the magnetron's output frequency —which depends on the number of times per second the electrons complete their circular path—may be as much as 30,000 megacycles, equal to 30,000,000,000 cycles per second.

Gas Tubes

The special tube types discussed so far in this chapter have been vacuum tubes. In the course of vacuum tube manufacture, every precaution is taken to remove as much of the tube's gas content as possible; the presence of any such unwanted substance would only interfere with the operation of the tube.

There are some special tubes, however, which de- mand the presence of chemically inactive gases for proper operation. While these gas tubes cannot be as finely controlled as vacuum types, they offer the ad- vantage of being able to carry much greater currents. Gifted with this and other valuable characteristics, gas tubes find a great many applications in electronic equip- ment, usually as diodes or triodes.

The Gas Diode

Like its corresponding vacuum tube, the gas diode contains a cathode and a plate. The cathode may be of the hot variety, emitting electrons when heated by the filament it encloses. If the plate of the hot cathode diode is given only a small positive voltage, the electrons drawn to it travel with low speed and therefore low energy. In the course of their movement to the plate, they collide with gas molecules, but lack the necessary energy to ionize them to any great extent (Chapter 1). Plate current will therefore remain small as long as the voltage applied to the plate is correspondingly small.

As the plate voltage is increased, the plate current will increase in proportion. Further increases in plate voltage, however, will attract electrons from the hot cathode with a velocity sufficient to dislodge many secondary electrons from the gas molecules struck. These secondary electrons join with the primary electrons in their march to the plate, smashing into other gas molecules as they go. As a consequence of these repeated impacts between electrons and molecules, a mass migration of electrons arrives at the plate. The tube reaching this point is said to have *fired,* and the potential supplied to the plate to initiate the heavy electron avalanche is known as the *firing potential.*

A similar phenomenon occurs in the *cold cathode* gas diode. The cathode in this type of tube is simply a small metal rod with no auxiliary filament. It is thus incapable of emitting primary electrons, but there are always free electrons among the gas molecules as a result of external radiation effects (Chapter 1). When a voltage is applied between the plate and cathode of the tube with the positive potential at the plate, the free electrons trapped in the electric field move in the direction of the attracting plate. If the voltage across the tube is then brought to the firing potential, electron flow within the tube becomes intense.

Because the gas diode carries an intense current in

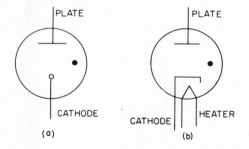

Fig. 6.12. *Schematics of Gas Diodes:* **The schematic of the cold cathode diode is shown in (a), that of the hot cathode tube in (b). The heavy dot inside the circles indicates that the tubes are gas-filled.**

firing, it behaves like a low resistance device. The voltage drop across the tube is therefore small, and its use in a circuit will allow that much more voltage to be developed across some other part of the circuit where high voltages should be produced. The gas diode is therefore an asset in heavy duty power supply circuits.

If the voltage drop across the firing gas diode is relatively low, it is also constant. It remains constant, furthermore, even if the current through it changes within certain limits. This peculiar characteristic gives the tube special value as a *voltage regulating* device in a power supply. In a poorly regulated supply, a heavy current passing through the bleeder resistor from other sections of the equipment depresses the positive d-c voltages furnished by the bleeder. What are supposed to be constant voltages thus become varying voltages. The way to steady the bleeder's d-c voltages is to connect a cold cathode gas tube across it, with the cathode of the tube joined to the negative terminal of the bleeder, and the plate to the positive terminal. With no filament to waste power, the cold cathode tube makes an economical voltage regulator when added to a power supply in this fashion. These tubes—their designations usually begin with the letters VR to indicate their function—are found in well-designed electronic equipment.

The Thyratron

When a grid is added to the gas diode to make it a triode, the resulting tube is generally referred to as a *thyratron.* The grid in the thyratron is nothing like the delicate wire of the vacuum tube triode; it is a rather massive metal cylinder.

In the thyratron, it is the voltage on the grid which does the firing. The plate is supplied with a fairly high positive voltage; but if the voltage on the grid is sufficiently negative before the tube is fired, the tube will be in cutoff. As the negative bias on the grid is reduced, a small plate current flow begins. If the bias continues to be reduced, a point will be reached at which the electrons moving through the grid travel at a sufficiently high speed to ionize the gas molecules in the tube. Then, of course, the tube fires.

Once firing takes place, however, the grid loses all control over the electron flow. The heavy gas molecules, now positively charged because they have lost electrons, feel the attraction of the negative grid and move slowly towards it. With the strong positive charge of these ions gathered around it, the effect of the grid's negative voltage is neutralized. Even restoring the cutoff voltage to the grid will not be able to stop the intense flow of electrons to the plate. The only way to halt the high plate current is to drop the applied plate voltage to the *de-ionization potential.* At this value, the plate voltage exerts less attraction on the electrons than the positive ions, the electrons are reunited to the ions, and the firing stops. With its positive ion sheath now de-ionized, the grid is once again in control.

The ability of the thyratron to control heavy currents is used in theater lighting circuitry. Just before the curtain rises on Act I, the house lights are dimmed. The performance of this task requires a gradual reduction of the immense amount of current the house lights draw. It is done by banks of heavy-duty thyratrons controlled from backstage switchboards.

GLOSSARY

Accelerating anode. An electrode given a high positive potential to speed up the moving electrons in the beam of a writing tube.

Aspect ratio. The 4:3 ratio of picture width to height in television.

Blanking. Cutting off the beam in a writing tube.

Cavity resonator. The metal chamber in a uhf oscillator which determines the frequency of oscillation.

Cold cathode gas tube. A gas-filled tube in which the cathode is not heated.

Decelerating ring. A metallic ring on the inner wall of an image orthicon tube used to slow down electrons in the scanning beam before they reach the target.

Deflection coils. Coils of wire in which the magnetic field used to swing the electron beam in writing tubes is generated.

Deflection yoke. The ring around the neck of a writing tube which contains the deflection coils.

Electromagnetic deflection. Swerving the beam in writing tubes by means of a magnetic field; i. e., by means of deflection coils.

Electron gun. The device in a writing tube which generates the electron beam.

Electron image. The pattern of electrons emitted by the image orthicon photocathode which corresponds to the light and shade in the object before the television camera.

Electron multiplier. A tube with several successive plates which multiplies electrons incident on the plates through secondary emission.

Electrostatic deflection. Swerving the beam in writing tubes by means of an electrostatic field; i. e., by means of deflection plates.

Firing. The heavy flow of electrons from cathode to plate in a gas tube.

Firing potential. The potential applied to the plate of a gas diode or the grid of a thyratron at which firing occurs.

Fluorescent screen. The coating on the inner wall of the face of a television receiver kinescope; the means of converting electrical energy into light.

Focusing coil. The coil in a writing tube which guides the electrons in the beam.

Gas tube. An electron tube into which a chemically inactive gas has been injected.

Horizontally-deflecting coils. The deflecting coils of a writing tube which exert a sidewise force on the writing beam.

Horizontally-deflecting plates. The deflecting plates in a writing tube which exert a sidewise force on the writing beam.

Image orthicon. A highly sensitive television camera tube.

Ion trap. A permanent magnet clamped to the neck of a kinescope which prevents ions from striking the kinescope screen.

Kinescope. The writing tube in a television receiver which converts the picture signal into light.

Klystron. A uhf oscillator tube containing its own cavity resonator, which depends on the bunching of electrons for its operation.

Lighthouse tube. A uhf triode resembling a miniature lighthouse.

Magnetron. A uhf diode oscillator containing its own cavity resonator, in which electrons are whirled in a circular path by a magnetic field.

Main bang. The burst of r-f emitted by a radar antenna.

Megacycle. One million cycles.

Oscillograph. A test instrument using a writing tube which shows the wave shape of an input voltage.

Oscilloscope. Same as oscillograph.

Persistence. The length of time in which the fluorescent screen of a writing tube holds the written image.

Photocathode. The electrode in the image orthicon which emits the electron image when struck by light from the televised object.

Photocell. A vacuum tube which converts light into electrical energy.

PPI. Plan position indicator; a type of radar scope on which the map of the area surrounding the radar antenna is plotted.

Slave. A piece of electronic gear under the control of signals from a master equipment.

Sync pulse. An electrical pulse transmitted to a slave circuit by the master equipment to operate the slave in synchronism with the master.

Sweep circuits. The circuits in equipment containing a writing tube which guide the movement of the beam in the tube.

Synchro generator. A shafted electronic component which emits a low frequency a-c signal proportional to the angle of rotation of its shaft.

Synchro motor. The reverse of a synchro generator; this device converts a 60 or 400 cycle per second signal into a proportional rotation of its shaft.

Target. The surface struck by the electron beam in a writing tube.

Target screen. The fine screen near the image orthicon target which takes up secondary electrons emitted by the target.

Thyratron. A triode gas tube.

Uhf. Ultra high frequency; the frequencies, roughly, in the 100 to 10,000 megacycle range.

Vertically-deflecting coils. The deflecting coils of a writing tube which exert an up and down force on the writing beam.

Vertically-deflecting plates. The deflecting plates in a writing tube which exert an up and down force on the writing beam.

Vhf. Very high frequency; the frequencies, roughly, in the 10 to 100 megacycle range.

Voltage regulation. The ability of a power supply to keep its output d-c voltage steady though drawing varying currents.

Waveguides. Hollow metal tubes used to interconnect points in uhf equipment.

Writing tube. A special type of vacuum tube in which an electron beam automatically writes or scans information on a target.

Chapter Seven

THE SUPERHETERODYNE

ABOUT TWENTY years after the invention of the triode, another development vital to the progress of electronics took place. This was the invention of the *superheterodyne*.

The superheterodyne was created in the early twenties, at a time when radio broadcasting as an industry had barely begun. Practical FM was still unknown, television was a science fiction writer's fancy, and not even the most advanced military tactician suspected that a weapon as powerful as radar would one day exist. Nor could any of these remarkable systems have been realized in their present advanced state but for the invention of the superheterodyne.

The TRF Receiver

Before the superheterodyne revolution in radio reception, the reigning instrument was the tuned radio frequency receiver, abbreviated trf. Like many receivers before and since, the trf adhered to the classic pattern of forward end, detector, and rear end (Chapter 3). The detector and rear end have carried almost intact to the present day. It was the forward end in the trf which offered so many difficulties that this type of receiver had to be abandoned.

The forward end of the trf consisted of a series—*cascade,* as electronic engineers term it—of tuned r-f amplifiers. As we saw in Chapter 5, the r-f amplifier consists of a transformer, a variable capacitor connected across the transformer secondary, and an amplifying tube circuit. The one component here which offers the greatest difficulty, as far as design is concerned, is the transformer. If the input signal across the primary winding of the transformer is to be stepped up in the sec-

ondary, the magnetic field created in the core of the transformer by the signal current must be a strong one. This is no problem in the power transformer, in which an iron core is used to concentrate the magnetic field. But the power transformer deals only with a-c voltages of low frequency, 60 or 400 cycles per second. For frequencies of 600 *kilocycles* per second and higher, the frequencies of carriers used in radio communication, the energy loss in the iron core of this type of transformer is so great that the transformer is practically useless. The transformers between the antenna and the first r-f amplifier and between the succeeding r-f stages in the trf receiver must therefore be wound around forms made of an insulating material, with nothing but air in the core of the form. The amplification of the trf's front end stages is therefore poorer than it might be.

A second and perhaps even more serious defect of the trf receiver is its low selectivity. For any one setting of the receiver's tuning dial, a narrow band of carrier frequencies is admitted to the receiver while all other frequencies are kept out. Suppose, for example, that the width of the admitted band is 10 kc and that the receiver is tuned to a transmitter whose carrier is 1000 kc. Expressed in the form of a fraction, the selectivity of the receiver is 10/1000 or 1/100. The value of that fraction could be doubled if some means were found to halve the carrier frequency to 500 kc; then the selectivity fraction would be 10/500, or 1/50.

Thus the root of the twin problems of poor sensitivity and selectivity haunting the trf set is the high frequency of the carrier signals. Its designers tried to combat those evils by adding more and more tuned r-f stages to the forward end. While this method worked to some extent with the low broadcast-band frequencies, it would fail dismally if it had to be applied to the much higher frequencies of FM, television, and radar. The superheterodyne receiver provides a better solution by making a direct attack on the root of the problem: it simply lowers the frequency of the incoming carrier through the physical principle known as *heterodyning*.

Heterodyning

Piano tuners are familiar with the phenomenon of heterodyning. If two neighboring tones on the piano are struck simultaneously—the effect is more pronounced if it is tried at the high end of the keyboard—the measured rise and fall of a third note is heard along with the two tones struck. This third note is the heterodyne or *beat note,* and its frequency is equal to the difference between the frequencies of the two original tones.

If heterodyning can be done with sound waves, it can be done also with electrical waves. A certain oscillator, let us say, puts out a voltage of 1000 kc, in frequency. If its output is added to the output of a second oscillator of 1455 kc in a detector circuit, a signal of 455 kc will emerge from the detector. This 455 kc signal is the beat frequency, equal to the difference between the original 1000 and 1455 kc signals.

We can take this one step further. Suppose the 1000 kc signal is amplitude modulated. If the signal added to it is an unmodulated 1455 kc signal, the output of the detector in which the two frequencies are combined will be a signal of 455 kc *carrying the same modulations as the original 1000 kc carrier*. This is the solution to the problem of high frequency carriers which the superheterodyne supplies. The original modulated signal is furnished by a single r-f amplifier stage, after the antenna, in the form of a received carrier. To the carrier signal, the unmodulated output of a separate oscillator is added. The output of the detector in which

these two signals are combined is a new version of the carrier, bearing the same modulations as the old, but having a much lower frequency. This new signal, known as the *intermediate frequency* (i-f) signal is amplified and then brought to a second detector—the diode circuit of Chapter 3. Here, the signal goes through a process we have already seen: the second detector strips the i-f carrier of its modulating signal—audio in AM and FM receivers, video in television and radar—and passes that signal to the appropriate amplifier. If the signal is audio, it will be transferred from the audio amplifier to the speaker for conversion into sound; if video, it will be brought from the video amplifier to a writing tube for conversion into light.

Superheterodyne Tuning

As we can see, the chief distinction between superheterodyne and trf receivers is the reduction in carrier frequency, and the consequent ease of amplification, typical of the former. The superheterodyne has another advantage: its tuning system is simpler.

Some of the old trf receivers had as many as four r-f amplifier stages ahead of the detector. Since each stage, including the detector, had to have a resonant circuit of coil and variable capacitor at its input, a total of five of these capacitors—to say nothing of the coils—was needed. Furthermore, since each stage had to be tuned precisely to the same frequency at the same time, the capacitor rotor plates were required to turn simultaneously whenever the operator of the receiver decided to change stations. This mechanical problem was solved by mounting all the tuning capacitors in a single unit, with the rotor blades of each condenser attached to a single shaft running through the unit. The shaft, in turn, was linked by a gear or pulley unit to the tuning knob. By turning this knob, the operator could thus tune his set at will. Some of these huge "ganged

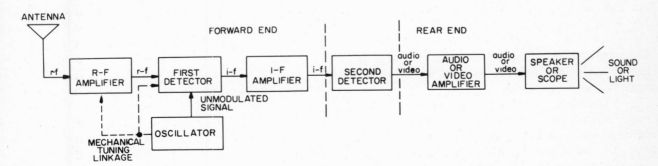

Fig. 7.1. *General Block Diagram of the Superheterodyne:* Arrows show the directions of flow and types of various signals. The dotted line between oscillator and r-f amplifier indicates mechanical ganging between tuning capacitors in the two circuits. Several amplifier stages may be included in the block labeled "i-f amplifier." Stages ahead of the second detector comprise the "forward end" of the receiver; stages after the second detector are the "rear end."

condenser" units, as they were called, are still to be seen in radio junk shops; they are now of no earthly use except for old radio buffs to cry over.

The superheterodyne did away with all that. In modern AM and FM receivers, there are units of three ganged condensers at most: one for the r-f amplifier, the second for the first detector, and the third for the oscillator. The r-f amplifier and first detector input circuits both tune to the same frequency—the r-f signal of the transmitter. Their capacitors are therefore identical in the number of rotor and stator plates each possesses. But the oscillator circuit, which must be tuned to a different frequency—usually a higher one than the r-f—requires a capacitor with fewer plates.

When the tuning knob of the superheterodyne is turned, the three capacitor rotors turn in step. Since the rotor of the oscillator capacitor is mounted on the same shaft as the others, *the difference between the r-f carrier frequency and the oscillator output frequency is always maintained*. If the dial of the receiver is set to the 1000 kc mark, for example, the r-f amplifier and first detector tuning capacitors are set to tune their circuits to that frequency; at the same time, the oscillator tuning capacitor is in position for an oscillator output frequency of 1455 kc. If the dial of the receiver is re-tuned to, say 800 kc, the r-f amplifier and first detector capacitors and their associated coils resonate to 800 kc while the oscillator capacitor's position is such that the circuit puts out a frequency of 1255 kc. Regardless of the setting of the tuning dial, the two signals entering the first detector of the superheterodyne are always 455 kc apart, and the output of the detector is always a 455 kc signal. This signal is passed on to the stages in the i-f amplifier section.

Obviously, if the signal coming into the i-f amplifier stages is at this same frequency of 455 kc regardless of the receiver dial setting, the i-f stages are relieved of the need to be tuned, and so are free of the necessity of continual adjustment.

The AM Superheterodyne

There is a definite reason for choosing as odd a figure as 455 kc in the foregoing example. This was the intermediate frequency decided upon by the Radio-Television Manufacturer's Association as the standard i-f for AM broadcast band superheterodynes, and it is the i-f still used in receivers of that type today. As a matter of fact, the example we have given is quite realistic: it not only points to a standard i-f actually in use, but also indicates that the frequency of the oscillator is almost always *higher* than the frequency of the incoming carrier signal. The superheterodyne principle would be just as valid if the oscillator frequency were lower

than the carrier frequency. As long as the difference between the two is the frequency to which the i-f amplifier stages will respond, the set will operate. But the effect of having the oscillator work at a higher frequency than the r-f carrier is to compress the frequency range covered and bring it within the compass of the r-f and oscillator tuning capacitors.

The CW Superheterodyne

In the AM system of broadcasting, the r-f carrier is a signal of constant frequency but varying amplitude. As we have seen (Chapter 3) the meaning the signal carries lies in the modulations of its peaks. It is possible, however, to charge a signal which varies neither in frequency nor in amplitude with meaning. Such a signal is called *continuous wave,* abbreviated CW; it is given its meaning through interruption into short and long trains of waves. These are the dots and dashes of the International Code.

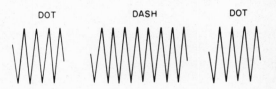

Fig. 7.2. CW Transmission: Unmodulated waves sent by a CW transmitter keying the letter R in International Code.

CW radio, nowadays, is mostly confined to ship and, to some extent, military communications. What with all the mechanical gadgetry designed to replace human CW radio operators, the art of handling a key seems to be a vanishing one. But the International Code is always a good thing to know, and so it is presented here:

INTERNATIONAL CODE

A	. —	N	— .
B	— . . .	O	— — —
C	— . — .	P	. — — .
D	— . .	Q	— — . —
E	.	R	. — .
F	. . — .	S	. . .
G	— — .	T	—
H	. . . .	U	. . —
I	. .	V	. . . —
J	. — — —	W	. — —
K	— . —	X	— . . —
L	. — . .	Y	— . — —
M	— —	Z	— — . .

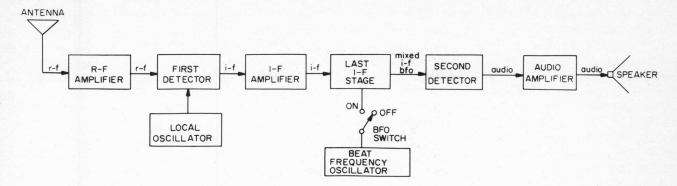

Fig. 7.3. *The CW Receiver Block Diagram:* When the BFO switch is in its ON position, the beat frequency oscillator is heterodyned with the CW i-f carrier to produce an audio tone. The oscillator in the front end of the receiver is often called the "local" oscillator to distinguish it from the bfo. For the sake of clarity, the last i-f amplifier is drawn as a separate block. With the exception of the bfo, the CW superheterodyne is the same as the AM superheterodyne.

The symbol R, for example, which in the radio operator's code book is the sign for "message received," would be transmitted by a group of separated short, long, and short train of waves. Since such waves are unmodulated, the diode detector in the receiver picking up the waves cannot produce an audio signal. At most, the speaker of the receiver would give faint clicks corresponding to the beginning and end of each wave section.

These CW wave trains, however, can be transformed into a singing tone easily heard by the radio operator. The method is to connect a separate oscillator, known as the *beat frequency oscillator,* to the last i-f stage of the receiver through a switch. If the "bfo" is tuned almost to the i-f, differing from it by a few thousand cycles per second, a signal equal in frequency to the difference between the i-f and bfo will appear at the output of the receiver second detector. Since the frequency of this signal is well within the audible range, it will come through the speaker as a tone of constant pitch. The frequency of the bfo is usually made variable to permit the operator to choose a pitch to his liking.

The principle behind this method of CW reception is the same heterodyning principle we have already seen. With the bfo tuned to 453 kc, for example, and the i-f at 455 kc, the signal appearing at the second detector output is a 2000 cycle audio note. This is amplified in the receiver audio amplifier, and comes through the speaker as a steady tone. Since the heterodyning between the i-f signal and the bfo signal can only take place if a train of waves comes through the i-f amplifier, the tone will be interrupted in the same way the received CW signal is interrupted. The purpose of the bfo switch, of course, is to permit the operator to hear either modulated or CW transmission as he pleases.

The FM Superheterodyne

Most people are accustomed to the idea that frequency modulation as a method of radio transmission was more or less an afterthought once amplitude modulation broadcasting had been developed. But records of the comparatively short history of electronic communication indicate that the first system considered was FM. Only when the problems of FM proved too tough for their limited resources did early experimenters fall back on AM as a better-than-nothing choice. It was not until the middle thirties, at a time when AM broadcasting was well on its way toward becoming a profitable industry, that the brilliant work of the American engineer Edwin H. Armstrong proved that frequency modulation was not

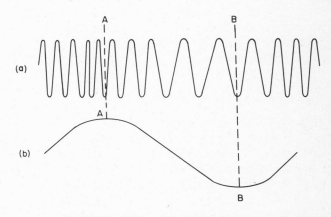

Fig. 7.4. *The FM Signal:* The carrier wave is shown in (a) and one cycle of modulating audio signal in (b). Waves in the carrier are compressed closest at point A, when the audio signal is at its maximum positive swing, and are most expanded at point B, when the audio signal is at its negative peak.

only practical, but was far superior to amplitude modulation as a system of radio broadcasting.

The fundamental idea of FM can be guessed from its name. If amplitude modulation consists of changing the amplitude of a carrier wave in accordance with an audio signal, then frequency modulation is the variation of the *frequency* of a carrier wave in accordance with an audio signal. A picture of the FM carrier would therefore be that of a wave which is compressed and expanded like the folds of an accordion. When the modulating audio signal reaches a high positive peak, the frequency of the carrier is at a high value. At that moment, the waves of the carrier are compressed; there are more waves in a given time interval. When the modulating audio signal swings to its negative peak, the carrier frequency is diminished. At that moment, the picture of the carrier is one of expanded waves, reflecting the condition of fewer cycles of carrier vibration per time interval. Between its positive and negative swings, the modulating audio signal goes momentarily through its zero voltage. The carrier at those times is at its *resting* frequency, the frequency it possesses when it is not under the audio's influence. All this can be summed up by the statement that the frequency of the carrier varies with the strength of the modulating audio signal at any particular moment.

The FM Band

By the time FM came out of the laboratory, in the World War II era, AM broadcasters were already solidly entrenched in the lower frequency bands. The Federal Communications Commission therefore licensed FM transmitters for operation in the 88 to 108 megacycle band, the present home grounds of FM stations. Since the FM receiver must respond to carriers of these frequencies, some 1000 times the frequencies of the AM broadcast band, it will naturally differ in some details from its AM relative. But the modern FM receiver is just as much a superheterodyne, follows almost the identical pattern, and even has identical names for its various stages. The important details in which the FM receiver differs from the AM receiver is, first, the much higher FM i-f of 10.7 mc—a natural consequence of the very high FM carrier frequency—and second, the circuit arrangement of the FM detector, which would have to be different from that of the AM detector since the basic principles of the two systems differ.

Like its AM counterpart, the oscillator in the FM receiver is usually at a higher frequency than the incoming carrier signal. The frequency of the oscillator is fixed for any one setting of the tuning dial. But the frequency of the FM carrier, even for the same dial setting, is continually being varied under the influence of the audio signal. Since the i-f is equal to the difference between the fixed frequency and the varying one, the frequency of the i-f signal will itself vary above and below its resting frequency of 10.7 mc. The i-f amplifiers in an FM receiver must therefore be equipped to amplify a range of frequencies around 10.7 mc.

The signal strengthened by the i-f amplifiers now enters the FM detector, which, like the AM detector, has the duty of picking the audio signal out of the carrier presented to it. But the FM detector's job is more complex: it reacts to the frequency variations in the i-f carrier by producing a positive peak signal when the carrier frequency shifts to one extreme, and a negative peak when the carrier frequency shifts to the other. By so doing, the detector circuit develops an audio signal which corresponds closely to the original audio signal at the transmitter studio. This signal is strengthened in the receiver audio amplifier, and is then fed to the speaker to be converted into sound.

The Television Superheterodyne

The superheterodyne, which can handle either AM or FM signals with ease, can do the same for television, which is a combination of both. But in handling tele-

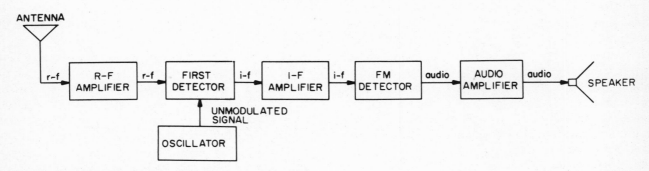

Fig. 7.5. *Block Diagram of the FM Superhetorodyne:* Compare this drawing with other block diagrams already given in this chapter.

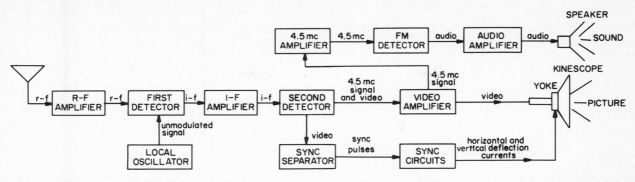

Fig. 7.6. *Block Diagram of the Modern TV Receiver:* The general pattern of the superheterodyne is apparent in this drawing. Separation of sight and sound signals occurs at the video amplifier. The sync circuits, which guide the scan-ning movements of the kinescope beam through the deflection yoke, are a special feature of receivers which appeal to the eye.

vision, the superheterodyne must be helped with additional circuits. These are the synchronization or *sync* circuits, entrusted with the job of sweeping the electron beam of the kinescope back and forth to paint the television picture.

The story of the TV superheterodyne picture naturally begins with the signals its antenna picks up, and which the receiver converts finally into sound and a picture. Every television transmitter sends out two carriers: a sound carrier, frequency-modulated by an audio signal, and a picture carrier, amplitude-modulated by a video signal. According to the regulations of the Federal Communications Commission, these carriers must be spaced 4.5 mc apart, with the sound carrier higher in frequency than the picture carrier. Both signals are picked up by the receiver antenna and are brought into the r-f amplifier. After being strengthened in that stage, the signals enter the first detector, where they are mixed with the output of a single local oscillator. The heterodyning which then takes place between the sound carrier and the local oscillator and between the picture carrier and the local oscillator, produces two i-f signals. One of these corresponds to the original sound carrier, and is consequently known as the sound i-f; the other corresponds to the original picture carrier, and is therefore the picture i-f. While these i-f signals carry the same modulations as the original carriers picked up by the receiver antenna, their frequencies are lower than those of the original carriers. The frequencies of the signals in many modern receiver models are 45.75 mc for the picture i-f carrier and 41.25 mc for the sound i-f.

Here, incidentally, we note a rather curious thing. Of the two r-f carriers picked up by the TV receiver antenna, the sound carrier is the higher; after conversion to i-f, the picture carrier is the higher. This mystery is solved when we recall that the oscillator is higher in frequency than either of the two received carriers. To take a practical example: a transmitter occupying Chan-nel 2 transmits a picture carrier of 55.25 mc and a sound carrier of 59.75 mc. These signals are picked up by the receiver and mixed with the local oscillator signal of 101 mc. The resulting picture i-f is 101 minus 55.25, or 45.75 mc; the sound i-f is 101 minus 59.75 or 41.25 mc. The picture i-f is thus the higher in frequency of the two. This example also indicates an even more important fact: the difference in frequency between the two carriers is 4.5 mc both *before and after* conversion to i-f.

Emerging from the first detector, the two i-f's are amplified together in the i-f strip—the engineer's term for the i-f amplifiers—and reach the second detector. This circuit is essentially the same as the diode detector of Chapter 3; it reacts to the amplitude modulated picture carrier as does any AM detector: it picks out the video signal, hands it on to the next stage—the video amplifier—and discards the carrier. But the detector performs another service as well. It sees the two approaching i-f signals as any heterodyne detector does, and operates in the same way to create a *new* signal of 4.5 mc, equal to the difference in frequency between the two parent i-f's. And, as in any heterodyning operation, the 4.5 mc beat signal retains the characteristics of both its parents: it is simultaneously amplitude *and* frequency modulated. The signal—also known as the intercarrier because it is derived from the interaction of two carriers—is fed to the video amplifier along with the video signal.

Separation of the intercarrier and video signals occurs in the video amplifier. The 4.5 mc signal, carrying the audio, takes a path along the sound strip—the circuits following the video amplifier. The first stage in this sound strip is the 4.5 mc amplifier, the purpose of which is to strengthen the signal to the point where it can adequately stimulate the next stage into operation. This next stage is the FM detector. Presented with a properly amplified frequency modulated signal, the detector can extract the audio and pass it along to the audio amplifier immediately following. The FM detector is insensitive to amplitude modulations; these variations in the inter-carrier signal are therefore ignored.

The strengthened video signal emerging from the video amplifier takes a less complicated path to its destination, the kinescope grid. What the kinescope does with this signal was described in the preceding chapter.

The Television Video Signal

Of the two signals borne by television transmitter carriers, the audio is the least complicated. Its only function is to describe electrically the transmitted sound. The video signal, however, has a triple function. The first is to furnish an electrical description of the light and dark elements in the televised image; this function is fulfilled by the *picture* signal.

Since the televised image is scanned in lines, there will be a series of picture signals, one for each line. We know, however, that the beam in the kinescope must be blanked out at the end of a line. Shutting off the kinescope beam is the second function of the video signal; it is performed by the blanking pulse which appears at the end of each line of picture signal. The blanking pulse reaches a voltage level negative enough to bring the kinescope grid to cutoff and quench the scanning beam. This voltage is known as the *black level* because, in the interval during which the pulse lasts, the screen is dark.

An extremely short moment after the blanking pulse

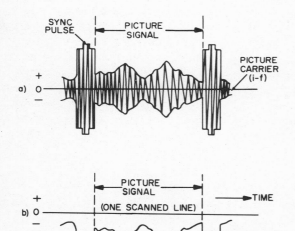

Fig. 7.7. *The Picture Carrier and Video Signals:* **The picture carrier is shown in (a), with the video signal in heavy lines. The video signal, made up of picture signal, blanking pulses, and sync pulses, is shown in (b). This is the signal applied to the kinescope grid. All of it is below the zero line, indicating that the kinescope grid is never permitted to become positive.**

begins, the sync pulse appears in the video signal. The sync pulse is even more negative than cutoff—voltages more negative than cutoff are called blacker-than-black—and so has no effect on the screened picture. But it satisfies the third function of the video signal: to trigger the sync circuits into sweeping the kinescope beam in step with the scanning beam in the transmitter's camera tube. The sync pulse is the connecting link between the transmitter and its slave, the receiver.

TV Receiver Sync Circuits

The description of kinescope operation given in the preceding chapter indicated that two sets of deflection coils, both housed in the tube's deflection yoke, are required to move the scanning beam horizontally and vertically. These deflection coils exert a force on the beam through their magnetic fields, and they can only possess those fields if they are supplied with current. It is the function of the sync circuits of the television receiver to furnish the coils with the properly varying current they need.

But if the scanning beam of the kinescope is to keep in step with the scanning beam of the transmitter's image orthicon, the sync circuits which control the movements of the beam through the deflection yoke cannot be left to operate as they please. They must come under the domination of the sync pulses. Consequently, a portion of the second detector video output is tapped off and fed into the first of the sync circuit stages, the sync separator. This stage might be called an electronic shears: it clips the sync pulses off the video signal supplied to it, and furnishes those sync pulses to the remainder of the sync circuits while discarding the rest of the video signal. Properly cued by the triggering sync pulses, the sync circuits supply the necessary deflection currents to move the kinescope scanning beam in step with the beam in the transmitter's camera tube.

The Radar Superheterodyne

Of the superheterodynes discussed in this chapter, two—the AM and FM receivers—were concerned only with sound, and one with both sound and light—the TV receiver. According to the logic of this scheme, there should be a receiver which is concerned wholly with light as an end product. Such a receiver is the radar superheterodyne.

Since the radar receiver is concerned only with producing a visible picture of some kind, its general pattern should be identical with that portion of the TV receiver devoted to the video signal. And so it proves, except for one complication: most radar systems include both a transmitter and receiver in the same unit. Moreover, the two divisions are tied together through their use of the

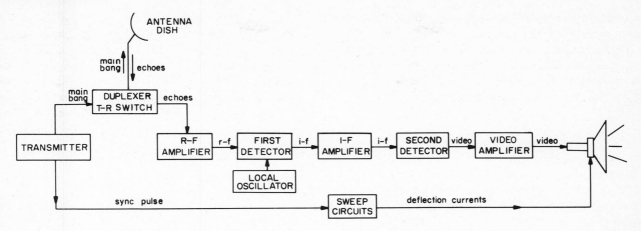

Fig. 7.8. *The Radar Superheterodyne:* **The transmit-receive (t-r) switch in the duplexer connects the transmitter to the common dish-shaped antenna during the main bang period. At the same time the receiver is closed off to the antenna. At the end of the main bang, echoes are picked up by the** **dish, and the receiver is reconnected to the dish to absorb the r-f echoes. Uhf radar receivers usually have no r-f amplifier, the echo pulses going directly to the first detector through wave guides. (See Chapter 6.)**

same antenna, and by the need of the receiver to be notified, through a sync pulse, of the precise moment at which the transmitter's main bang is set off. (See Chapter 6). Since the transmitter is so intimately connected with the receiver, the effect of the transmitter must enter any discussion of the radar superheterodyne.

The use of a single antenna for both receiver and transmitter requires some device to close the receiver input while the transmitter is issuing its r-f bang. This device is called the *duplexer*. In it is a transmit-receive switch which functions automatically to connect the transmitter to the antenna while the main bang is in progress. At the same time, the t-r switch short-circuits the receiver input to keep the power loosed by the transmitter out of the receiver. The t-r switch thus protects the receiver from harm during the main bang period. The input circuits of the receiver are designed to take only small quantities of r-f energy, and could certainly not sustain the powerful thrust of the transmitter's main bang.

The instant the main bang is completed, the duplexer acts to connect the antenna dish—so called because of its shape—to the receiver input. The echoes from objects intercepting the r-f now return to the dish, and are brought into the r-f amplifier of the superheterodyne. After amplification, they go on to the first detector where they are mixed with the uninterrupted output of the local oscillator. The i-f signal produced is, in many radar equipments, 30 mc. For a single reflecting object in the radar's antenna field, the echo is a single r-f burst resembling the main bang in everything but amplitude. Even though the local oscillator output is continuous, the i-f obtained from that single-burst echo will consist

only of a single burst since the 30 mc beat frequency cannot appear while the r-f is missing.

After amplification, the echo i-f signal is applied to the detector. The echo burst, like the main bang, is neither amplitude nor frequency modulated, but it has a square envelope. Acting on this wave in the same way it acts upon an amplitude-modulated signal, the second detector of the radar superheterodyne selects either the positive or negative envelope, and discards the carrier. This square pulse is increased in amplitude by the video amplifier stages and applied to the radar scope.

In the PPI system, the radar antenna continually rotates, gathering a succession of echo wave trains as it goes, while the video pulses corresponding to those trains are fed to the scope grid. In other radar systems, however, there may only be a single meaningful video pulse for every burst the transmitter sends out. This pulse,

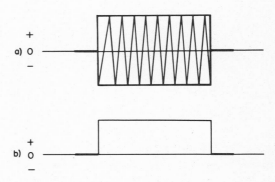

Fig. 7.9. *Radar Signals:* **The echo burst is shown in (a), with the positive and negative envelopes in heavy lines. The detected video pulse is shown in (b).**

emerging from the video amplifier, is applied to the vertically-deflecting plates of the tube in the same way that an a-c wave is applied to the deflecting plates of an oscilloscope for observation (Chapter 6). The video pulse then appears on the radar screen as a "blip" representing the object of the radar's scrutiny.

GLOSSARY

Bfo. Beat frequency oscillator; the oscillator in a CW receiver which heterodynes with the i-f signal to produce an audio note.

Beat frequency. The difference frequency between two heterodyned signals.

Black level. The cutoff voltage on the TV kinescope grid.

Blacker-than-black. A voltage more negative than the black level.

Blanking pulse. The negative pulse that cuts off the kinescope electron beam.

Blip. The pulse on a radar screen representing the object tracked.

Cascade. A succession of amplifying stages.

Dish. The reflector of a radar antenna.

Duplexer. The device in a radar unit which cuts the receiver off from the antenna while the transmitter is in operation.

First detector. The heterodyne detector in a superheterodyne.

Ganging. Mounting the rotor plates of two or more tuning capacitors on a common shaft.

Heterodyning. Mixing two signals in a detector to obtain the beat frequency.

I-f. Intermediate frequency; the signal in a superheterodyne which appears at the output of the first detector.

I-f strip. The intermediate frequency amplifier stages in a superheterodyne.

Intercarrier signal. The 4.5 mc signal in a TV receiver.

Local oscillator. The front-end oscillator in a superheterodyne.

Picture carrier. The television carrier modulated by the video signal.

Resting frequency. The frequency of the unmodulated FM carrier.

Second detector. The detector in the superheterodyne which extracts the audio signal from the modulated i-f carrier.

Sound carrier. The television carrier modulated by the audio signal.

Sound strip. The stages in a TV receiver concerned with the sound program.

Superheterodyne. A receiver in which carrier frequencies at the forward end are reduced through heterodyning.

Sync circuits. The circuits in radar and television which control the movements of the scope beam.

Sync separator. The circuit in the television receiver which separates the sync pulses from the video signal.

T-r. Transmit-receive; the switch in a radar-duplexer.

Trf. Tuned radio frequency; a radio receiver in which the forward end consists only of tuned radio frequency amplifier stages.

Chapter Eight

THE SUPERHETERODYNE FRONT END

TECHNICAL LANGUAGE is a feature of every profession on earth. The lawyer speaks of torts, replevins, and felonies; the doctor of seizures, occlusions, and embolisms; the accountant of credits, mortgages, and capital gains. What is completely comprehensible to one person is often so much gibberish to another. Members of the *same* profession may have trouble understanding one another because some of the terms they use are too loosely defined.

We might begin this chapter, then, by strictly defining two phrases which sound the same but have somewhat different meanings: *forward end* and *front end*. The first term refers to those stages ahead of the demodulating detector, and may apply either to trf or superheterodyne receivers. The second term, however, applies only to superheterodynes, and consists of the r-f stage, the local oscillator, and the first or heterodyning detector. We intend, in this chapter, to explore each of these three stages.

The r-f stage in any superheterodyne is the first stage to receive the transmissions the antenna receives. We can therefore learn how an r-f stage is supposed to work if we first attempt to unravel a mystery about broadcasting stations and the signals they emit.

AM Side Bands

The Federal Communications Commission rules state that a station in the AM broadcast band must limit its transmissions to a band 10 kc wide. The radio page of a newspaper, on the other hand, lists that AM station as having a single frequency. A question now arises: does an AM station occupy a whole *band* of frequencies, or does it occupy just one frequency? The answer, curiously enough, is that it can do both.

At the beginning of its broadcasting day, an AM transmitter puts its carrier on the air for testing. During this test period, no announcements are made, no entertainment of any kind is permitted to be broadcast. Consequently, there is no audio signal, and the carrier is simply an unmodulated, continuous wave. It then occupies one frequency and one only—that listed in the newspaper radio page.

Let us suppose that part of the test involves sounding a tuning fork in front of the microphone. The sound of the fork is translated by the microphone into an electrical audio signal and the carrier is modulated. Since the amplitude of its wave is now varying under the influence of the audio signal, the carrier has lost its resemblance to its original, unmodulated state. It is, in a sense, distorted; and because of this "distortion," two new frequencies are generated. One is equal to the *difference*

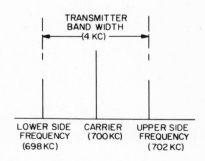

Fig. 8.1. *The Band Width of an AM Transmitter:* **This drawing illustrates the band width occupied by an AM transmitter broadcasting a pure audio signal (2 KC). The amplitudes of the side frequencies are equal to each other but less than that of the carrier, as indicated by the relative heights of the three vertical lines.**

between the carrier frequency and the frequency of the tuning fork; the other to the *sum* of the two frequencies. The first is called the lower side frequency; the second, the upper side frequency.

If, for example, this transmitter being tested has a carrier frequency of 700 kc, and the frequency of the test tuning fork is 2 kc, the lower side frequency will be 698 kc, and the upper, 702 kc. The station is then occupying a band width of 4 kc. Once this station begins its regular schedule of entertainment, its carrier will be modulated by a whole range of audio signals, from the deep bass tones of its male announcer to the shrill notes of a violin in its upper register. The band width of the station continually expands and contracts as a result, depending on the highest frequency of the audio signal doing the modulating.

This is where the FCC ruling comes into effect. To be on the right side of the law, the station must limit its audio signal to 5 kc at most. At that limit, the upper side frequency is 705 kc, the lower side frequency is 695 kc, and the total band width is 10 kc. These legal limits are necessary in the AM broadcast band especially. The carriers of the transmitters occupying this band are crowded so closely together that the band width of each station must be kept from overlapping that of its neighbor.

R-F Amplifier of the AM Superheterodyne

As we discovered in Chapter 5, the r-f amplifier strengthens the signal that its resonant circuit of coil and tuning capacitor selects. For any one station to which the amplifier is tuned, the resonant circuit will have to respond not only to the station's carrier, but to its side frequencies as well. Thus the response of the resonant circuit must be broad enough to include the transmitter's band width. Another way of putting this is that the *band width* of the r-f amplifier must be at least equal to the band width of the transmitter to which it is tuned. However, the range of frequencies the r-f amplifier admits to the receiver should not be much larger than the band width of the transmitter. If it is, it may receive two stations simultaneously.

The plate load of the r-f stage is usually the primary winding of an air-core transformer, with the secondary winding of the transformer connected to the input of the following stage, the first detector.

The Local Oscillator

The local oscillator—it is given the epithet "local" to distinguish it from other oscillators that may be present in the superheterodyne—may have any number of de-

signs. Whatever its form, the oscillator always has two elements basic to its operation: the first is an amplifying device; the second, a resonant circuit.

The function of an oscillator is to emit energy in the form of an a-c wave, usually of high frequency. In order to do so, it must develop a surplus of energy—that is, it must develop more power than is lost inside its circuit. Hence, it must have an amplifying device. If the wave the oscillator emits is to have a definite frequency, the oscillator circuit must be equipped with a resonant device to determine that frequency.

The Armstrong Oscillator

A common form of circuit is the Armstrong oscillator, named for its inventor—the same Armstrong who was the father of FM broadcasting, and who contributed so much to the progress of electronics. (Armstrong is also generally credited in this country with having invented the superheterodyne, but other nations have put forward equally valid claims for their favorite sons.) In this circuit, the amplifying device is a vacuum tube triode, and the resonant device the same combination of coil and capacitor that we have seen before.

The secret of the oscillator lies in the coupling between the plate and grid circuits. The plate of the triode is connected in series with a small "tickler" coil and the B voltage source of the power supply. The purpose of the latter, of course, is to provide the plate with the high positive voltage it needs for the tube to operate properly (Chapter 4). As for the tickler, it is wound on the same form as the resonant circuit coil. Since the magnetic fields of both coils are thus allowed to interact, the surplus energy developed across the tickler through the amplifying ability of the tube can be fed back to the input grid circuit to keep the oscillations going.

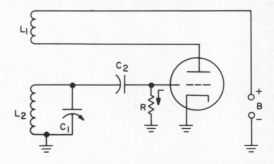

Fig. 8.2. *The Armstrong Oscillator:* The tickler coil (L$_1$) is coupled to the resonant circuit coil (L$_2$), resulting in feedback of energy from plate to grid. R is the grid leak, and C$_2$ the grid by-pass capacitor. The direction of d-c current flow through the grid leak is indicated by the arrow. The frequency of the oscillator output is determined by the setting of the variable capacitor C$_1$ in the resonant circuit of C$_1$ and L$_2$.

Repeated pulses of voltage keep the resonant circuit of coil and tuning capacitor electrically vibrating. As more pulses are fed to the circuit, the grid voltage swings increasingly positive and the grid begins to draw electrons. The resulting d-c current flowing through the grid resistor puts the grid at a highly negative potential, somewhat below cutoff. Hence the odd term *grid leak* for this resistor; it serves as a leakage path for electrons accumulating on the grid. Because of this high negative grid bias, the current in the plate circuit consists of pulses. These, in turn, are fed to the tickler coil, and thence to the resonant circuit coil. The process is thus a circular one, with the circuit continually building up the strength of the electrical vibrations to the point where the circuit emits its excess energy.

A fixed capacitor connected between the grid leak and the resonant circuit has the important function of bypassing the alternating component of the grid current. In addition to the d-c bias, a signal voltage is fed to the grid from the resonant circuit. This signal imparts to the grid current an a-c component which must be kept out of the grid leak to maintain a constant grid bias. Thus the fixed capacitor—known as the grid bypass—acts in similar fashion to the capacitor of the cathode bias arrangement (Chapter 4). Some variations of the Armstrong oscillator, in fact, have the grid leak and grid bypass capacitor wired in parallel.

Although the energy fed to the resonant circuit is in the form of voltage peaks—that is, parts of a cycle—the electrical vibrations within the circuit are complete voltage cycles. This phenomenon is the result of what has been called the "flywheel effect." If a flywheel is given a sudden rotational push, the sheer weight of the heavy wheel will help carry it through a complete rotation. The electrical equivalent takes place inside the resonant circuit: only part of a voltage cycle is required to put the circuit through a complete cycle of its vibration.

The Hartley Oscillator

The Armstrong oscillator is a popular choice to fulfill local oscillator duties in a superheterodyne. But it has a rival. This is the Hartley oscillator, which operates in a similar way, but offers other attractions.

The distinctive characteristic of the Hartley oscillator is the tapped resonant circuit coil. This tap is connected to the cathode of the tube. However, the plate of the tube is at chassis potential for a-c signals. This is the reverse of that in the Armstrong oscillator, in which the cathode is at chassis potential while the plate is connected to a coil extended from the resonant circuit coil. Thus the small portion of the coil between the tap and chassis is doing the work of the tickler. In all other respects, the operation of both oscillators is much the same.

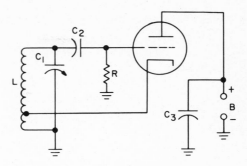

Fig. 8.3. *The Hartley Oscillator:* **This circuit is very similar to the Armstrong, but offers the added advantage of having only one coil. The capacitor C_3 allows the passage of a-c. Hence, it puts the plate of the tube at chassis potential for a-c.**

For economy-minded receiver manufacturers, the Hartley oscillator holds the attraction of having only a single coil with three terminals while the Armstrong requires a four-terminal double coil. But both types are used.

The Crystal Oscillator

A third type of oscillator which is widely used throughout the electronics industry is the crystal oscillator. This type takes advantage of the principle of *piezoelectricity* exhibited by a section cut from a quartz crystal. The prefix "piezo" means "pressure." When pressure is applied to such a crystal section, the crystal generates a voltage in one direction; when the pressure is released, the crystal generates a voltage of opposite polarity. A varying pressure applied to the crystal will thus produce a varying voltage. The converse is also true: a varying voltage applied to the crystal causes it to vibrate mechanically. Depending on the way it is cut from the parent crystal, its dimensions, and other factors, the piezoelectric crystal will vibrate strongly when voltage of a particular frequency is connected across it. The

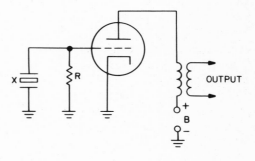

Fig. 8.4. *Piezoelectric Crystal Oscillator:* **The crystal (X) takes the place of the resonant circuit. R is the grid leak. No bypass capacitor is necessary since the crystal's electrodes are, in effect, capacitor plates. The output may be taken off the secondary of a transformer, as shown.**

crystal, therefore, can be used in place of the resonant circuit in an oscillator.

From different points of view, the crystal oscillator is both desired and unwanted. Its most desirable characteristic is that its frequency is less likely to wobble than that of the other two oscillators discussed. Consequently, it is used a great deal in transmitters, which work on a single frequency and must stay on that frequency. But the fact that its frequency cannot be readily varied makes it a bad choice for the local oscillator of a superheterodyne receiver, a circuit which is subject to frequency changes as often as its owner tunes in a new station. Any engineer using a crystal oscillator in a radio receiver would find that he has produced a set capable of picking up only one transmitter.

The First Detector

The outputs of the r-f amplifier and local oscillator could be applied to a simple diode detector like that discussed in Chapter 3 to obtain the intermediate frequency. But there is a better method. The first detector stage should amplify as well as detect, thus causing an increase in signal strength. Since added strength is always useful, the tube in the first detector is usually a pentode or better. The meaning of this phrase, "or better," will be apparent shortly.

In the early days of the superheterodyne, each of the three stages in the front end—the r-f amplifier, the local oscillator, and the first detector—had its own tube. But

engineers soon found a way of combining the local oscillator and first detector tubes into one envelope. To this single tube they applied the term "converter" because it is able to convert the radio frequency fed to it from the r-f amplifier into the intermediate frequency. Perhaps the most popular converter now in use for AM and FM receivers is the *pentagrid* type, given this name because it has a total of five grids.

The electrodes of the pentagrid converter are arranged in concentric fashion around the central element of the tube, its cathode. Like the cathode in any other vacuum tube, this one is brought to correct operating temperature by the heater enclosed within it. The first element immediately beyond the cathode is a grid which functions as the control grid of the oscillator, while the second grid serves as the virtual plate of the oscillator. Thus the pentagrid converter contains within it an oscillator triode comprising the cathode, the first grid, and the second grid.

Surprisingly enough, the tube also contains a pentode. This is made up of the cathode, grid number 3, grid number 4, grid number 5, and the plate of the tube. In this pentode, the r-f signal is applied through a resonant circuit to grid 3, which thus fulfills the function of control grid. This electrode is therefore provided with the avc voltage normally given to control grids of tubes in the receiver's forward end. (See Chapter 4). Grid 4 is the screen of this pentode, and grid 5 the suppressor. Since grids 4 and 2 are doing duty as screen and oscillator plate respectively, they both should be provided

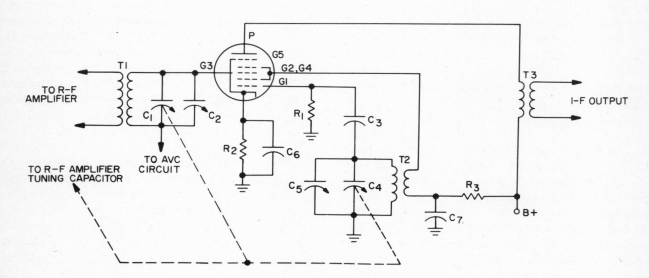

Fig. 8.5. The Pentagrid Converter: The oscillator circuit here is an Armstrong, with the first grid (G₁) as the oscillator grid and the second grid (G₂) as virtual plate. The secondary of T₂ is the tickler coil, C₄ is the oscillator tuning capacitor, R₁ the grid leak, and C₃ the grid bypass. Dotted lines indicate mechanical ganging of rotors for oscillator and r-f tuning capacitors. C₂ and C₅ are small trimmer capacitors for fine adjustment of oscillator and r-f tuning. R₃ and C₇ are screen dropping resistor and bypass capacitor respectively.

with a highly positive voltage. They are therefore connected together, usually within the tube. In the circuit, they are wired to the B+ point of the power supply through a dropping resistor.

The electron stream through the tube from cathode to plate varies at both oscillator and r-f frequencies because of the activity of the oscillator and r-f grids. Since this stream is always in one direction, as in an ordinary diode, the tube is also acting as a detector. Hence the plate current of the tube has an intermediate frequency component. If the primary of a transformer is inserted in the plate circuit, an i-f voltage will develop across the coil and will be transferred to the secondary. From this point the i-f signal goes on to the i-f amplifier.

Tracking

Before a manufactured receiver leaves the factory, an adjustment is made to ensure that the correct frequency difference between r-f and oscillator signals is maintained over the entire tuning range. This adjustment is known as "tracking." It is done by making fine adjustments on trimmer capacitors connected in parallel with each of the tuning capacitors in the receiver. The trimmers are tiny condensers, each with only two metal plates held together by a screw. The adjustment is made by properly setting this screw.

When the tracking procedure is finished, both r-f amplifiers will tune precisely together, while the oscillator will tune to the required frequency. A receiver which is not too badly abused in the customer's home—"abuse," here, means tinkering by an untutored hand—will rarely require a second tracking process.

FM Band Width

Earlier in this chapter, we found that the tuned circuits of the AM receiver front end should tune broadly enough to admit a band of frequencies 10 kc wide. If this is the range of frequencies an AM broadcast band receiver requires for any one setting of its dial, how much band width must the FM receiver front end admit for any one setting of its dial?

We found, in the last chapter, that the FM carrier remains at a constant frequency as long as it is unmodulated. Once modulation begins, the carrier frequency increases and decreases depending on the strength of the modulating audio signal. Applying the technical term *deviations* to the changes in the carrier above and below its resting frequency, we can say that the band width of the FM station is equal to the difference between the maximum positive and the maximum negative deviations of its carrier. Suppose, for example, that a soprano is performing in an FM broadcasting studio. In the course

of a gentle passage, she keeps her voice at a low volume. The corresponding audio signal is weak, and may move the carrier to no more than 5 kc above and 5 kc below its resting frequency. At this moment, then, the positive and negative deviations are 5 kc each, and the total band width is 10 kc. Her voice may swell later on; if she is a Wagnerian soprano, in fact, she may let loose a healthy volume of sound. If the level she hits at this moment is three times as loud as it was before, the positive and negative deviations in the carrier frequency will be some 15 kc each, making a total band width of 30 kc.

The band width of an FM station thus changes continually, depending on the amplitude of the modulating audio signal. Since frequency space is at a premium in the FM band, the FCC sets a limit on the modulation an FM carrier can assume. According to the FCC regulations, the positive and negative deviations can be no more than 75 kc each. The maximum band width of the FM transmitter is therefore 150 kc. FM receiver manufacturers, then, design the front ends of their sets to permit the entrance of a band width of 150 kc for a setting of the tuning dial.

Radio Receiver Front Ends

Two factors in modern radio communication tend to simplify things for designers of receiver front ends. One is the excellence of modern vacuum tubes; the other, that most of the receivers manufactured today are used in areas which boast at least one local transmitter.

The first factor just about explains itself. A modern vacuum tube can do much more than its ancestor of a generation ago; consequently, today's receiver has less tubes and is therefore simpler than its predecessor. The effect of the second factor is also fairly obvious. If the stations the set owner depends upon for entertainment are much closer to his home, a really powerful receiver is unnecessary. The exceptions are such equipment as automobile and farm radios which often are quite distant from the nearest transmitter. These latter usually need a full complement of tubes, but general run of mill radio receivers can get along quite well without an r-f amplifier. By getting rid of this superfluous stage, the manufacturer of the receiver can economize on costs and pass the economy on to the buyer.

Consequently, the first stage into which the receiver antenna feeds is usually the converter. Many receivers of the AM and FM type are simplified in this fashion. The front ends of both are about the same. A radical difference, however, is the antenna each uses. The FM receiver generally has a built-in *dipole,* an antenna frequently found in vhf equipment. AM receiver antennas are also built-in, but take a form more suitable for the much lower frequencies of the AM broadcast band, a

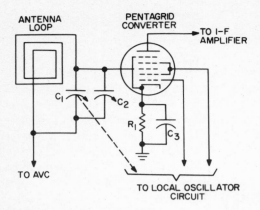

Fig. 8.6. *Radio Receiver Front End:* **The antenna loop and tuning capacitor C_1 make up the r-f resonant circuit. C_1 is ganged to the oscillator tuning condenser (not shown) as indicated by the dashed line. C_2 is the r-f trimmer capacitor, and R_1 and C_3 the cathode bias circuit. Automatic volume control voltage is fed to the r-f control grid (grid #3) through the antenna loop.**

form known as the *loop antenna.* The loop is usually a wire wound in coil fashion on a flat surface— in many sets the flat surface is the cardboard backing of the cabinet —and serves also as the coil of the resonant circuit connected to the converter's r-f signal grid. Since there is no r-f amplifier, a gang of only two tuning condensers is necessary. One of these, tuning to the incoming r-f signal, is connected in parallel with the antenna loop; the second occupies its regular place in the oscillator circuit and performs its normal function of tuning the oscillator to the correct frequency. Since the converter combines the function of both first detector and oscillator, the whole front end of many AM and FM sets is thus built around a single tube.

Some of these receivers are further simplified by a clever method which dispenses with the tuning capacitors. Here, the idea is to tune the coils of the r-f and oscillator resonant circuits rather than the capacitors. The antenna loop is a hollow tube around which are wound many turns of wire. Inside this tube and inside a corresponding tube for the oscillator circuit is a moveable core of powdered iron. The cores of both coils are moved in unison by a pulley system tied to the front panel tuning knob. This method of *slug tuning* has the beauty of simplifying the problem of packaging by permitting the use of miniature capacitors.

The TV Band Width

We have seen, in this chapter, that the band width required by an FM receiver is about 15 times that for the AM receiver. Compared to the band width the TV receiver must have, however, those of AM and FM are badly outmatched. The preceding chapter, with its ex-

planation that the sound and picture carriers are 4.5 mc apart, has already hinted at the enormous frequency range covered by a single TV channel. That frequency range is actually considerably larger than 4.5 mc.

The band width of the modulated sound carrier in TV can be immediately established at 150 kc, the same as it is for FM broadcasting. Aside from the fact that the sound carrier in the TV transmitter is only one part of the total signal emitted, it is identical to that of the audio FM transmitter. In both, frequency deviations up to 75 kc are permitted by FCC regulations. If the total width of the sound frequencies is only 150 kc, it is evident that most of the television band width is occupied by the modulated picture carrier.

Some clear thinking, based on knowledge of amplitude modulation, indicates that the video signal is responsible for the enormous width of the picture signal frequencies. As we saw at the beginning of this chapter, the band width of an AM signal is set by the highest modulating signal. If the signal doing the modulating is audio—the electrical signal corresponding to sound— the band of frequencies transmitted cannot be very wide. The highest sound frequency audible to the average man is about 10 kc, although there are people who can hear frequencies much higher. Consequently, an AM transmitter concerned solely with audio modulation would not have to have a band width of much more than 20 kc even if no limits were put on it by FCC regulations. The eye, however, is a much more sensitive and demanding instrument than the ear. Where an audio signal of up to 10 kc in frequency is enough to provide satisfactory sound in a radio receiver, video signals of up to 4 mc— 400 times as much as the 10 kc audio—are required to produce a satisfactory picture.

Some simple figure-juggling will show why the frequency of the video signal must be so high. Let us begin by assuming that the picture appearing on the face of the kinescope is a striped pattern made up of 50 vertical black lines separated by as many white stripes equally spaced across the screen. As the beam of the kinescope scans across the face of the tube, the video signal applied to the kinescope grid varies from a high to a low negative value. It is highly negative for the black stripes and much less negative for the white stripes between. In going through its high and low negative value, the video signal varies through one cycle. Since there are 50 black and white stripes, the video signal goes through 50 cycles in the time it takes for the beam to sweep once across the screen's width. That time is 1/15,750 of a second (Chapter 6). Actually it is somewhat less, since the 1/15,750 figure covers also the very small retrace time the beam takes when it reaches the end of one scanned line and scurries back across the screen to start scanning the next one. For the sake of making the calculation

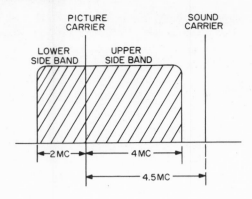

Fig. 8.7. *Vestigial Side Band Transmission:* The total band width of the picture r-f signal is shown in shaded area. This is an idealized picture since it is almost impossible to cut the upper and lower limits as sharply as indicated. The "vestige" is the 2 mc remaining of the lower side band.

easier, however, let us say that the beam scans one line in 1/15,000 of a second.

Now, if there are 50 cycles of video in 1/15,000 of a second, there will be 50 times 15,000 cycles in a full second. And 50 times 15,000 is equal to 750,000 cycles or 750 kc. In order to give this picture of fifty vertical stripes, then, a video signal of almost 1 mc is necessary. If the system now in use were to permit a video signal of at most 1 mc, the picture of fifty stripes could appear, but the edges of the stripes would be rather fuzzy. To sharpen the detail, the FCC has allowed a system of picture transmission in which video signals of up to 4 mc can be used. Even more detailed pictures could be achieved if frequencies higher than 4 mc were permitted, but there has to be a limit somewhere. At this maximum of 4 mc for the video signal, the total band width of one television transmitter would be 8 mc, exclusive of the sound. This is more than enough to swallow up not only the whole AM broadcast band but blanket a good chunk of the FM band as well.

There is always a fierce race to get frequency room on the airways. Consequently, the band held by a single transmitter must be cut to a minimum consistent with good picture transmission. The FCC has therefore decreed that television transmitters must use special equipment to cut part of one side band to 2 mc, thus allowing a total coverage of 6 mc—four on one side of the picture carrier, two on the other. This system is known as *vestigial side band transmission.* There is no harm done in cutting the lower side band. As long as one side band with the full range of video frequencies remains, the picture received will be a complete one.

The TV Channels

There are now 12 regular vhf television channels in operation all over the country. Relatively small communities are usually serviced by a single transmitter; a city the size of New York, however, with over a million television receivers in operation, is covered by seven transmitters. Surprisingly, this is the maximum number of vhf channels available to one city. The frequency range occupied by any one channel is so close to that of its neighbor that the FCC allocates alternate channels to a particular area, leaving the channels in between to cities just outside the line-of-sight range. Thus New York City—the great antenna atop the majestic Empire State Building serving as its base of television operations—occupies Channels 2, 4, 5, 7, 9, 11, and 13, while smaller cities nearby are allotted the remaining channels. Channels 4 and 5 are not cheek by jowl; they are separated by a band width of 4 mc.

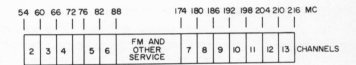

Fig. 8.8. *VHF Television Channels:* Each channel occupies a six megacycle width. The FM broadcast band begins where channel 6 ends, and runs up as far as 108 mc. Note separation between channels 4 and 5.

TV Receiver Front End

Every TV receiver—even the "portables" with their built-in antenna gadgets—has two screw terminals reserved for an outdoor antenna connection. The usual TV antenna is a *dipole.* In its simplest form, this consists of two horizontal metal rods, perhaps adjustable in length, insulated from each other, and lying along the same line. It is installed on its mast with the line of its poles broadside to the direction of the transmitter.

The two antenna poles are connected to the screw terminals on the receiver through a flat "ribbon" lead-in, a length of flat rubber resembling a miniature railroad track. The two slightly bulging "rails" of the ribbon each enclose a wire running the ribbon's length. Each of these wires is joined solidly to the antenna pole at one terminal and to one of the screw terminals at the other. With the ribbon in place, the front end of the TV receiver is ready to admit signals the antenna receives.

Once, in the dim past of commercial television's

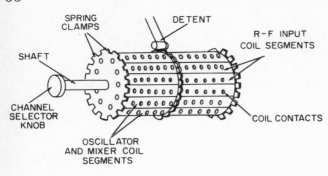

Fig. 8.9. *The Turret Tuner:* **Five contacts in the r-f input coil segments include three for the primary and two for the secondary. There are three coils in the oscillator and mixer coil segments, hence six contacts, two for each coil. The segments are held in place by spring clamps.**

history, receivers were made with mechanical tuning systems similar to the gradual, knob-rotating system of the radio receiver. But too many viewers found the process beyond their patience. As a result, the switch method of tuning is followed in just about all modern TV sets. The tuning device is a rotating drum, known as the *turret*, which is held at each of the twelve channel positions by a mechanical detent arrangement. The tuning knob is mounted on the shaft of the turret. Thus the knob can be switched to any channel without the necessity of having to tune carefully.

Around the length of the turret cylinder are twelve pairs of insulating segments, one pair for each channel. Underneath the segments, on the inside of the drum, are small coils, their terminals soldered to metal projections on the segments' top surfaces. These projections make contact with switch points in the front end circuit. For any particular channel indicated by the tuning knob—in most receivers, the knob is called the "channel selector"—the coils in one pair of segments are switched into the circuit of the front end. One of each pair contains two coils which form the input transformer between the antenna and the first stage of the receiver. The coils of the other share the same magnetic fields, but are shielded from the coils of the first segment by a metal plate which prevents interaction between the two. It is through the magnetic coupling between the coils of the second segment that the r-f signals—the sound and picture carriers—are brought into the first detector along with the constant signal output of the local oscillator.

Here, incidentally, is another possibiilty of confusion in technical terminology, the theme on which this chapter was begun. The term "first detector," which has been used heretofore to describe the heterodyning detector stage in the superheterodyne, is duplicated by the word "mixer." Both mean exactly the

same: the first seems to be preferred in the more formal prose of engineering textbooks; the second is the less stiff-necked term. The word "converter," on the other hand, is usually reserved for those economical stages in which the first detector and oscillator are combined into one. There are many engineers, however, who use all three terms in the same sense.

Detailed Explanation of the TV Front End

The schematic diagram of the television receiver front end given in this section has been chosen because of its interesting features. The input circuit, that of the primary of the r-f amplifier, is known as a balanced input. This coil is tapped at its electrical center while the two end terminals are connected through the ribbon lead-in wires to the antenna dipole. Most television receivers use this balanced input arrangement because it is the best method of bringing in the antenna signal.

As the voltage picked up by the antenna varies first in one direction and then in the other, current surges through each half of the input coil. As it does so, it creates a varying magnetic field inside the coil form. The secondary coil shares this varying field, and therefore adopts the voltage in the balanced primary. This voltage is amplified in the pentode. Biasing for the control grid of the pentode is obtained from the agc system (Chapter 4) and applied to the tube through the secondary of the input transformer.

The secondary coil at the input to the pentode has no capacitor wired across it, yet in itself it is a resonant circuit. Between the windings of every coil exists what is termed *distributed capacitance*: the turns of wire are in effect parallel metal plates separated by some insulating substance—air, or the insulation around the wire. At the high frequencies of television, this normally small capacitance bulks quite large in the scheme of things. It cannot be varied, but the slugs of powdered iron in both the input coils can. The adjustment of the slugs is a factory tuning procedure to set each switched-in coil of the turret to the frequency of the proper channel.

The resistor connected across the secondary winding of the input transformer is responsible for broadening the response of the resonant circuit to the point where the circuit will admit the 6 mc band width of the TV transmitter. It is a peculiarity of resonant circuits that increasing the resistance in the circuit tends to broaden the band of admitted frequencies. Hence a resistor is deliberately inserted into the resonant circuit of the coil and its distributed capacitance at the control grid of the r-f amplifier pentode.

The amplified signal at the output of the pentode is

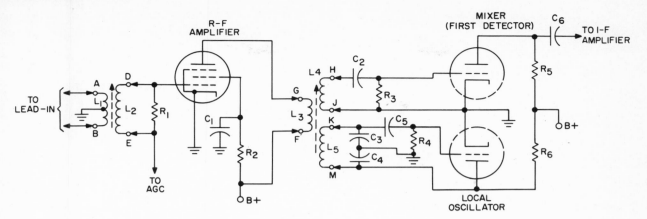

Fig. 8.10. *TV Receiver Front End:* Coils L_1 through L_5 are in the turret tuner; A, B, D, E, F, G, H, J, K, M are switch points connecting tuner coils to corresponding terminals in the front end circuit. The mixer and local oscillator are two triodes, both within a single envelope; the half-dotted circle around each is the usual method in schematics of indicating combinations of different units within the same tube. Dotted arrows alongside coils indicate slug tuning. L_1 and L_2 are the coils in one of the tuner's segment pair; L_3, L_4, and L_5 are in the second of the pair.

coupled through a transformer to the grid of the first detector or mixer. Also fed to the mixer by the same method is the output of the local oscillator. The type of oscillator used in this particular design is a Colpitts, named for its inventor, which resembles the Hartley oscillator described earlier in this chapter. Here, however, the tap is not taken from the coil part of the oscillator resonant circuit, as in the Hartley, but at the junction between two unequal capacitors. The connection between tap and cathode is made through the chassis of the receiver. One of these capacitors is fixed, the other, however, is variable, and its shaft is brought out to a knob on the front panel of the receiver. This capacitor is called the *fine tuning* condenser; its function is to restore the oscillator to its correct frequency if its signal should tend to slip away from the true value. The knob controlling the fine tuning capacitor is usually mounted concentrically with the knob controlling the turret tuner, but the rotation of one has no influence mechanically on the rotation of the other.

Operating as the first dectector is a triode, in a circuit known as a *grid leak detector*. This type of detector is really an amplifier operated approximately Class B (Chapter 4). The positive swings of the signal applied to the grid cause the grid to draw current. As this flow of current passes through the grid resistor, a negative voltage appears at the grid. The electron flow through this resistor does not vary as the input signal does because of the bypass capacitor between the grid resistor and the coupling coil at the detector input. This capacitor allows the varying component of the grid current to flow away from the resistor. Hence the voltage across the resistor is fairly constant, biasing the grid at about cutoff. With the grid biased at this

potential, the current flow in the plate circuit reproduces only one half the signal. But this, as we found in Chapter 3, is precisely how the detector works. The triode in this circuit therefore operates as a combination amplifier and detector, and because of its action in the latter capacity, the signal flowing in its plate circuit is a composite signal of the picture and sound i-f's. This signal is then brought through a capacitor to the i-f amplifier stages which follow the first detector.

The oscillator coils in the tuner segments can be adjusted with a screwdriver through a hole in the tuner. This is an adjustment made at the factory, but it occasionally does get out of kilter. Symptomatic of its incorrect adjustment is the inability of the fine tuning control to bring in a good picture even though the knob of the control is turned through its entire range. An adjustment of this type is a rather ticklish one. If the screwdriver with which the adjustment is made is metallic, the tool's blade will act like the plate of a capacitor and upset the oscillator frequency, thus making the adjustment difficult. Radio parts shops sell non-metallic adjustment screwdrivers for viewers brave enough to tinker with their own sets. But it is the better part of valor to have a trained serviceman do the job.

The Radar Band Width

If band width is a problem in AM and FM communication systems, it is equally a problem in radar. The echoes returning to the radar receiver from the reflecting object are modulated, as the drawing of the radar signal in the preceding chapter shows, by sharply rising and falling square pulses. The information obtained by the radar is reliable only if the shape of the pulse

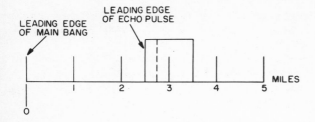

Fig. 8.11. *Radar Scope Blip:* **The distance between the main bang leading edge and the blip leading edge is the range of the target, 2½ miles on the scale. If the leading edge of the blip is cut off (dotted line) the target is assumed to be further away than it actually is. The error here is about ¼ mile.**

is maintained, and the radar receiver front end must be receptive to a broad band of frequencies to maintain the pulse shape. The evidence for this is presented in the following episode—a fairly common one—in the life of a wartime radar installation:

The problem the radar is required to solve is the range of an enemy warship. The transmitter sends out its r-f bang, and the echo burst is received very soon afterwards. If the warship is a long way off, the echo takes a longer time to return; if the ship is nearby, the echo arrives sooner. Hence the range of the warship is measured by the time elapsed between the beginning of the radar's main bang and the beginning of the returned burst. The operator of the installation makes that measurement by observing the position of the blip representing the echo on his scope. If the blip is not an accurate picture of the echo pulse, its leading edge will not be where it should on the scope, and the defending guns will be given the wrong range information. Thus the accuracy of the radar depends on the preservation of the shape of the echo burst in its progress through the receiver from antenna to scope.

But the echo burst is the same, except for amplitude, as the main bang of the radar transmitter. Consequently, the observed blip should have the same shape as the main bang. In creating this main bang, the transmitter oscillator must jump suddenly from a completely inactive state to its rated frequency of perhaps 1,000 megacycles or more per second, and then drop just as suddenly when the main bang is over. Although it does so in a very short time, it must run through a tremendous frequency range. It follows, then, that the receiver should be able to admit all these frequencies in the echo burst if the blip on the scope is to be an accurate representation.

It would seem, from all this, that the band width of the receiver should be extremely wide. But the designer of the radar receiver front end finds that he must pay the penalty of low gain to derive the advantages of a broad band. The front end, which concentrates on just

a few frequencies to amplify, can certainly be more effective for these few than a broad-band amplifier of corresponding strength can be for its whole variety of frequencies. Since gain is highly important for radar—the strength of the echo signal is so small that every precaution must be taken to bring up its strength—there is an equally good argument for a narrow-band front end. Faced with these two opposing needs, the designer of the radar front end has to compromise. What his compromise will be depends on the purpose he wants the radar to serve. If it is to work as an accurate ranging device, gain has to be sacrificed for band width.

The gain of the radar receiver can be improved by providing its front end with an r-f amplifier. But here the designer is faced with another necessary compromise. An r-f amplifier not only amplifies the desired signal but also introduces noise. Electrical noise pulses are visible on the radar scope, sometimes to the point where they obscure the target blip. Furthermore, the noise hazard increases with increasing frequency. Most of our present-day radar equipments operate in the uhf region for greater accuracy. It follows, then, that designers of modern radar equipments would rather do without the r-f stage than run the risk of increasing the already high noise level.

The Radar Receiver Front End

The antenna assembly of a radar system consists of a reflector, an antenna horn, and a waveguide leading from the horn into the duplexer. The horn is situated at the focal point of the reflector to receive echo waves striking the reflector surface, and the waves are led down the waveguide to the duplexer. Once the main bang is over, the path of the waves to the receiver mixer cavity is cleared by the transmit-receive switch in the duplexer. The local oscillator signal is also injected into the mixer cavity through a probe which picks up the signal in the oscillator cavity. Another probe in the mixer cavity conducts the echo r-f and oscillator signals from the mixer cavity to a crystal diode. This latter, in a circuit closely resembling the simple detector of Chapter 3, converts the signals into an i-f which consists of echo bursts at the intermediate frequency. The i-f amplifiers succeeding the radar receiver front end then bring the i-f signal up to proper strength.

The radar receiver is a powerful illustration of the value of the superheterodyne principle. Frequencies are so high in the receiver front end that cavities and waveguides take the place of circuits and wires, and the stages ahead of the crystal detector become a mess of what radar engineers jocularly refer to as "plumbing." The title is quite apt; the right-angle turns and twists of the various waveguides not only look like but

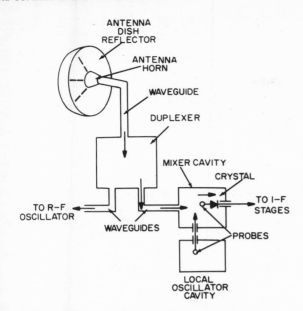

Fig. 8.12. *Radar Receiver Front End:* Echo signals are focused by dish into the horn. The r-f signals pass through duplexer into mixer cavity. Oscillator signal is picked up by probe from local oscillator cavity. The mixed signals in the mixer cavity are brought through a probe to a crystal detector. The output of the detector is the i-f signal.

perform functions similar to the lead-pipe tubing in water supply systems. Once the signals involved get by the crystal detector, however, the frequency of the signal drops to some 30 mc—i-f's in radar may vary from system to system—a frequency low enough to free the engineer from the plumbing business and send him back to designing circuits in the style to which he is accustomed.

Fashions in electronics have a way of coming back, like women's hemlines. In the days when radio was considered to be a pleasant toy with no conceivable future, the crystal of galena—a bright, silvery mineral—was the unanimous choice as a detector. With the coming of the vacuum tube, the crystal retired from radio history. Now the crystal is back again in a revived, new version, and is proving so useful in radar as well as every other branch of electronics, that it seems to be chasing the vacuum tube into retirement.

GLOSSARY

Antenna horn. An enlarged opening of a waveguide at the focus of a radar reflector.

Antenna loop. A flat coil of wire which serves both as antenna and as part of the input resonant circuit of a receiver.

Armstrong oscillator. An oscillator in which feedback is achieved through coupled plate and grid circuit coils.

Band width. The frequencies emitted by a transmitter and picked up by a receiver; any range of frequencies.

Colpitts oscillator. An oscillator in which two resonant circuit capacitors are used, with a tap between the two capacitors.

Converter. A single stage combining the functions of local oscillator and first detector.

Detent. The mechanism in a TV tuner which holds the tuner to a particular channel.

Dipole. A double antenna often used in vhf and uhf systems.

Distributed capacitance. The virtual capacitance existing between adjacent loops in a coil.

Fine tuning capacitor. The small variable capacitor in a TV tuner for fine adjustment.

Flywheel effect. The effect of a resonant circuit in which an input electrical pulse of less than one cycle produces a complete output cycle.

Frequency deviation. The swing of an FM carrier away from its resting frequency.

Front end. The stages between antenna and i-f amplifier in a superheterodyne.

Grid bypass. A small fixed capacitor which bypasses the signal away from the grid leak.

Grid leak. A grid resistor through which d-c grid current flows.

Grid leak detector. A detector which depends on the flow of grid current for its operation.

Hartley oscillator. An oscillator circuit in which the coil of the resonant circuit is tapped.

Leading edge. The initial rise of a square pulse.

Negative frequency deviation. A drop of the FM carrier frequency below the resting frequency.

Pentagrid converter. A converter tube with five grids.

Piezoelectric crystal. A crystal which converts mechanical pressure into an electrical signal, or converts a signal into pressure.

Plumbing. The term applied to waveguides and cavities in uhf equipment.

Positive frequency deviation. A change in the FM carrier to a frequency higher than its resting frequency.

Reflector. The dish or similar device which in radar equipment reflects the main bang outward from the horn or reflects the echo bursts into the horn.

Ribbon lead-in. The two-conductor wire interconnecting the dipole antenna and the front end of the TV receiver.

Side band. The range of frequencies above and below the unmodulated carrier put out by a transmitter.

Side frequency. A single frequency in the side band.

Slug tuning. Tuning a resonant circuit by varying the powdered iron core of the coil.

Tickler coil. The plate circuit coil in the Armstrong oscillator.

Tracking. The adjustment of a superheterodyne front end to insure the uniformity of the receiver's i-f over the whole range of the tuning dial.

Trailing edge. The drop in voltage at the end of a square pulse.

Vestigial side band transmission. Transmission of the TV signal in which a portion of the lower side band is cut off.

Chapter Nine

INTERMEDIATE FREQUENCY AMPLIFIERS

THE THEME OF technical language, with which the preceding chapter was begun, might well carry into this one. Technical terms are meant to be precise, but what with the pressure of history and the loose talk of people who should know better, these terms begin to lose their precision and come to mean just about anything.

One of these terms is radio frequency, which we have been conveniently abbreviating r-f. Before the radio industry bloomed into its present eminence as the electronics industry, its domain was a narrow one and the language it used to describe that domain was correspondingly narrow. In those days, radio transmission and reception was more or less confined to the AM broadcast band, and so the term r-f referred to those frequencies ranging roughly from 600 to 1600 kc. Nowadays, however, what with the tremendous range of frequencies used by communications services of every type, the term r-f can mean just about anything from 600 kc on up.

The term "audio frequency" is more definite, since it is tied to sound; but even here there is some difficulty. It is hard to set an upper limit to the audio frequencies because the limit of hearing varies with different people. A minority—with youth on its side—can hear sounds of up to 16 kc (16,000 cycles per second) without straining. Possibly this is the upper limit. For the same reason, it is equally difficult to put a lower limit to the audio frequencies. Perhaps it is best to put the audio band in round figures and say that it is anything up to 20,000 cycles.

As long as the old trf receiver held sway, radio engineers spoke in terms of r-f and a-f. But with the coming of the superheterodyne, they were faced with the problem of giving the signal at the output of the superheterodyne's first detector a name. They solved that problem by calling the signal "intermediate fre-

quency"—that is, a signal with a frequency lower than r-f but higher than a-f. And "intermediate frequency" it remains to the present day. As we have seen, the i-f can be just about anything, depending on the system in which it is found.

The Broadcast Band I-F

The i-f chosen for AM broadcast band superheterodyne receivers is 455 kc. A number of important considerations were taken into account when this figure was chosen, most of them pointed toward keeping interference in the desired signal at a minimum.

For one thing, the i-f should not be located in a band used by local stations. If the frequency to which the i-f amplifiers in the receiver are tuned is being broadcast by a powerful local transmitter, the transmitter signal may be picked up by the i-f amplifier wiring. It will then be amplified in the i-f circuits, and the audio signal it carries will be reproduced in the receiver's speaker as sound. In the meantime, the receiver is working in normal fashion to reproduce the modulations carried by the broadcast band station to which its front end is tuned. Thus the undesired signal interferes with the desired one. The remedy, of course, is to choose an i-f outside the frequency lanes of heavy local radio traffic; the 455 kc figure satisfies this condition.

While the i-f must be lower than the lowest r-f signal in the broadcast band—about 600 kc—it should not be too low. Suppose, for example, that the i-f chosen were as low as 100 kc. With the r-f resonant circuit tuned to a transmitter operating on a frequency of 800 kc, the local oscillator of the receiver would have to be set at 900 kc to produce a 100 kc i-f. If the band width of the r-f resonant circuit of the receiver is also large enough to admit a signal of 1000 kc, the 900 kc oscillator beating with it produces the same difference frequency of 100 kc. Thus the signals of both the 800 and 1000 kc transmitters would be amplified in the i-f stages, and the listener would hear the clashing nonsense of two simultaneous transmissions. This type of *image interference*—the 1000 kc transmitter is said to be the image of the desired 800 kc station—is a disease peculiar to superheterodynes with a low i-f. As this example shows, the desired station and its image are separated by a frequency equal to twice the i-f. For the normal superheterodyne receiver with an i-f of 455 kc, the image of 800 kc frequency would be twice 455 or 910 kc from the desired 800 kc signal. The image is therefore 800 plus 910, or 1710 kc, which is so far away from the desired frequency that it would be kept out of the input resonant circuit of the receiver.

The AM I-F Amplifier Circuit

Although the resonant circuits of the i-f amplifier stages in the broadcast band receiver are tuned to the fixed value of 455, they cannot be depended on to stay that way forever. The effects of aging, of varying temperature and humidity all affect the components in the amplifiers and tend to change their electrical characteristics. Manufacturers of receivers have therefore made the i-f amplifier tuned circuits variable to permit an occasional tune-up when the i-f tuning shows signs of going astray. The variable factor in the resonant circuit is either a trimmer capacitor or a slug-tuned coil.

The coil portions of the i-f amplifier circuits are in the form of transformers, the primaries and secondaries of which are shunted by a small capacitor. As the input

to the i-f circuit, the primary of the first transformer is the plate load of the converter. Thus a signal voltage of 455 kc appears across this primary. If both coils are tuned properly, the 455 kc signal applied to the grid of the i-f amplifier tube is a strong one, and the amplitude of the signal after the strengthening effect of the tube is many times that of the signal at the converter's output. This amplified version of the signal appears across the plate load of the i-f amplifier tube, a load which consists of a coil-capacitor combination tuned to the i-f. In AM broadcast band receivers of the simpler type, only one i-f amplifier stage is present; the better receiver may have two. What with the excellent amplifier tubes manufactured nowadays, receivers with more than two i-f stages are rare.

In accordance with modern practice, the i-f amplifier tube control grid is fed avc voltage. Most i-f amplifier tubes are therefore of the remote cutoff pentode variety (Chapter 5). The avc voltage alone may not be sufficient to bias the grid of the pentode properly, so a cathode biasing circuit of a resistor shunted by a fixed capacitor is often used. The tube is thus adapted for Class A operation by the combined effects of avc and cathode bias.

I-F Shielding

Unless proper precautions are taken in the design of the i-f amplifier, the stages may oscillate. Any receiver afflicted by this kind of ailment will howl like an anguished animal.

One cause of oscillation is magnetic interaction between the input and output transformers of an i-f stage. The signal at the output transformer is an amplified version of the i-f signal, and therefore is more than

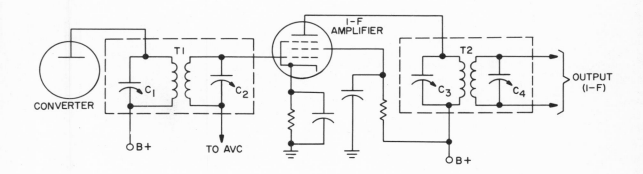

Fig. 9.1. *The AM Receiver I-F Amplifier:* The connections of the remote cutoff i-f amplifier pentode are standard. Capacitors C_1 through C_4 are the i-f trimmers. If i-f transformers T_1 and T_2 are slug-tuned, the capacitors are fixed. The dotted lines indicate shielding.

enough to restore energy lost in the circuit if it is fed back to the input of the circuit. Hence oscillation occurs. In a compact receiver, it is difficult to arrange things so that the output transformer is far enough away from the input transformer to prevent such unwanted coupling. The next best thing is to isolate the two transformers from each other by *shielding* both of them.

The process of shielding consists in covering both transformers with oblong metal "cans" in which holes are left open at the top to permit access to i-f trimmers or slugs. The cans are solidly held to the chassis either by screws or small rivets, and thus make excellent electrical contact with it. As a result, the magnetic field inside one of the i-f transformers is restricted to its own bailiwick. This shielding could be abetted by fastening metal plates not only to the bottom of the chassis but also its open sides to keep outside electrical influences from getting into the i-f's through those chinks in the set's armor. However, this is expensive and therefore not usually provided in home receivers. Military electronic equipment is very carefully shielded and is consequently thoroughly dependable.

FM Receiver I-F Amplifiers

The i-f amplifier stages in the FM receiver resemble those of the AM receiver. Except for two factors, the two would be identical. One of these factors is the relatively high frequency of the FM i-f, which at 10.7 mc, is more than twenty times as high as the i-f of the AM receiver. The second factor is band width. The heterodyning process reduces the resting frequency of the received FM signal to the i-f value, but it has no corresponding effect on the band width occupied by the FM signal. If in some interval the carrier of the FM transmitter is undergoing a positive and negative devia-

tion of, say, 50 kc for a total band width of 100 kc, the corresponding signal in the i-f of the receiver undergoes that same total deviation of 100 kc.

This second factor makes for some difficulty in the design of i-f amplifiers in FM receivers. Suppose an FM receiver is tuned to a 99 mc station occupying a band width of 100 kc. This 100 kc band width, equal to 1/10 of a megacycle, does not amount to much compared to the resting frequency of 99 mc. After conversion in the receiver's first detector, however, the 99 mc signal becomes an i-f resting frequency of slightly less than 11 mc. Compared to this i-f figure, the band width of the signal bulks 9 times as large.

The method used in many FM receivers for coping with this problem of band width in the i-f stages is to make certain that the resonant circuits of the stages contain a good amount of resistance. We have seen the effect of such band-broadening resistors in the preceding chapter. Thus the width of the FM i-f amplifier can be broadened either by inserting a separate resistor into the tuned circuit, or by using i-f transformers made of wire so fine that the resistance, so to speak, is built-in.

The fact that the frequency of the FM i-f is so much higher than the AM i-f actually tends to simplify the design of FM i-f amplifiers. Since operation at higher frequency generally permits the use of smaller components, only small capacitors are needed for the tuned circuits in the i-f stages of the FM receiver. In fact, the capacitors are so small that they can be cut out altogether, and the distributed capacitance of the transformer windings used in their place. With no "lumped" capacitance present, any adjustment necessary in tuning the i-f strip is made through slugs in the transformer coils.

Shielding is a necessity in all i-f transformers, FM

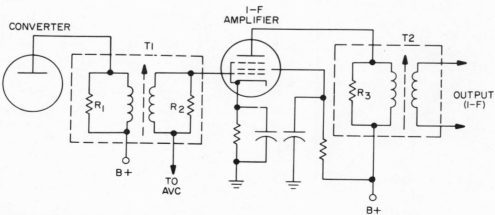

Fig. 9.2. *The FM Receiver I-F Amplifier:* R_1, R_2, R_3 are band-broadening resistors. The dotted arrow between the windings of T_1 and T_2 represent slug tuning.

as well as AM. In general, the higher the frequency with which a piece of electronic equipment deals, the more careful the shielding should be.

TV Receiver I-F Amplifiers

If the band width of the FM receiver presents some problems to the designer of its i-f stages, the problems involved in designing i-f stages for the television set are much more complicated. At most, the FM band width covers slightly more than 150 kilocycles; but the TV band width covers some 6 megacycles. Since this is equivalent to 6,000 kc, the band width of TV is more than 30 times that of FM.

Fortunately for the TV engineer, however, all the frequencies in this tremendous band width need not be amplified by the same amount. In fact, the receiver will behave better if the i-f sound carrier, at 41.25 mc is not amplified too much. As for the higher frequencies in the TV i-f band width, those around the picture carrier of 45.75 mc, they too may be somewhat neglected without hurting the resulting picture unduly. The important thing is that all the signals be amplified in the i-f strip at least to the extent that they will play a part in producing a clear picture accompanied by clear sound.

Achieving a band width of this extraordinary range would be futile if only ordinary means, such as band-broadening resistors, were used. Certainly, such a band width cannot be achieved by a single stage. The fact of the matter is that it takes several stages of amplification to do justice to all the frequencies that have to be strengthened. Furthermore, the resonant circuits of all these stages have to be tuned in special fashion. If all

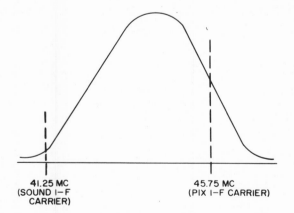

Fig. 9.3. *TV Receiver I-F Bandwidth:* The height of the humped curve indicates the comparative strengths of the various frequencies amplified in the i-f stages. Thus the amplitude of the sound i-f carrier is fairly low, and the amplitude of the picture carrier is about ½ the maximum strength.

the stages were tuned to one particular frequency, the total amplification effect would be very strong indeed. But it would be restricted to only a narrow band of signals immediately above and below the frequency to which the resonant circuits respond.

It is far more logical to tune the resonant circuits of the i-f stages to strategically spaced frequencies in the desired band width. For example, one of these resonant circuits could be tuned to the frequency of 43.5 mc, which is just about at the middle of the band width. The effect of this circuit is to increase the response of the i-f amplifier strip to the frequencies immediately above and below 43.5 mc. Tuning the resonant circuit of a second i-f amplifier stage to, say, 45 mc improves the response of the i-f strip to the higher frequencies of the i-f range. And, in similar fashion, tuning the resonant circuit of a third stage to a frequency slightly higher than 42 mc would build up the frequencies at the lower end. This method of tuning the various stages of i-f amplification, usually three in number, to different frequencies for the sake of achieving broad band coverage is known as *stagger tuning*. The reason for the name is not hard to see; the tuning of the i-f strip's circuits is staggered at spaced frequencies rather than concentrated on a single band section.

The Television I-F Circuit

Although stagger tuning is the basic method through which the broad-band response of television i-f amplifier stages is obtained, it often is allied with another method found to be effective: the band-broadening resistor. A resistor used in conjunction with one of the i-f resonant circuits broadens the band of frequencies that circuit will admit. If the resonant circuit of the following i-f stage is similarly treated by a resistor, the frequencies covered by each will overlap, thus offering better amplification for the range *between* the two favored frequencies. The method of inserting these resistors is the same as that used in the FM i-f stages: the resistor is connected across the resonant circuit.

As for the resonant circuit itself, it consists as always of a coil of wire and a capacitance. But in television, as in FM, the frequencies involved are high, and the capacitance involved can be the distributed capacitance of the coil windings. Since no trimmer condenser is connected across the coil, the schematic drawing shows no condenser in that position. Any necessary alignment that may have to be made by the serviceman in tuning the i-f stages can be done by screwing the powdered iron slugs of the coil in or out, as the occasion demands.

Bias is furnished to the i-f amplifier control grids from the agc system through the resonant circuit and band-broadening resistor. In some television receivers,

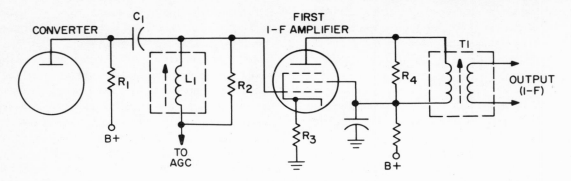

Fig. 9.4. *TV Receiver I-F Stage:* C_1 is a coupling condenser which permits the i-f signal output of the converter to be applied to the control grid of the first i-f amplifier tube and prevents the B+ voltage at the plate of the converter from getting to the i-f amplifier grid. R_2 and R_4 are band-broadening resistors. R_3 is a small stabilizing resistor. L_1 and T_1 are the resonant circuits.

the familiar resistor-capacitor arrangement in the cathode circuit of the tube helps supply the necessary d-c grid voltage. Many times, however, the schematic of an i-f stage will show only a resistor in the cathode circuit, without its accompanying capacitor. Such a resistor is a rather small one, too small to provide bias voltage of any real value. Its true function is to keep the amplifier stable. The resistor operates in this fashion:

When the signal on the i-f amplifier tube swings in the positive direction, the current flowing through the plate circuit increases. This current comes up from chassis, and enters the stabilizing resistor to return to the tube cathode. Since the point at which current enters a resistor is always negative, the chassis end of the resistor is negative with respect to cathode. The control grid of the tube, however, is also connected to chassis through the agc system. Consequently, the voltage at the chassis end of the resistor is applied also to the grid. If the grid of the tube swings in the positive direction, therefore, the action of the resistor will bring to the grid a modifying negative influence. The same would be true if the grid were given a strong negative voltage; the resistor would then oppose that voltage slightly by a counter positive swing. Thus the resistor tends to keep the operation of the i-f amplifier within manageable limits by feeding back an *out-of-phase* signal to the input of the tube.

Radar Receiver I-F Amplifiers

Like the i-f amplifiers of other superheterodynes, the i-f strip in the radar receiver is designed to handle the frequencies in the band width of the received signal. The previous chapter indicated that the width of the frequencies in the received signal depends on the type of radar system. It follows that the design of the i-f amplifier of a particular receiver depends on the function that receiver is designed to fulfill.

As we saw, in the preceding chapter, the receiver in accurate range-finding radar must have a front end equipped to receive a wide band of frequencies. After conversion to i-f, the signal occupies just as wide a band, and the i-f strip must produce an amplified version of all those frequencies. Such a band is often wider than that involved in television. Where the TV receiver i-f strip requires a coverage of up to 6 mc, with only indifferent amplification at the outer fringes of this band width, the radar receiver i-f strip may have to cover 8 mc with better amplification. Thus, with 30 mc as the center of the band width, the i-f strip will have to amplify signals in the 26 to 34 mc range.

This is done in just about the same way as it is in the television receiver i-f strip, through stagger tuning aided by band-broadening resistors. Since the band of frequencies amplified in the radar i-f is broader, the i-f strip usually has more stages—four and possibily five. Thus at least four frequency points in the band width can be selected for amplification to strengthen the voltages of the various frequencies within the band.

GLOSSARY

I-f alignment.   The process of tuning the resonant circuits in the i-f strip to their proper frequencies.

I-f trimmer.   A small variable capacitor in the i-f amplifier resonant circuits of an AM broadcast band receiver.

Image interference.   A failing peculiar to superheterodynes in which two stations separated by a frequency equal to twice the i-f of the receiver may be simultaneously received.

Shielding.   A method of preventing interaction between circuits by surrounding the circuits with metal plates.

Stabilizing resistor.   An unbypassed resistor in the cathode circuit of an i-f amplifier tube which helps keep the tube from being overloaded.

Stagger tuning.   A method used in TV and radar receivers of broadening the i-f band, in which the resonant circuits of the i-f strip are tuned to various points in the i-f band width.

Chapter Ten

THE AM RECEIVER

IN THE BEGINNINGS of radio broadcasting history, the radio enthusiast got his feet wet by building a simple receiver like that shown schematically in Chapter 3. But diode vacuum tubes in those early days were quite expensive. So, as a cheap and convenient substitute, the galena crystal was the popular choice among radio amateurs for the detector device. As a matter of fact, the amateur lost nothing by making this choice: for one thing, although the galena may have been difficult to adjust at times, it had no heater and hence required no batteries; for another, it was on a par with the vacuum tube diode as far as amplifying ability was concerned. Neither had any.

This last item, amplification, makes the big difference between the crude "hook-ups" of those times and the sleek, efficient equipment of today. The pioneer radio amateur had to use every bit of power caught by his antenna. To make certain that he would get as much of the broadcast power as possible without spending any of it in the process, he took a great deal of time and trouble setting up an antenna that could withstand the assault of wind and weather, and yet give efficient service. Rooftops in those days were forests of antenna masts; in fact, not a few enterprising men erected antennas reaching between roofs of adjoining buildings.

The Loop Antenna

Today, no one but the dedicated amateur would dream of going to all that bother for a mere antenna. There is no need to. The modern built-in loop inside most AM receivers picks up much less energy from the broadcasting transmitter than did the elaborate rigs of the past, but the tubes in the modern set are more than equal to the task of amplifying that bit of energy into a useful signal.

The description of the modern AM receiver therefore begins with the loop antenna. Since the loop is wound as a coil of wire, it can serve as the coil element in a resonant circuit. Connected across the loop is a variable condenser, the other element of the resonant circuit. Such a circuit has the ability to vibrate in sympathy with a received signal provided it is set for the frequency of this signal. By varying the position of the tuning capacitor, therefore, the operator of the receiver can have it resonate to frequency of any transmitter signal he chooses.

If the receiver has an r-f amplifier (Chapter 5) the resonant circuit is connected to the control grid of the tube. The electrical vibrations of the tuned-in signal are amplified by the action of the tube, and appear across the plate load, which is usually the primary of an air core transformer. Unless proper bias voltage is applied to the grid of the tube, however, the amplified signal may be distorted. Such bias is supplied by a circuit in the tube's cathode made up of a resistor in parallel with a condenser. The tube also has a second bias source: the avc voltage. This negative d-c voltage (Chapter 4) is applied to the grid of the r-f amplifier through the antenna loop. When the incoming signal is strong and threatens to overdrive the r-f amplifier with resulting distortion, the avc voltage goes highly negative and reduces the amplifying power of the tube. For a relatively weak incoming signal, the avc voltage goes less negative, and the tube's ability to amplify is increased. The avc system and the voltage it produces thus act as a sort of automatic brake to keep the signal under control and hold the volume of speaker sound within reasonable limits.

The Converter

If the receiver has no r-f amplifier—true of many AM receivers—the resonant circuit of antenna loop and tuning capacitor is connected to the signal grid of the converter, a tube which combines the functions of first detector and oscillator (Chapter 8). The first two grids of this five-grid tube act as the grid and plate of an oscillator tube. The important remainder of the oscillator circuit is its resonant circuit, which determines the frequency of the signal the oscillator emits. Since this frequency must always be 455 kc higher than the incoming r-f, the resonant circuits of both have to be varied simultaneously whenever the receiver owner decides to tune in a different station. The tuning capacitor of both resonant circuits, therefore, is mounted on a common rotating shaft.

The r-f signal, brought into the converter by the r-f resonant circuit, and the oscillator signal, generated in its resonant circuit, are combined in the plate circuit of the converter. The tube's action as first detector gives its plate current a 455 kc component, equal to the difference between the r-f and oscillator frequencies. Avc operation also controls the amplification which the converter lends the r-f signal; consequently, avc

voltage is fed to the converter signal grid through the coil of the resonant circuit.

The I-F Amplifier

The i-f signal of 455 kc (Chapter 9) appears across the plate load of the converter. This plate load is the primary coil of what is usually a powdered-iron core transformer. Because the secondary winding of the transformer shares the magnetic field with the first, the i-f signal voltage also appears across the secondary, from which it is brought to the control grid of the i-f amplifier pentode. The coil of the secondary is part of a resonant circuit—a fixed capacitor is usually the complementing part if the transformer is slug-tuned—set to the i-f of 455 kc. In common with the stages ahead of it, the i-f amplifier tube is controlled by avc voltage.

The amplified i-f signal appears across the plate load of the i-f amplifier, the primary coil of a second i-f transformer. This coil and its fellow, the secondary, are both tunable, and are available to the serviceman when he performs his occasional tune-up operation.

Detector and AVC

It is this i-f transformer which, in the modern AM receiver, introduces the i-f signal to the detector diode. As a matter of fact, the coil in the detector schematic

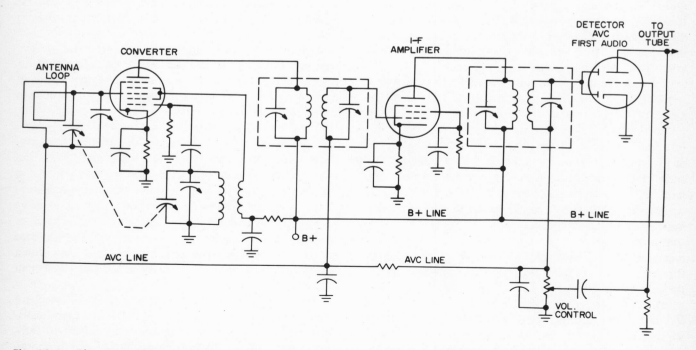

Fig. 10.1. *The AM Receiver, First Three Stages:* This schematic is the result of combining the converter, i-f amplifier, and detector-avc-first audio circuits given in chapters 8, 9, and 5 respectively.

of Chapter 3 is really the secondary of the transformer following the i-f amplifier tube. The signal from this tube is just as much a carrier as is the incoming r-f, except that its frequency is lower. By performing its rectifying operation on this signal and its sidebands, the detector circuit produces the audio signal.

Chapter 4 explained the operation of the detector further, and demonstrated how both the detector and avc diodes work in the duo-diode triode tube—the heart of the detector, avc, and first audio amplifier circuits. The coil winding which brings the signal to the two connected diode plates is the secondary of the i-f transformer. This latter is the transformer between the single i-f amplifier tube which many AM receivers contain, and the detector.

The load for the detector circuit is the resistance element of the volume control. If there were no filtering here, the current flowing through the resistor would be a combination of i-f, audio, and a negative d-c voltage. However, a small capacitor connected across the resistor removes the i-f signal, which is no longer needed. The remaining voltage consists of d-c and audio signals. The avc filter removes the audio, selecting only the d-c. It is this negative voltage, varying with the strength of the signal, which is fed back as avc to the i-f amplifier, the converter, and the r-f amplifier if there is one.

A different path is taken by the audio signal from the volume control. As the operator of the receiver adjusts the control, more or less of the audio is picked off by a tap and brought through a capacitor to the grid of the triode portion of the duo-diode triode tube. If the volume control is turned up, the amplitude of the audio signal brought to the triode grid is increased; if the control is turned down, the audio signal voltage falls. The amplified audio signal appears across the load resistor in the triode plate circuit.

The Rear End

In many AM broadcast receivers, the rear end consists of two stages. The first of these is, of course, the first audio amplifier discussed in the preceding section of this chapter and in Chapter 4. The second and last stage before the speaker is the power amplifier or output stage.

Primarily a voltage amplifier, the first stage is only incidentally concerned with developing audio currents. But strong audio currents as well as voltages are needed; the speaker is a mechanical device and requires electrical *power*—a combination of voltage and current—to produce a good, strong sound level. Consequently, a second tube with a heavy current as well as voltage output is used. Such a tube, as described in Chapter 5, is the beam power amplifier.

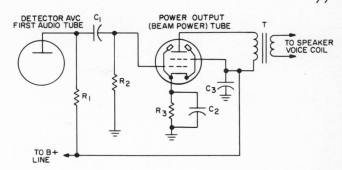

Fig. 10.2. *The Output Stage:* The method of resistance coupling is used between the first audio and power output stages. C_1 is the coupling capacitor which keeps the high positive B+ voltage away from the output tube grid, yet carries the audio signal to it. R_3 and C_2 make up the familiar cathode biasing circuit, T is the step-down output transformer, and C_3 is the screen bypass capacitor. R_2 provides the necessary d-c path between control grid and chassis.

The Output Stage

The output tube obtains its audio signal through a capacitor from the plate of the first audio amplifier. This capacitor is large enough to couple the low frequency audio signal through to the control grid of the beam power tube; it has the additional virtue of blocking the B+ voltage fed to the triode from the beam power tube grid. Descriptive technical terminology for capacitors so used becomes rather vague; they may be called coupling capacitors, blocking capacitors, or even both.

Bias for the beam power tube is provided by the customary cathode resistor-capacitor circuit. A resistor is connected between the control grid of the tube and the receiver chassis to provide a d-c path for bias voltage from the chassis end of the bias circuit.

These are standard devices that we have seen before. At the output circuit of the beam power tube, however, there is a novelty, the output transformer. Since the frequencies of the audio signal it handles are low, the transformer, has as can be expected, a heavy iron core. What is rather surprising is the fact that its primary winding, connected between the plate and screen of the beam power tube, has many more turns of wire than its secondary. The transformer thus steps down the voltage of the audio signal before the signal can get to the speaker.

The reason for this state of affairs is the need for stronger audio power for the speaker. The output transformer thus aids the beam power tube's efforts to provide increased current for driving the speaker properly. In addition, a well-designed transformer in this position has the helpful effect of transferring most of the frequencies in the audio range from the output stage to the speaker, hence improving the quality of the reproduced sound.

The Speaker

The speaker has been described as a device which converts electrical energy into sound energy. This statement is perfectly true: electrical energy in the form of an audio signal is put into the speaker, and out of the speaker comes sound. But there is an intermediate mechanical process. It would be more precise to say that conversions of electrical to mechanical to sound energy are performed in the speaker.

The mechanical energy in the speaker is obtained by using the principle of the electric motor. An electric motor consists of a coil surrounded by a magnetic field. When current is passed through the coil, a second magnetic field appears inside the coil. These two fields interact in forces of either attraction and repulsion, and these mechanical forces cause the coil to rotate.

This is a rather simple explanation of the motor principle, but it offers the requirements necessary for that principle to act. Those two requirements are the magnetic fields, one of which is already present, the other appearing only when a current is passed through the coil. In the speaker, these same two requirements are achieved: the first is provided by a permanent magnet of cylindrical form which fits into, but does not touch, a cylindrical extension of the speaker cone. Around the cone extension is wound a coil of just a few turns, known as the *voice coil*. The voice coil is connected to the secondary winding of the output trans-

former in the radio receiver. It therefore fulfills the second requirement of the motor principle, the coil through which a current is passed and in which a magnetic field is generated.

The permanent magnet is simply a piece of metal which has been strongly magnetized and is capable of preserving its magnetism for a long time. Since it is permanent, its north and south poles are fixed. The magnetic field of the voice coil, however, continually changes in polarity because the audio current passing through it alternates first in one direction and then in the other. When the pole at one end of the coil is the same as the corresponding pole of the permanent magnet, there is a force of repulsion, and the cone of the speaker is pushed in one direction. When the current through the voice coil is reversed, the pole of the voice coil field is reversed, and the consequent force of attraction between the two fields pushes the cone in the opposite direction. The cone therefore vibrates mechanically back and forth in response to the variations of the audio signal. As it does so, it compresses and decompresses the air in front of it, and this train of alternate compressions and decompressions reaches the listener's ear as sound waves.

The wide mouth of the speaker cone is attached to its rim through corrugations in the stiff cone material. These corrugations, which run around the cone's circumference, give the cone an elasticity permitting it to vibrate back and forth against the unyielding rim without damage.

Short Waves

For the listener who is bored with AM broadcasts emanating from local stations in the broadcast band, there is the excitement of overseas broadcasts. Many of the AM transmitters in foreign countries operate on frequencies much higher than those of our domestic broadcast band transmitters, for the most part between 20 and 40 mc. These are the so-called "short wave" bands. The word "short" in this term refers to the wavelength. The length of any wave depends on its frequency: the greater the frequency, the smaller the wavelength; and conversely, the lower the frequency, the longer the wavelength.

Observation of a fairly common spectacle, a tall man walking side by side with a small boy, can prove this last statement. The length of one of the walker's strides corresponds to the wavelength of the radio wave, and the number of times per second his right foot hits the pavement corresponds to the wave's frequency. Now, since the man's strides are naturally longer than the boy's, the boy must hurry his pace—that is, his frequency must increase—if he is to stay with his com-

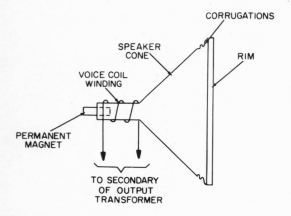

Fig. 10.3. *The PM Speaker:* The a-c audio currents passing through the voice coil generate a magnetic field which interacts with the field of the permanent magnet. A vibratory motion of the cone is thus produced. The corrugations around the cone at the rim of the speaker give the cone its resiliency.

panion. To keep within the spirit of the comparison, both the man and boy must remain side by side by maintaining the same velocity of travel; all electromagnetic waves, regardless of frequency, travel at the same velocity in free space. This is the cornerstone, as laid down by Einstein, of the whole structure of modern physics.

Lying in the frequency region between the broadcast band and the lowest of the television channels, the short waves enjoy a strategic advantage. The short wave station can project its transmissions further than either the broadcast band or the vhf transmitter, assuming that all characteristics except frequency are the same for each. A layer of charged particles, known as the *ionosphere*, is responsible for this. The ionosphere surrounds the earth at an altitude just beyond the atmosphere, and is filled with charged particles capable of bending a radio wave sent at a skyward angle. The amount by which the wave is bent depends on its frequency. A low frequency wave is quite sharply curved, so that it will return to the earth a short distance from the point at which it was transmitted. If the frequency of the wave is increased, the bending effect is more gradual, and the distance of its travel—known as the *skip* distance—may span a continent.

Since the short waves are at the right frequency for tremendous skip distances, they are the logical vehicles for transoceanic broadcast. Every nation beaming out

wisdom, misinformation, or propaganda uses them. There is a small but vigorous cult of long distance fans, on this side of the Atlantic and Pacific, who pick up these broadcasts regularly. For the sake of these stay-at-home global wanderers, some manufacturers of AM receivers have equipped their sets with a switch almost magical in its possibilities. By means of this "SW-BC" switch, together with its associated circuits, the listener can eavesdrop in every corner of the civilized world.

The Broadcast-Short Wave Receiver

Setting this remarkable switch in one position, the receiver owner can pick up the ordinary AM broadcast band transmitters he knows so well; setting the switch in the other, he can navigate among the short waves. Now the upper limit of the broadcast band is roughly 1600 kc, while the short wave stations operate around the 30 mc frequency region. Since 1600 kc is equivalent to 1.6 mc, the r-f circuits of the combination broadcast band and short wave receiver must be able to skip through the tremendous range of 1.6 to 30 mc. The tuning capacitor of an AM broadcast band receiver working with a single coil just about gets through a one megacycle range in rotating from minimum to maximum capacitance; it is obviously asking too much of it to cover the short waves as well.

The combination receiver manufacturer solves this

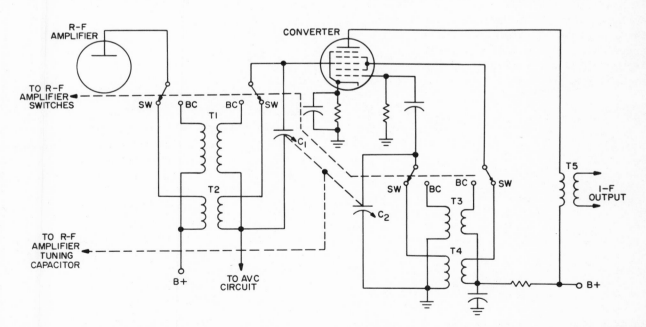

Fig. 10.4. *The Broadcast-Short Wave Receiver:* **The dotted line between switches indicates that all are ganged to the BC-SW knob on the receiver front panel. With the switches in the SW position, as shown, T_2 and T_4 are active while T_1 and T_3 are inactive; with the switch in the BC posi-** tion, the opposite is true. Capacitor C_1 operates with the secondary of either T_1 or T_2 for tuning; C_2 works with either the T_3 or T_4 secondary. Tuned circuits and switches for the r-f stage are not shown for the sake of simplicity. Compare the circuit of this converter with that of Chapter 8.

problem by having two tuned circuits for every one that is normally used. One of these circuits covers the broadcast range; the other covers the short wave range. The local oscillator, which must always keep company with the r-f, also boasts a pair of tuned circuits. All of these are controlled by the switch with the magical properties, which brings either the broadcast or short wave circuits into the receiver arrangement as desired. The switch knob on the receiver front panel has two positions, one marked BC, for broadcast, the other, SW, for short wave. This one knob simultaneously operates several sets of switches: one for the resonant circuits of the r-f amplifier—if there is one—a second for the circuits of the converter, and a third for the oscillator.

The switch and the extra resonant circuits are all the alteration needed to tailor the broadcast band receiver to reception of short waves. The extra resonant circuits need not consist of both coil and tuning capacitor. A single condenser can cover both bands provided it is given two separate coils to work with. Beyond the receiver front end, no further change is required. Regardless of the position of the BC-SW knob, the difference between r-f and oscillator frequencies is always 455 kc. The i-f amplifier is therefore always in tune for either short wave or broadcast band reception, and so is the detector. Some of these receivers may be refined to give the listener the added advantage of listening to CW transmissions, used by many transmitters working the short wave band. This refinement requires the addition of a beat frequency oscillator or bfo (Chapter 7).

GLOSSARY

Blocking capacitor. A fixed condenser which simultaneously blocks the d-c voltage at the plate of one tube from the grid of the next, and transfers the output a-c signal of the first tube to the input of the second.

Output transformer. A step-down, iron core transformer between output tube and the speaker voice coil.

PM speaker. A speaker in which the constant magnetic field is supplied by a permanent magnet.

Short wave. International AM broadcasting in the frequency vicinity of 20–40 mc.

SW-BC switch. The switch on some AM receivers which sets the receiver for either standard broadcast or short wave reception.

Voice coil. The coil of few turns around the cylindrical extension of the PM speaker cone.

Wave length. The distance (usually given in meters or centimeters) between the peaks of two consecutive waves in a wave train.

Chapter Eleven

THE FM RECEIVER

AS A SYSTEM of broadcasting, frequency modulation has had some bad breaks. Its first misfortune was to be born a younger brother to the still lusty AM system, thus having to take up residence in the colder climate of the 88 to 108 mc range. Its second was even more disastrous: before it had much time to grow up, it was given a baby brother so lively as to hog the entire electronic stage.

Any comparison between FM and its fascinating kid brother TV is, of course, unfair to the former. FM is purely a system of reproducing sound; television, with its FM sound system, provides the same benefits as FM, but also has the most attention-getting device any electronic system can possess—a lifelike motion picture. But a comparison between FM and AM can be made; and in such a comparison, the former must inevitably come out the winner. The AM system is still amazingly popular. But from the technical viewpoint, at least, FM is vastly superior despite its handicaps. In this chapter we shall take a closer look at the FM receiver and see how it achieves its technical triumphs.

The Receiver Antenna and Front End

By the time FM sets came to be manufactured, radio set buyers had already become accustomed to receivers with built-in antennas. FM set manufacturers have therefore followed the same custom. The antennas they install usually consist of two wires shaped into the T form of the dipole, with half the length of each wire forming half the horizontal bar of the T, and the remaining half of each descending to the two input terminals on the chassis of the receiver. Because the frequencies of FM carriers are so high, the dimensions of the dipole wires

need not be very large. They are easy to install, either by tacking them to the rear edges of the cabinet, or by concealing them on the inside of the cardboard partition which is screwed to the back of many sets.

Through the input terminals on the receiver chassis, the dipole wires are connected to the ends of the primary winding of a transformer, with the center tap of that winding connected to the chassis. The input circuit is therefore balanced by having an equal number of windings on either side of the grounded tap. Signals picked up by the dipole are transferred from the primary to the secondary winding of the transformer. As part of a resonant circuit, the secondary winding is paralleled by the variable tuning capacitor. If the receiver has an r-f amplifier, the tuned circuit is connected to the control grid of the r-f amplifier tube; if no r-f amplifier is pres-

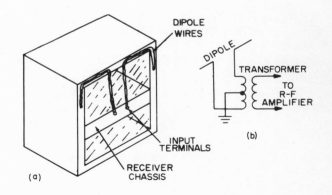

Fig. 11.1. *The Built-in FM Dipole:* (a) The insulated wires of the dipole are tacked down to the rear edges of the FM receiver cabinet; (b) The dipole and input circuit in schematic form.

ent, the tuned circuit is connected to the control grid of the converter tube.

Except for the antenna, the front end of the FM receiver really differs little from its corresponding portion of the AM set. The local oscillator circuits of the two receivers are also just about the same. Most FM receivers are equipped with local oscillators of either the Armstrong or Hartley type; while Colpitts circuits are somewhat rarer. Since the i-f in an FM receiver is 10.7 mc, the frequency of the local oscillator signal is higher than the received signal by that amount.

I-F Amplifiers

The i-f amplifier strip in the FM receiver usually has two stages, each featuring a pentode tube. Bias voltage for the control grids of these tubes are supplied both by cathode biasing circuits and by avc, the latter operating as a control voltage to prevent the i-f signal from being overamplified. Like all pentodes operating with avc, the i-f tubes are of the remote cutoff type. Transformer coupling is used between stages. The i-f voltage developed across the primary winding, in the plate circuit of the first stage, also appears across the secondary. The avc voltage is applied to the tube grid through the turns of the secondary winding. Both windings of the transformers may be adjusted by moving powdered iron slugs. Fixed condensers are sometimes connected across these windings to provide the capacitance necessary for resonant circuits; however, in many receivers, the distributed capacitance of the transformer windings is depended upon to do the trick.

The FM Detector

Transformer coupling is also used between the last i-f stage and the FM detector which follows it. The transformer used here, however, generally has three windings. Two of these are tuned by powdered iron slugs, and are set for the normal 10.7 mc i-f frequency; the third coil, known as the *tertiary* is untuned.

A glance at the schematic of the FM detector shows that the circuit of the detector is *balanced*. The tertiary winding (L_3) and its series resistor (R_1) are connected between the center tap of the transformer secondary (L_2) and the midpoint of two equal capacitors (C_1, C_2). This series arrangement of tertiary and resistor thus occupies the electrical center of the circuit, with the two diodes (D_1, D_2) grouped symmetrically around it. The two diodes are connected to aid each other. If current flows in one diode, from cathode to plate, it will pass through resistor R_2, and be in the proper direction to flow also through the second diode (D_2). When the i-f voltage applied to the diodes changes polarity, neither

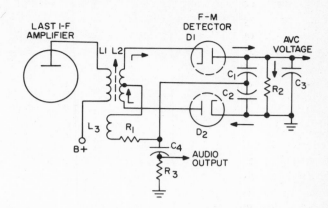

Fig. 11.2. *The FM Detector:* The circuit is balanced if the incoming i-f signal is at the resting frequency. The voltage at midpoint of bypass capacitors C_1 and C_2 is then zero. For a positive frequency deviation of the i-f signal, the voltage at the midpoint is positive; for a negative deviation, the voltage is negative. The output audio voltage appears across R_3 after the d-c component is removed by capacitor C_4. A large stabilizing capacitor, C_3, keeps the voltage across the two capacitors constant. Arrows show the direction of current through the diodes. The dotted portion of the circles enclosing the diodes indicates that both diodes are in one tube envelope.

diode can pass current. But the large stabilizing condenser C_3, connected across the resistor, acts to maintain a constant voltage across the resistor. It is enabled to do so by its size, large enough to hold an electric charge for some time. If the voltage across R_2 is held constant, then the voltages across the two small capacitors, C_1 and C_2, will also remain fixed.

The i-f signal is brought into the detector circuit in two ways: the first, by the coupling between the two tuned coils, L_1 and L_2; the second, by the coupling between L_1 and the untuned tertiary, L_3. In the first method, the i-f is brought through a circuit tuned to 10.7 mc, and in the second, through an electrically neutral branch. The effect of this apparent duplication is to measure the frequency of the incoming i-f signal against the frequency of 10.7 mc. If the i-f is not being deviated, its frequency will be the same as the resonant frequency of L_2. The circuit will then remain in electrical balance, and the voltage across each of the two capacitors C_1 and C_2 remain the same. The net voltage at their midpoint is therefore zero.

Under the influence of the audio signal, however, the i-f signal shifts in frequency. If there is a positive frequency deviation, the balance of the circuit is upset, and the voltage across C_2 becomes larger than that across C_1. The net voltage at the junction of the two capacitors is then positive; thus a positive deviation in the signal becomes a positive d-c voltage. A negative deviation in the i-f produces a corresponding negative d-c voltage. Thus the voltage at the point between the two capacitors is a d-c version of the audio signal the circuit extracts from the frequency modulated carrier. When this point is connected to chassis through a capacitor (C_4) and a resistor (R_3), the d-c component of the resulting current flow is removed by the condenser, and the voltage across the resistor is pure audio. Thus R_3 is the audio load resistor.

The ability of the large capacitor C_3 to hold its charge for some time lends the FM detector the advantage of being insensitive to changes in amplitude of the i-f signal. But the capacitor cannot keep its voltage constant forever. It will steady, or *stabilize,* the circuit against small amplitude changes for some time; but if the change in amplitude is a gradual one, covering relatively large periods of time, its voltage will change. Now, such a voltage is exactly what is needed for avc control. An avc voltage, as we found in Chapter 4, is one which varies with the strength of the signal. Such a voltage is supplied by the stabilizing capacitor in the FM detector to the control grids of the tubes ahead of it in the receiver.

Noise in FM Signals

One of the important advantages the FM system holds over the AM system is the fact that the FM receiver gives noise-free service, while AM reception is bedeviled by the snaps, crackles, and pops of what is known as *static.* Static is the common name for the various natural and man-made electrical noises which inhabit the airwaves. These noise waves are small in amplitude compared to the transmissions of a local station. But they are disturbing because they add to and subtract from the amplitude of the transmitted signal, and thus produce an amplitude modulation of their own.

If some circuit were added to the AM receiver to get rid of these noise modulations, the circuit would also get rid of the desirable audio signal modulation. The cure, therefore, would be worse than the disease. But the FM signal does not depend on amplitude changes to convey its message; an FM detector which overcomes the changes in amplitude produced by noise will only eliminate the noise. Hence the *ratio detector*—as the circuit described above is usually called—gets rid of noise through its insensitivity to the small and rapidly varying variations in amplitude caused by the noise signal.

The Discriminator

The ratio detector is used in practically all FM receivers nowadays. But in earlier sets, FM detectors were classi-

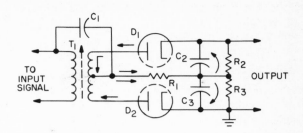

Fig. 11.3. *The Discriminator:* The input signal is coupled to the circuit through a capacitor (C_1) and transformer (T_1). The primary and secondary of the transformer are tuned to the frequency of the input signal. Currents of both diodes (D_1, D_2) (indicated by arrows) flow in the same direction through R_1, but in opposite directions through R_2 and R_3. C_2 and C_3 are bypass capacitors.

fied as *discriminators.* While the discriminator circuit works quite well in its function of converting frequency changes in the carrier into audio, it also responds to amplitude changes in the carrier. Additional circuits are therefore needed to eliminate the resulting noise.

While the circuit of the discriminator resembles that of the ratio detector, there is one important difference. In the discriminator, the diodes are connected with each diode plate tied to each terminal of the input transformer secondary.

As in the ratio detector, the primary and secondary coils of the input transformer are tuned to the frequency of the incoming signal. The signal is introduced into the balanced circuit at the circuit's electrical center through a capacitor (C_1), and also through the tuned circuit by means of the transformer. But where the output of the ratio detector is taken from one half of the rear end of the circuit, the output of the discriminator is taken from the whole of the rear end—that is, across *both* the series resistors, R_2 and R_3 in the accompanying schematic.

When the input signal is at the same frequency as that to which the secondary coil of the transformer is tuned, the d-c currents flowing through both diodes are equal. Both flow in the same direction through the central resistor (R_1), but flow in *opposite* directions through the equal resistors R_2 and R_3. The voltage across these resistors is therefore equal and opposite, and the net voltage across both is zero.

Suppose, now, that the input signal undergoes a positive deviation in frequency. The circuit is then unbalanced, and the diode D_1 allows more current to flow than diode D_2. A greater d-c current now flows through R_2 than through R_3, and the net voltage at the ungrounded end of the two resistors is positive. Thus, for a positive deviation in frequency of the input signal, a positive d-c voltage is obtained.

When the input signal suffers a negative deviation in frequency, the opposite diode (D_2) conducts the greater current, and the output is a negative d-c voltage. As far as detecting frequency changes in the signal is concerned, then, the discriminator performs the same function as the ratio detector. But where the ratio detector cannot be unbalanced by changes in amplitude of the signal, the discriminator can. Nor can this be cured by connecting a stabilizing capacitor across the discriminator output. Such a condenser would hold the voltage constant and therefore choke off the output audio signal.

The Limiter

In spite of the fact that the discriminator responds to noise, the FM receivers of a few years ago were as noiseless as modern sets. The clue to that secret is provided by a circuit known as the *limiter*. The limiter, as its name implies, limits the amplitude of the i-f signal applied to the discriminator to a constant level, and so defeats noise modulations. Because it must rid the signal of its amplitude variations before it arrives at the discriminator, the limiter is placed between the last i-f amplifier and the discriminator itself.

Like the i-f stages it follows, the limiter is an amplifier. Unlike them, however, its amplification takes place within such narrow limits that a strong signal fed to it has its positive and negative peaks cut off. In Chapter 4, we found that an overdriven amplifier has the effect of shearing off the peaks of the signal it amplifies. The limiter is an amplifier which is deliberately overdriven; as a consequence, the positive and negative peaks are cut off, thus removing the noise variations in signal

amplitude. Frequency variations in the signal, however, are unaltered, and the legitimate audio signal is thus preserved.

The tuned input circuit of the limiter is set for 10.7 mc, the i-f frequency. On positive swings of the signal, current is drawn by the control grid, and a bias voltage is developed across the grid leak in the circuit. A bypass capacitor across the leak keeps the bias at a constant value. Both the plate and screen voltages are kept low by a large dropping resistor; consequently, the positive peaks of the signal easily drive the tube into saturation, and are not reproduced in the circuit's output. The bias value set by the grid leak is such that the negative peaks of the signal drive the tube into cutoff. Thus the negative signal peaks are sheared away. Plate current of the tube therefore consists of a signal with its frequency variations unaffected, but with no amplitude variations. Such a signal, when presented to the discriminator circuit which follows the limiter, cannot produce noise simply because its noise-producing peaks are no longer present.

Automatic Frequency Control

In any superheterodyne, the intermediate frequency is created by mixing the received r-f signal with the signal generated by the receiver's local oscillator. Since transmitters are careful to keep their carriers at the correct frequency, the incoming r-f can be depended upon. But unless similar precautions are taken by receiver designers to keep the frequency of the local oscillator constant, the set may produce badly distorted sound.

The i-f amplifier in an FM receiver is like an archway broad enough to allow a number of men marching

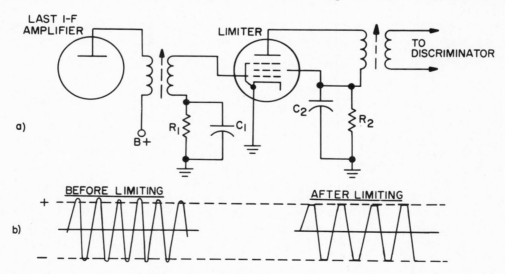

Fig. 11.4. *The Limiter:* The schematic is shown in (a). R_1 is the grid leak and C_1 the bypass capacitor. A dropping resistor (R_2) keeps the plate and screen at low d-c potential. C_2 is the bypass capacitor for the dropping resistor. Effect of the limiter on the FM i-f signal is shown in (b). The dotted lines are the positive and negative limiting levels. There is no amplitude variation after limiting.

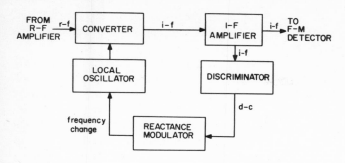

FROM
R-F
AMPLIFIER → r-f → CONVERTER → i-f → I-F AMPLIFIER → i-f → TO F-M DETECTOR

LOCAL OSCILLATOR

frequency change

REACTANCE MODULATOR

DISCRIMINATOR

d-c

Fig. 11.5. *AFC System, Block Diagram:* The addition of two circuits, the discriminator and reactance modulator, provide the FM receiver with an automatic frequency control system. The discriminator samples the frequency of the i-f signal, sends corrective d-c signals to the reactance modulator, and the reactance modulator automatically adjusts the local oscillator to the correct frequency.

is 88 mc, which means that the local oscillator must work at a frequency of 98.7 mc. At a frequency this high, the oscillator is likely to slip unless it is carefully controlled. In the better types of FM receiver, a special device called the automatic frequency control circuit (abbreviated *afc*) does the job.

One of the stages in the afc circuit is the discriminator, discussed earlier. The second is the *reactance modulator,* a circuit containing a pentode amplifier. This circuit acts like a variable capacitor, the amount of its capacitance depending on the d-c voltage applied to the control grid. A circuit of this sort, connected in parallel with the tuning capacitor of an oscillator, will become part of the total capacitance in the oscillator's resonant circuit. Even with the oscillator's regular tuning capacitor unrotated, a variable d-c voltage fed to the grid of the reactance modulator can vary the frequency of oscillation.

This explanation of the reactance modulator's work, plus the explanation already given for the discriminator, provides us with the tools we need for understanding the afc system. In the usual way, the i-f energy developed in the last i-f amplifier of the receiver is fed to the FM detector. But part of the signal is diverted to the discriminator, whose input circuit is tuned to the 10.7 mc i-f. As long as the local oscillator behaves and stays on frequency, the discriminator's output voltage is zero. The grid of the reactance modulator, connected to the discriminator's output circuit, receives this zero voltage and consequently has no effect on the oscillator.

A tendency of the oscillator to rise above its normal frequency, however, meets with action from the afc circuit to check that rise. The discriminator detects the increase in frequency and responds by emitting a positive voltage. This d-c voltage, placed on the control grid of the reactance modulator, increases the capacitive effect of the circuit, thus increasing the total capacitance

abreast to pass through; the men, of course, represent the frequencies covered by the modulated i-f signal. As long as the oscillator stays on frequency, the center of the frequency range covered matches the 10.7 mc to which the i-f amplifiers are tuned, and all the frequencies can be properly amplified. The marching men, that is to say, can all move safely through the archway as long as the center of their ranks matches the center of the arch. But if the line of march should swerve from its path, only a part of the troop will manage to enter the archway. Exactly the same thing occurs when the frequency of the local oscillator drifts. The center of the i-f signal range is no longer 10.7 mc, and some of the frequencies in it cannot get to the FM detector to be converted into sound.

In general, the higher the frequency at which an oscillator operates, the greater its tendency to drift. The lowest r-f to which an FM receiver front end will tune

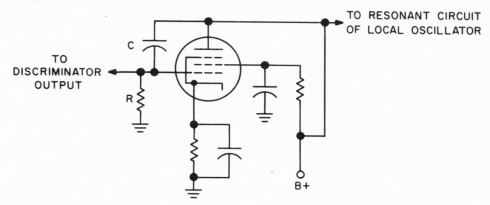

TO RESONANT CIRCUIT OF LOCAL OSCILLATOR

TO DISCRIMINATOR OUTPUT

C

R

B+

Fig. 11.6. *The Reactance Modulator:* The effect of the capacitor C is several times that of R; the circuit therefore operates as a capacitor. Changes in the circuit's capacitive effect are produced by d-c voltages applied to the grid from

the discriminator output circuit. When the circuit is connected in parallel with the local oscillator resonant circuit, the frequency of the oscillator is controlled by the d-c input signal.

in the oscillator. Now, an increase in the capacitance of a resonant circuit means a drop in the frequency to which that circuit vibrates. Consequently the frequency of the oscillator will fall off and readjust until the discriminator output is zero once more.

The same action in reverse occurs in response to an erratic drop in the local oscillator frequency. The discriminator reacts with a negative output voltage, the capacitive effect of the reactance modulator is decreased, and the frequency of the oscillator is forced to rise. In short, the afc system anticipates every frequency deviation of the local oscillator and acts to oppose it. The system, however, is not so powerful as to force the oscillator frequency to stay where it is even though the receiver is re-tuned to another station. Regardless of the station picked up, the i-f is always the same, and the discriminator responds as before.

Undoubtedly, the afc circuit is an asset to the FM receiver, but like all assets, it has its balancing liabilities. The liability of the afc circuit is its drain on the power that, in the end, will be delivered to the speaker. An FM receiver unequipped with afc can take advantage of all the power delivered by its i-f amplifiers since the total output of those stages is confined to a single path —the path to the detector. In a receiver which has the control system, however, part of the output power of the i-f stages must be diverted to the discriminator section of the afc system, which means that less power will be available to the detector. Given two receivers equal in every way except that one contains afc while the other does not, the latter will be the more sensitive.

The answer to this problem adopted by many manufacturers is to provide a front panel switch labeled AFC

IN-OUT. When the listener chooses a strong transmitter on his tuning dial, he places the switch in its IN position. The afc system is then doing its share of work in the receiver's operation, and the listener can sit back and enjoy the program with the assurance that it is not likely to suffer distortion. Of course, he will note a slight drop in volume when he makes the switch; but if the input signal to the receiver is strong, there is power to spare. If the listener chooses, however, to seek some weaker station on his dial, he may find it necessary to switch out the afc if he is to hear that station at all. But then he must take his chances on encountering the distortion bugaboo.

The AM-FM-Phono Combination

While the television set is usually the electronic center of the American home, equipment devoted to the purely tonal arts of music and the spoken word has certainly not been neglected. There are many individual FM and AM radios still in use and in production, of course, and there are also a good many combinations of these instruments with the added benefit of the phonograph. One of these combination radiophonographs is described here.

The important controlling device of this combination is a four-position switch. The four positions of the front panel knob through which this switch is operated are labeled AM, FM, FM-AFC, and PHONO. There is no secret here, of course. When the knob is set to the AM position, the combination works as an AM receiver for the broadcast band stations; in the FM position, the receiver is set to receive stations in the FM broadcast band, but without the benefit of automatic control; the

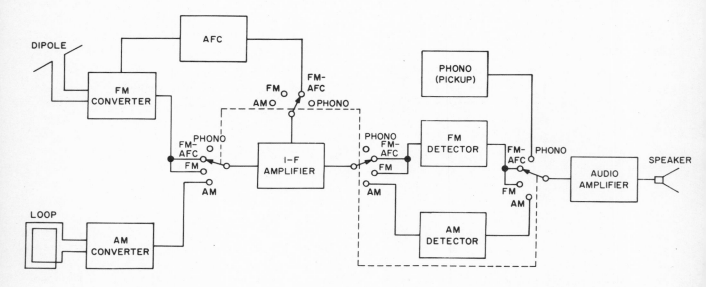

Fig. 11.7. AM-FM Combination Receiver, Block Diagram: All four switches are ganged, and are controlled by a front panel knob. The switches are shown in the FM-AFC position.

FM-AFC setting of the switch offers FM reception with automatic frequency control; the final switch position has the combination working as a simple phonograph.

Looking inside the combination, we find that the switch knob controls the ganged rotating arms of four switches. When the knob is set to the AM position, the switches interconnect the purely AM stages of the combination. The line-up of these stages are, in the order of signal travel: the built-in loop antenna, the AM converter, the i-f amplifier stages—perhaps two of them—the AM detector, the audio amplifier, and finally, the speaker. As long as the switch remains in this position, the stages in the FM receiver and the pickup arm of the phonograph turntable are idle.

When the listener wants entertainment from an FM station whose transmissions are not particularly strong in his area, he will turn to the FM broadcast band but keep the afc system from operating. This he does by clicking the switch knob into the FM position. The four switches now interconnect the dipole, FM converter, the i-f amplifier, the FM detector, the audio amplifier, and the speaker. The afc system is excluded from the circuit, the stages of the AM receiver are isolated from each other, and the phonograph pickup is still inoperative.

Perhaps because he is dissatisfied with the performance of the receiver without the blessings of afc, our listener now places the knob in its FM-AFC position. No change occurs in the line-up of stages for FM reception, but the two circuits of the afc system—the discriminator and the reactance modulator—are now switched in between the i-f amplifier and the oscillator circuit which is part of the FM converter stage. As before, the AM stages and the phonograph pickup are inactive.

But the programs offered by the FM stations are not very gratifying at that particular time of day, so the listener decides to put on a few of his own records. He therefore switches the knob to the PHONO position. Now all stages in the radio reception channels are out of operation, but the pickup arm of the phonograph turntable is connected to the audio amplifier. When our listener starts the automatic mechanism of the turntable, the pickup needle settles to the surface of the rotating record, and the audio signal can pass from the needle cartridge to the audio amplifier and thence to the speaker.

The Combination's I-F Amplifiers

In the preceding explanation, we are struck by two odd, but noteworthy items. One is the fact that, alone among the stages in the radio circuits, the i-f stage is used in common by both AM and FM. In view of what we have found—that the AM i-f is 455 kc and the FM i-f at the much higher frequency of 10.7 mc—how is it possible for both systems to use the same stages? The answer

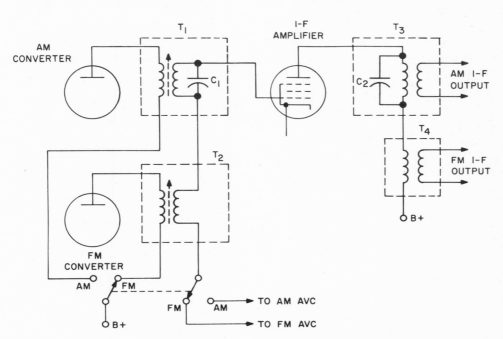

Fig. 11.8. *I-F Stage in Combination Receiver:* The secondary of T_1 responds only to 455 KC, and the secondary of T_2 responds only to 10.7 mc. The signal in one will not interfere with the signal of the other. This is also true of the primaries of T_3 and T_4. Dotted lines between switches represent ganging; dotted lines around transformers indicate shielding.

to that question lies in the peculiar characteristics of resonant circuits.

Two of the ganged switches controlled by the switch knob of the receiver are in the converter and i-f circuits. When the knob is set for either FM or FM-AFC, the plate circuit of the FM converter tube is connected to B+; the AM converter is simultaneously deprived of this necessary voltage. Only the FM converter can then operate. The 10.7 mc i-f flowing in its plate circuit is transferred to the secondary winding of the transformer between converter and i-f amplifier. The 10.7 mc signal therefore appears on the control grid of the i-f amplifier tube. It is true that the 455 kc resonant circuit for AM is also connected to the grid of the tube; but since this circuit is completely unaffected by a frequency so much higher than the one to which it is tuned, it might just as well not be in the circuit; its coil acts merely as a conductor—as would any ordinary wire—between the avc system at one end and the control grid of the tube at the other. The same is true when the set is switched to AM operation. Then the AM converter is active and the 455 kc resonant circuit at the input to the i-f amplifier responds, while the coil of the 10.7 mc resonant circuit is really a simple conductor.

The switch in the grid circuit is necessary because there are two sources of avc voltage, one at the AM detector, the other at the FM detector. When the switch knob of the receiver is placed in the AM position, only the AM detector is active. The switch must then be in position for connecting the AM avc voltage to the grid of the i-f amplifier. Or, if the receiver is set for FM operation, the switch must connect the grid with avc voltage from the FM detector.

Some Tips on Repair

The second item worth noting about the combination AM, FM, and phonograph combination is the common audio amplifier. This is only to be expected. All of these sound systems produce an audio signal which must be amplified before it is applied to the speaker for the final sound conversion. Consequently, all the services the set offers are funneled through the one audio amplifier section.

In many types of electronic equipment, the weakest link is the tube. Nor is it difficult to understand why that should be so, in view of the fact that the tubes are usually the hottest of all the equipment's components. A serviceman faced with the problem of putting a disabled combination radio receiver back into operation will, likely as not, begin by checking its tubes. Now most tube failures are caused by the snapping of the heater filament. In most instances, therefore, a set can be repaired by opening its cabinet, hunting for a cold, dark tube, and replacing it with a new one.

The problem in a complex receiver of this kind, though, is where in it does one look for the bad tube? An intelligent understanding of the symptoms and their causes can help solve that problem.

The breakdown of a tube in the audio amplifier of a combination set will naturally mean the breakdown of all the services which the set offers. The same symptom of complete inactivity can also be caused by a bad rectifier tube in the power supply. Fixing the responsibility for trouble in this way is based on logic: since both the audio amplifier and the power supply are continuously in operation for every job the set does, one of the two must be guilty if the set refuses to do anything.

What if the set will not work on AM or FM, but will on PHONO? The audio amplifier must be in good shape if the phonograph is working as it should, and the power supply is also beyond suspicion for the same reason. Since it is extremely unlikely that two tubes will simultaneously "blow" in different parts of the set, the guilty tube must be in a stage or stages used in common by AM and FM. The only stages answering this description are the i-f amplifiers. Thus the search for the bad tube narrows down to two possible suspects at most.

By the same token, the i-f amplifiers must be guiltless if the set works on either AM or FM but not both. If the AM system is good, then either the FM r-f amplifier—if one is present—the FM converter, or the FM detector must be at fault; if the FM radio works, the corresponding AM tubes are suspect.

Many manufacturers paste a plan of the receiver chassis on the inside of the cabinet. The tubes in this plan are indicated by circles, with the tube type number printed inside the circle, and possibly the function of the tube—converter, detector, and the like—underneath. This little label can, at times, be quite valuable because it shows where every tube in the receiver is placed.

The Benefits of FM

We can sum up the subject of FM radio by presenting a tally sheet of its faults and attractions. Possibly its outstanding disadvantage, from a technical viewpoint, is its need for operating in the very high frequencies. But the afc system goes a long way to provide the antidote for that.

With this one prominent debit thus canceled out, the FM system is the superior method of broadcasting. For one thing, it is free of the electrical noise that often bedevils AM reception. For another, it is capable of giving a richer tonal quality to its reproduced music or speech provided it is properly used. We have already seen the technical proofs of the first point; let us see now what we can make of the second.

A pure tone, struck from a tuning fork for example, sounds thin and naked compared to the richer tone of identical pitch and volume drawn from a violin. The two tones are the same in everything except what is known as *quality*. A scientific analysis of the tuning fork would show that its tone is composed of a single note called the *fundamental*. The violin tone has this same fundamental—hence, the same pitch—but has in addition a number of other frequencies called overtones or *harmonics*. These harmonics have frequencies of vibration which are multiples of the fundamental frequency. If the fundamental of the violin's note is 500 cycles, for example, harmonics of 1000 cycles, 1500 cycles, 2000 cycles, and so on, equal to twice, three times, and four times the fundamental, may also be present. None of these harmonics is as loud as the fundamental, which explains why both the tuning fork and the violin notes have the same pitch. But if all those harmonics were eliminated from the violin tone, leaving only the fundamental, that tone would lose its lovely timbre and sound as lifeless as the tuning fork.

A man whose range of hearing stops dead at 5000 cycles per second can hear the fundamental and all of the harmonics of the violin up to that limit, but is deaf to all the harmonics beyond. For him, then, the violin does not quite have the charm that it has for a second man with a better ear. But what is the position of this second man who listens to a radio unable to reproduce sounds of higher than 5000 cycles? To all intents and purposes, he is as deaf as his friend.

If a transmitter on the AM broadcast band wants to stay within the limits set for it by the FCC (Chapter 8) its carrier cannot be modulated by audio signals higher than 5000 cycles. The most perfect AM receiver, picking up that transmission, cannot then capture the complete tonal quality of a violin being played in that transmitter's studio. But no such limits are set for the FM transmitter. The FM carrier does have to operate within frequency limits, certainly; but those frequency limits reflect only the volume, or amplitude, of the audio signal, and not its frequency. All other things being equal, then, the FM transmitter provides a much wider range of audio frequencies, and the FM receiver tuned to that station furnishes its owner an incomparably richer tone.

GLOSSARY

Afc. Automatic frequency control; a system involving a discriminator and reactance modulator for controlling the frequency of an oscillator.

Combination set. A receiver combining AM, FM, and phonograph. Some of these sets also include television and a tape recorder.

Discriminator. A balanced, duo-diode detector circuit which converts frequency deviations into a variable d-c or audio signal.

Fundamental. The basic frequency of a vibrating object emitting sound.

Harmonic. A frequency equal to a whole-number multiple of a fundamental.

Limiter. An overdriven amplifier which, in the FM receiver, eliminates electrical noise from the i-f carrier.

Quality. The color or richness of a musical tone.

Ratio detector. The duo-diode detector used in most modern FM receivers.

Reactance modulator. A circuit capable of acting as a variable capacitor. A second variety of reactance modulator acts as a variable inductance or coil.

Stabilizing capacitor. The large capacitor which steadies the operation of the ratio detector.

Static. Natural or man-made noises of electrical origin.

Tertiary. The third winding of the transformer interlinking the last i-f stage with the ratio detector in an FM receiver.

Chapter Twelve

HIGH FIDELITY AMPLIFIERS

IN THE EARLY 1950's, electronics had just about settled down to a peaceful state, after the eruptions of FM and television, when a new revolution in the art occurred. Unkind observers called the uprising the "hi-fi craze." Whether the demand for high fidelity equipment—which, incidentally, is still in progress —has grown out of a sincere desire for the best in music or is just another adventure for status-seekers bored with sports cars, is a question best left to sociologists. As far as the engineer is concerned, high fidelity is what the customer wants, and high fidelity is what he intends to give him.

The engineer is therefore ready to go all out to supply bigger and better sound equipment. But an engineer is not only a scientist, he is also a business man. He is aware that customers' tastes are usually well ahead of their pocketbooks, and he is consequently aware that he is likely to lose his buyers if he presents them with a product which is too expensive because it has every anti-distortion circuit known to man. He then pursues the usual course followed by people faced with a dilemma: he compromises.

He understands, if he is designing an AM broadcast band receiver, that he cannot give the customer full fidelity. In a system which rarely affords an audio signal higher than 5 kc in frequency, hi-fi is out of the question. Rather than give the set a complex amplifier system in what is obviously a lost cause, he simply tacks on to the AM detector the two-stage audio amplifier we have seen in Chapter 10. It is far from being the best of amplifiers, but it is good enough for AM and it is the type of amplifier to be found in many broadcast-band receivers now manufactured.

When the engineer considers designing a television receiver, his thinking is apt to turn into psychological rather than electronic channels. Is the TV viewer really interested in hi-fi? Not really. The viewer is just that —a viewer; he would rather see than hear. If he wants the best in sound reproduction in addition to a good picture, he can be accommodated, of course. But he will have to have his set custom-built. The mass-produced TV receiver is carefully designed to give as good a picture as possible for its price; but the audio amplifier in its sound system is rarely equipped with anything better than the same two stages of the broadcast band radio. Within its limits, such an amplifier provides good quality in a set devoted to television reception.

The FM radio receiver, however, is a different matter. Under the FM system, this set is capable of giving stunning reception if it is provided with a high fidelity audio amplifier. It would seem, therefore, that it should have one. But the question arises: is the receiver to be a small, portable job or is it to be contained in a large cabinet for the living room? If the former, an expensive audio amplifier is really pointless. The portable receiver is housed in a small box, its speaker is correspondingly small, and it is simply a waste of money to build a luxurious audio system ahead of a speaker that cannot possibly reproduce the rich harmonics the system supplies. But the living room cabinet model can house a large speaker or even a system of speakers, and consequently deserves a good, meaty audio amplifier.

In these days of luxury living, though, the large-cabinet living room receiver capable only of FM reception is relatively rare. It is more likely to be a combination—"combo" in the lexicon of the electronics industry—with not only FM, but AM, TV, short wave, an automatic phonograph turntable and record changer, and a tape recorder. A complete sound system, in other words. To do all this justice, a brilliantly designed and brilliantly performing audio system is a must.

The rabid hi-fi fan, however, resents putting a lot of money into a fancy cabinet when he can spend the surplus on more elaborate electronic equipment. He therefore prefers to buy *units*—that is, a separate tape recorder, phono turntable, FM tuner, audio amplifier, and so on—and hook them all together according to directions given him by the supply house he patronizes. What he has when he gets done may be deplorable, from the point of view of an interior decorator, but is a treat to the cultured ear.

It would seem that such a set-up is the ultimate in electronic sound reproduction, but as hi-fi set-ups go, it is only half what can really be done. The true high-fidelity seeker aims further than accurate reproduction; he wants nothing less than the full depth of tone evoked by a performance in a live concert hall. For him the magic word is *stereophony*.

The stereophonic sound reproducer is to the modern living room what the stereoscope was to the living room of three generations ago. Back in those days, it was customary to ward off boredom by peering through two lenses at a postcard bearing what seemed to be twin pictures. The effect was startlingly lifelike. Objects in the foreground seemed close enough to touch; those in the background receded in space. Stereophonic equipment attempts the same three-dimensional effect in sound.

What Is High Fidelity?

It is as impossible to define high fidelity as to define good cooking. Both are really a matter of taste. The listener who prefers a good booming bass will never see eye to eye with the individual who worships "tonal balance," nor can the vegetarian dreaming of a platter of radishes, carrots, and tomatoes come to terms with the gourmet whose idea of heaven is lobster *a la Newburg*.

All other things being equal, however, a good audio amplifier is the necessary foundation for any electronic sound-reproducing structure. What we propose to do in this chapter is to investigate some of the favorite circuits of the audio engineer and show how they work. In the next, we shall take a closer look at some of the devices mentioned in these introductory paragraphs.

Troubles of the Two-Stage Amplifier

In damning the two-stage audio amplifier of Chapter 10 with faint praise, we have not as yet given it a fair

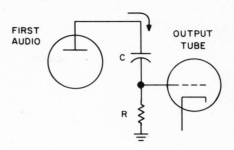

Fig. 12.1. *Simplified Schematic of Interstage Coupling Circuit in Two-Stage Audio Amplifier:* Audio current flows in the plate circuit, through coupling capacitor C and resistor R. Since the capacitor offers less opposition to high frequencies than to low, the voltage across R is predominantly high in frequency. This voltage is amplified by the output tube, with the result that the output of the amplifier favors the treble tones against the bass.

hearing. What, if any, are its defects?

First, it shows a tendency to overload easily. For the most part, this tendency is caused by the type of tube chosen for the first triode tube, a *sharp cutoff* amplifier. Unlike the grid of the remote cutoff type (Chapter 5), the grid of the sharp cutoff triode has regularly spaced turns. This characteristic gives it the benefit of better amplification, but the amplification provided is without distortion only if the input audio signal is held to small swings. Once the amplitude of the input signal increases, distortion is likely to set in—a distinct possibility since the signal is not directly controlled by any automatic system.

A second defect is the amplifier's unfair discrimination between audio signals of different frequencies. The note played by even a single musical instrument, as was pointed out in the preceding chapter, is made up of a number of different frequencies. If some of these frequencies are strengthened at the expense of the others, some alteration in the quality of the note takes place, and the amplifier can be accused of distortion. The one component in the two-stage amplifier responsible for that type of distortion is the coupling (or blocking) condenser between the plate of the first tube and the control grid of the second. Like any capacitor, this one offers little opposition to the flow of high frequency audio currents and tends to oppose more strongly the passage of lower frequency currents. What is then available to the following stage and ultimately to the speaker are mostly the high frequency elements in the audio signal. As a result, the sound reproduced by the speaker is shriller than it should be.

In many radio receivers using the two-stage amplifier, this shrillness is balanced out by connecting a fixed condenser from the plate of the output tube to chassis.

The idea here is that the condenser will bypass the higher audio frequencies away from the output transformer which leads to the speaker, thus giving the speaker a bassier quality. But this scheme smacks too much of robbing Peter to pay Paul. No attempt is made to restore the low frequencies lost through the action of the coupling capacitor; instead, a good portion of the high frequency audio range is whacked off by way of compensation.

These twin evils of *amplitude distortion* of the audio signal through overdriving and *frequency distortion* caused by loss of some part of the audio frequency range, are hard to battle in simple amplifiers of this type. But some good attempts can be made.

D.C. Amplifiers

The "d.c." in the heading of this section stands for "direct coupled," in which the audio signal developed at the output of the first stage is brought to the grid of the next tube by a direct wire rather than through a coupling capacitor. The advantage of this method is obvious: it gets rid of the troublesome condenser. However, it requires some fancy juggling of voltages. Since there is no capacitor to keep the high B+ at the plate of the first stage off the grid of the following tube, the voltage at the cathode of the second tube must be correspondingly increased.

Suppose, to begin with, that there is no audio signal in the d.c. amplifier. The +90 volts normally applied to the plate of the first tube through the plate load resistor is also given to the grid of the second tube. Now, if the cathode of that tube were connected to

chassis, it would be a full 90 volts lower than the grid. Its electrons would therefore be attracted to the grid (90 volts positive with respect to cathode) with such force that the heat of their impact could conceivably destroy it. The solution is to apply a d-c potential of +95 volts to the cathode of this second tube. When that is done, the grid of the second tube, at +90 volts, will be 5 volts less than the cathode. The grid voltage is therefore −5 with respect to cathode; this is the value of the grid bias.

The voltage normally supplied to the plate and screen of the second tube is some +150 volts d-c. But this is only true if the cathode voltage is approximately zero. With the cathode at +95, the plate of the tube must be raised by this same amount of 95 volts to keep it 150 volts above the cathode potential. The plate, consequently, is given the total voltage of +245 volts—or, in round figures, +250. So, also, is the screen.

But this is not the end of the voltage juggling. It must be remembered that the second tube has a heater, and that this heater has across it a voltage of, usually, 6.3 volts a-c (Chapter 5). If the cathode is at +95 volts, there is a difference of some 90 volts between these two electrodes. But the *distance* between them is extremely small. It is therefore likely that arcing—a continuous flashing of sparks—will take place across the tiny gap under the heavy electrical pressure of 90 volts, and that this incessant arcing will ruin the tube in short order. The possibility of arcing is foiled by connecting +90 volts d-c to the heater, thus equalizing its potential with that of the cathode. Many a fine design has turned out a failure for lack of this simple precaution.

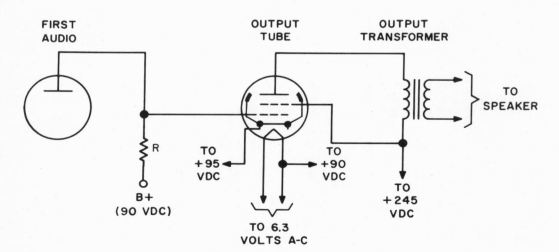

Fig. 12.2. *The D.C. Amplifier:* No blocking capacitor is needed here. The control grid of the output tube is −5 volts d-c with respect to cathode—a normal value. The plate and screen voltages of the tube are also normal at +150 with respect to cathode. Application of +90 volts d-c to heater of the output tube is necessary to prevent arcing. R is the plate load resistor of the first audio stage.

Degenerative Feedback

The d.c. amplifier goes a long way toward correcting frequency distortion. But it is helpless in the face of amplitude distortion, in which the peaks of the audio signal are lopped off or otherwise mangled. A second method, called *degenerative feedback*, is useful in fighting both.

The term "feedback" has come up several times in the course of this book; it reappears again and again, not only in electronics but in technical literature of all types. Feedback is the act of obtaining some of the surplus energy at the output of some device and conveying that energy back to the input. *Regenerative* feedback takes place when the energy at the output is fed back in such fashion as to aid the energy at the input. An example of such aiding feedback is the oscillator, described in Chapter 8. A feedback method which has the reverse effect is said to be *degenerative*. Here the energy at the output is brought back in such fashion as to oppose the energy at the input; an example is afforded by the stabilizing resistor described in Chapter 9. One way of obtaining degenerative feedback in the audio amplifier is through the use of just such a resistor, connected in the same manner, and working along identical lines.

This resistor is connected in the cathode circuit of the audio amplifier tube. When signal current flows through it, the resistor feeds back to the grid of the tube a voltage opposed to the applied voltage. Any blemish in the shape of the audio wave is thus diminished by a weaker image of itself in the opposite direction. The system thus corrects its own faults. If the blemish is an extra hump in the wave peak caused by amplitude distortion, the voltage fed back has the same hump, but of opposite polarity. The amplitude distortion is then diminished. A blemish of frequency distortion is similarly corrected. If the amplifier tends to favor the higher frequencies against the lower, the current in the degenerating resistor is made up predominantly of these higher frequencies. These are fed back negatively to the input in greater quantity than the lows, and the tendency is to restore the balance in the distribution of frequency strength.

This method of degenerative feedback seems at first blush to be a perfect one, but it shows a fault when carefully examined: the fed-back voltage consists not only of the blemish but also of the desired audio signal. Consequently, the desired audio signal is weakened. This loss, however, means little to a powerful audio amplifier, and is a fair exchange for better fidelity.

The Push-Pull Amplifier

Amplifiers consisting of two single stages like the triode and the beam power tube of Chapter 10 are said to be *single-ended*. Each stage has a single active end, the plate; the opposite end, its cathode is a more or less grounded electrode. By an adroit use of two tubes in place of the single one of each stage, the stage can be converted into a *double-ended* amplifier in which one tube "pushes" while the other tube "pulls." The push-pull amplifier is like the carrot-and-stick method of moving an obstinate donkey. Beating him with a stick at one end is helpful; it is doubly effective to appeal also to his other end with an appetizing carrot.

A glance at the schematic of the push-pull amplifier shows it to be balanced—schematics of the circuit are

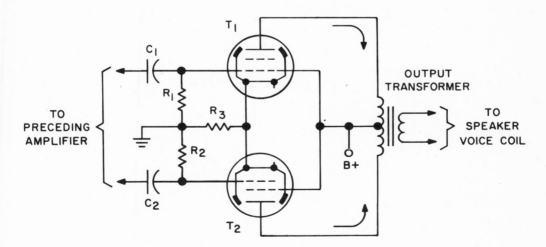

Fig. 12.3. *The Push-Pull Amplifier Output Stage:* The circuit is balanced. B+ voltage for the plates and screens of the tubes is fed to the electrical center of the output transformer primary winding; R_1 and R_2 are equal resistors, and C_1 and C_2 equal coupling capacitors. Arrows show direction of plate currents of both beam power tubes.

usually drawn in this fashion, with the symbol of one tube inverted with respect to the other, to emphasize the circuit symmetry. The input capacitors are equal, the grid load resistors of both tubes are equal, the two tubes have as nearly identical characteristics as possible. The B+ voltage fed to the plates and screens of both tubes are applied at the electrical center of the output transformer primary, and the chassis point at the input is centered between the identical grid load resistors.

If we begin our analysis of the circuit by assuming that there is no input audio signal, we can immediately see some outstanding advantages. Because the upper and lower halves of the circuit are balanced, the plate current flow of each tube is equal. The current through the upper tube flows *down* the upper half of the output transformer primary to the B+ point; the current through the lower tube flows *up* through the lower half of the same coil. The net current through the entire coil is therefore zero. Consequently, the core of the transformer is unmagnetized in its resting state, and can operate more efficiently when an audio signal is put into the circuit. This same balancing effect also tends to reduce hum in the circuit arising from insufficient filtering in the power supply (Chapter 2). By opposing each other in the primary of the output transformer, the hum currents buck themselves out and are not transferred to the secondary coil and the speaker.

But the real beauty of the push-pull amplifier is unmasked when its behavior with an input audio signal is examined. The positive half of the audio signal cycle is applied to the control grid of the top tube through its capacitor (C_1). At the same time, a negative version of this same half-cycle is applied to the control grid of the opposite tube. With a positive-going signal encouraging the flow of electrons through the top half of the circuit, the plate current in the circuit is strengthened; as a result, the top terminal of the transformer primary is depressed to a negative peak with respect to the center tap. A simultaneously weakened current passes through the lower half of the circuit, and the voltage at the lower end of the primary is raised to a positive peak. Both halves of the transformer primary then resemble two batteries connected in series, their total voltage being equal to twice the voltage of each. Corresponding to a half-cycle of input audio, then, an audio half-cycle of at least twice the strength appears at the output of the circuit.

When the input signal goes through the opposite half of the cycle, the behavior of the circuit reverses itself. Now, a weakened current passes through the upper half at the moment that a strengthened current passes through the lower. The result is a greatly enlarged half-cycle of audio in a direction corresponding to the new

input peak. Looking at the operation of the circuit as a whole, we can see how it gets its name: stimulated by the positive voltage applied to its grid, one tube pulls; the corresponding stimulus of the negative voltage causes the other tube to push. Or, in the language of the carrot-and-stick figure, the positive input peak is the carrot to attract our donkey of a circuit forward, while the negative peak beats the donkey from behind.

The push-pull amplifier can be operated Class AB (Chapter 4) without fear of distortion. This type of amplification offers the attraction of improved efficiency. As for the distortion bugaboo, that is typical only of single-ended amplifiers operated in this class; in the double-ended amplifier, the balancing feature of the circuit helps remove the distortion just as it helps cancel out hum.

The Single-Ended Phase Inverter

A powerful amplifier, the push-pull circuit cannot do its best if it is given a weak audio input signal to work on. It therefore cannot immediately follow the detector circuit of a receiver, the pickup of a phonograph, or whatever the original source of audio happens to be, but must follow a *preamplifier*. The function of this latter circuit, of course, is to strengthen the output of the original audio source to the point where it is adequate to drive the push-pull circuit.

But the preamplifier is more than an ordinary amplifier stage. It should also be able to supply the push-pull circuit with its carrot and stick. That is to say, the preamplifier should furnish, for every half-cycle of audio put into it, a positive and a negative half-cycle. Such a device is called a *phase inverter* because of its

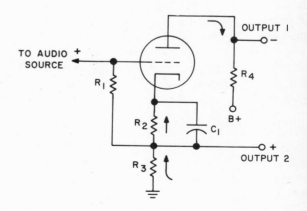

Fig. 12.4. *Single-Ended Phase Inverter:* An audio half-cycle of positive phase on the grid of the triode produces a negative half-cycle across R_4 and a positive half-cycle across R_3. The circuit of R_2 and C_1 is for bias; R_1 is the grid load resistor. Arrows indicate the direction of plate current flow.

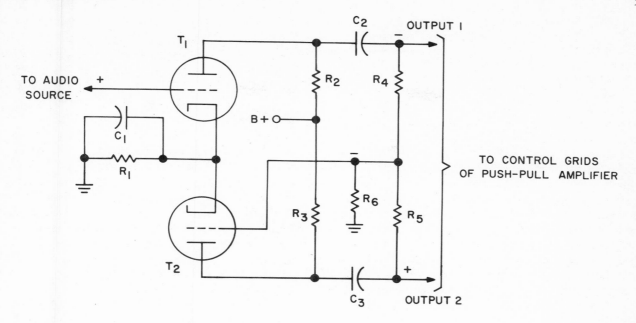

TO AUDIO SOURCE

TO CONTROL GRIDS OF PUSH-PULL AMPLIFIER

Fig. 12.5. *Double-Ended Phase Inverter:* For a positive input half-cycle at T_1, audio current flows through R_4 and R_6. The negative voltage appearing at R_6 is fed to the grid of the second tube, T_2. Thus a negative output half-cycle appears at R_4 and a positive half-cycle at R_5. These output voltages can be applied directly to the control grids of the push-pull amplifier.

ability to produce a signal of inverted as well as of the same phase as its input signal.

The simpler or single-ended type of phase inverter is usually a triode with two load resistors, one at the plate and the other in the cathode circuit. When an input half-cycle of positive phase is applied to the grid of the triode, the plate current increases. It flows through the plate load resistor to B+, through the power supply to B— and chassis, and from chassis back to the cathode of the tube via the cathode load resistor. Since the current is an increasing one, it depresses the voltage at points of entry into both resistors in the negative direction. Thus the output voltage of the load resistor is negative. The output of the cathode resistor is taken from the terminal of the resistor *opposite* to that at which plate current enters. That voltage is therefore positive. For a single positive half-cycle of input audio, the circuit supplies a negative half-cycle output at the plate and a positive half-cycle output at the chassis-connected resistor in the cathode. And when the input half-cycle is negative, the negative half-cycle appears at the cathode resistor output point, and the positive half-cycle at the plate output.

In the schematic of the single-ended phase inverter, incidentally, it is worth noting that the grid load resistor is returned not to chassis, but to the junction of the two cathode resistors. The voltage applied to the grid from the cathode circuit is therefore only the bias voltage across the upper resistor (R_2).

The Double-Ended Phase Inverter

The value of the single-ended phase inverter can be multiplied by converting it into a double-ended system; then the full advantages of balancing—the cancellation of hum noise and distortion—come into play.

Balance is achieved in the double-ended phase inverter through the use of two matching triodes, with equal condensers and resistors in the circuits of each. The input audio signal is fed to the grid of one triode (T_1 in the schematic). When that signal is in its positive phase, a strong audio current flows through the blocking capacitor C_2, and the series resistors R_4 and R_6 to chassis. In its passage through R_4, this increasing current puts a negative voltage at the top of the resistor. The negative half-cycle thus formed is the inverted output. A similar negative voltage appears at the ungrounded side of R_6, and is brought directly to the grid of the second tube. This tube now does its amplifying work on the negative half-cycle fed to it, and produces in its plate circuit a positive half-cycle which is put through the second blocking capacitor (C_3) to give an output of the same phase as the input. A similar analysis proves that the reversal of the input audio signal to a negative phase produces changes in phase at the two output points.

The two output terminals of the double-ended phase inverter can be connected directly to the grids of the following push-pull amplifier. As for the single input terminal, at the grid of the first triode, that may be connected through a switch selecting audio from one of several sources. We have already noted that such a source may be the detector of a receiver or a phono pickup. It might even be the microphone in a PA—public address—system, the kind used in the sound trucks which roam the streets at election time. If the latter, an additional stage of amplification might be needed for the microphone, a device with a weak output. The amplifier would then consist of a single-ended stage, a double-ended phase inverter, and a push-pull amplifier.

Additional power can be secured by adding a second stage in push-pull amplification, a procedure which will have to be followed if the amplifier is to supply audio power to several speakers. But there is a limit to the benefits of amplification, a limit set by the noise level of the system. As the amplification is increased, the noise level is progressively increased to the point where it interferes seriously with the desired signal.

Tone Controls

Most amplifiers are equipped with electronic circuits for varying the tone of the sound reproduced. These circuits are called tone controls, and their function is to adjust treble and bass—the high and low frequency components—in the audio signal according to taste. Any change made in the amplifier's audio signal is reflected in a change in quality of the sound emitted by the speaker system; by varying the size of circuit elements through the tone control knobs, the listener can alter the tone to suit his mood of the moment.

There are many different types of tone controls. Most

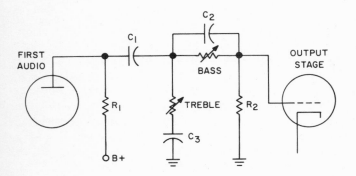

Fig. 12.6. *Tone Controls:* The bass and treble tone controls are variable, as symbolized by the arrows drawn through the resistor symbols, each working with a capacitor (C_2, C_3). C_1 is the usual blocking and coupling capacitor, R_1 the plate load of the first audio stage, and R_2 the grid load resistor of the output stage.

of them are networks of capacitors and resistors in which the variable element is a resistor. In the simpler types, the treble tone control takes the form of a series connection of variable resistor and fixed condenser, the whole wired in parallel with the input of one of the amplifying tubes; the bass control is a variable resistor shunted by a condenser, both in the line between the plate of one amplifier tube and the grid of the tube following. The shafts of both variable resistors project through the front panel of the sound system—or of the amplifier, if it is an individually packaged unit—and are capped with knobs labeled TREBLE and BASS.

Like any capacitor, the condenser in the treble circuit tends to oppose currents of low frequency more than those of high. Because it shunts the input to an audio stage, it would ordinarily bypass the high frequency components to chassis before they could reach the amplifier input circuit, and so lend the sound issuing from the speaker a predominantly bassy quality. The condenser, however, does not exist by itself, but is in series with a variable resistor; the setting of the resistor therefore determines the extent to which the highs will be drained out of the audio signal. An extreme counterclockwise turn of the TREBLE knob cuts out most or all of the resistance in this tone control circuit. The treble circuit then consists only of the capacitor, and the resultant tone is the booming bass people of the virile type usually dote on. Clockwise rotations of the knob from that extreme position bring in more resistance, increase the opposition of the circuit to the draining flow of highs, and consequently makes more of the high frequency signal available to the following stage and ultimately to the speaker. Hence the treble coloring in the tone is touched up.

Those frequencies in the audio signal which are not discarded by the treble circuit are then passed on to the bass control circuit. With the BASS knob turned to its extreme counterclockwise position, all of the variable resistance is introduced into the circuit, and the parallel capacitor is important in the circuit. Since the capacitor discriminates against the lows in the audio signal, the effect of maximum resistance is to reduce bass reproduction. As the knob is advanced in the clockwise direction, the resistance in the circuit is reduced until it is practically zero at the end of the knob's run. The capacitor is then virtually short-circuited; it is no longer capable of resisting the low frequency currents, and the bassy tone of the sound system is heightened.

The treble and bass circuits thus regulate the composition of the audio current flowing through the grid load resistor of the stage following the controls. As a consequence, only the frequencies passed by the controls can be amplified and sent on to the speaker. The controls act much like hot and cold water faucets emptying into a single pipe: they permit the resultant mixture to be blended to its user's comfort.

Equalization

There is nothing the hi-fi fan loves so dearly as an amplifier with flat characteristics—an amplifier, that is, which shows no discrimination among frequencies but amplifies them all equally. Such an amplifier provides excellent reproduction of an audio signal from almost any source. However, for accurate phonograph record reproduction, the amplifier requires a special type of tone control known as an *equalizer*. The function of the equalizer is to compensate for certain frequency distortions in the record.

A phonograph record is "cut" by a vibrating stylus tracing a groove in a wax blank rotating under it. The side-to-side oscillations of the stylus are controlled by the input audio signal. At low input audio frequencies, the movement of the stylus is slow and fairly free of mechanical inhibitions. But the higher frequencies demand so rapid a motion that the sidewise travel of the stylus is limited by its own inertia. Given high and low frequencies of the same amplitude, then, the stylus tends to cut wider swathes at the lows than at the highs; and the recording engineer must reduce the amplitude of the low frequency signals to prevent the stylus from cutting into the adjacent groove. The amplifier in the recording studio is therefore adjusted to attenuate, or reduce, the low frequency components of the signal fed into the cutting head.

A circuit for boosting the upper frequency limits also finds a place in the recording studio amplifier, but for another reason. Its ultimate purpose is to compensate for the hiss of needle scratch when the record is played back. Now needle hiss is a high-pitched sound and so corresponds to a high frequency audio signal. By overamplifying the highs in the audio fed to his cutting head, the engineer in effect overcomes the hiss.

To compensate for these deliberate distortions in the tone of the played-back record, the equalizer in the home amplifier reverses the deficiencies and exaggerations of the recording studio amplifier. It overamplifies the lows and thereby restores their strength. It underplays the highs and so reduces needle hiss to impotence.

In many modern radio-phono combinations, the function switch controlling the operation of the combination has an additional setting labeled RIAA. These mystic letters stand for Recording Industry Association of America. When the switch is placed in the RIAA position, the equalizer circuits are cut into the amplifier to adapt it for playback of the records manufactured by this industrial group.

Amplifier Curves

Advertisements of high fidelity amplifiers are often accompanied by an engineer's "curve" indicating the type of performance to be expected of them. These amplifier curves are much like the band width curves shown in earlier chapters of this book (Chapter 9). In both drawings, horizontal distances correspond to frequency, and vertical distances to the strength of the signal. There is this important difference, however. Where signal strength in the band width curve is rated in units of volts, signal strength in the audio amplifier curve is rated in *decibels,* abbreviated "db." This latter unit was developed to fit the characteristics of the human ear, which responds to the intensity of sound in not quite the same way as do scientific instruments.

The hi-fi fan's idea of glory is an amplifier whose curve is absolutely flat from zero to 20,000 cycles—an amplifier, that is, which responds equally to just about every audio frequency vouchsafed to man. Like most ideals this side of heaven, such an amplifier is an impossibility. There are, however, many good amplifiers with not quite so extensive a range, but with a fairly uniform response for the range they do cover. But they are expensive. It is safe to say that the flatter an amplifier's curve, the flatter the purchaser's pocketbook.

GLOSSARY

Arcing. Sparking across a narrow gap between conductors.

Bass. The low frequency tones in sound.

Cutting head. The device holding the stylus in disc recording.

Db. Decibel; the unit in which the intensity of sound is measured.

D.c. amplifier. Direct coupled amplifier; an amplifier in which the coupling between the plate of one stage and the grid of the succeeding stage is made through a conductor rather than a condenser.

Degenerative feedback. A type of feedback in which the returned output signal is opposite in phase to the input signal.

Double-ended amplifier. A two-tube amplifier with a symmetrical circuit arrangement.

Equalizer. An elaborate tone control system designed to compensate for frequency distortion in phonograph records.

Frequency distortion. A type of distortion in which certain frequencies are lost or discriminated against.

Hi-fi. High fidelity.

PA. Public address; an amplifying system for large audiences.

Phase inverter. A type of amplifier which supplies a positive and negative half-cycle of output for every half-cycle of input voltage.

Preamplifier. A one or two-stage amplifier required to strengthen the output of a weak electrical device to the point where it can drive a main amplifier.

Push-pull amplifier. A double-ended amplifier often used as the power output stage in an audio amplifier system.

Regenerative feedback. A type of feedback in which the returned output signal is in phase with the input signal.

RIAA. An equalizer for the playback of modern phonograph records.

Sharp cutoff tube. An amplifier which provides high amplification but is prone to overloading.

Single-ended amplifier. A single-stage amplifier using one tube.

Stylus. The cutting needle which, in the recording process, etches the grooves of a record master.

Tone control. A circuit for setting the bass or treble response of an amplifier to the listener's satisfaction.

Treble. The high frequency tones in sound.

Chapter Thirteen

HI-FI COMPONENTS

OF ALL AVAILABLE bores in this world, the hi-fi fan is possibly the worst. He will prattle constantly of degeneration, distortion, and decibels, and can only be diverted from gabbling about his amplifier by another hi-fi fan dying to talk about *his*. It is only when this subject palls, if it ever does, that either of them is willing to begin describing his other possessions.

Generally, these possessions are sources of audio in the form of speech, music, and—the hi-fi enthusiast's delight—the hisses, bells, and whistles of a steam locomotive. Such items as AM and FM tuners as well as microphones are responsible for the speech and music; the recording devices—the phonograph turntable and the tape recorder— generate the fantastic noises most hi-fi fans seem to adore. All of these audio sources plug into the front panel of the amplifier housing, and thus connect with the amplifier's input circuits.

At the output of the amplifier are, usually, a group of speakers. The word "usually" is inserted in the preceding sentence as a necessary precaution, for there is a hi-fi cult whose members would rather look at curves than listen to music: these people are in the habit of connecting an oscilloscope (Chapter 6) to their amplifier output terminals. However, this chapter is not meant to be a catalog of human oddities; we shall therefore restrict it to a discussion of high fidelity components.

The Tuner; the Cathode Follower

The hi-fi fan who has equipped himself with a good amplifier and speaker system already has the electronic rear end of a radio receiver—one, furthermore, which is likely to be superior to anything he might find in the best of manufactured radio sets. He would be foolish to buy a complete receiver when he knows that part of his money will go for a pale imitation of something he already has. So, if he wants the benefits of AM or FM reception, he buys a tuner.

The tuner is in all respects a radio receiver—it is equipped with its own power supply—which stops short at the detector. Its output can therefore be applied to the hi-fi fan's own amplifier and speaker system to give him a radio receiver with superb audio performance. While the output of the detector circuit in the tuner can be fed directly to the amplifier input, a more efficient method of linking tuner and amplifier is the circuit known as the *cathode follower*. This circuit is usually provided in the tuner after the detector.

The cathode follower is usually a triode in which the input signal is, as usual, fed to the grid, and the output is taken off a cathode resistor which is not

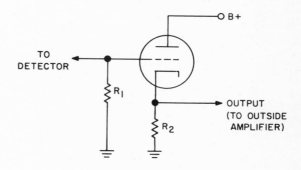

Fig. 13.1. *The Cathode Follower:* **The audio signal at the tuner detector output is fed to the grid across the grid resistor R$_1$. The output voltage is developed across the cathode resistor, R$_2$.**

bypassed. In the positive phase of the audio signal applied to the grid, the plate current of the tube increases, and a corresponding positive voltage appears at the output terminal. Similarly, a negative output voltage follows the appearance of a half-cycle of the same phase given to the grid. Thus the circuit gets its name from the tendency of the cathode voltage to follow the voltage applied to the grid.

Because the cathode resistor causes a degenerative feedback (Chapter 12) the circuit is a poor voltage amplifier. But it has the advantages of efficiently interlinking the detector circuit of the tuner and the input of the external audio amplifier, and of providing greater power than the unaided detector.

The Microphone

The microphone is an instrument which converts sound energy into electrical energy. It consequently has a thousand uses, from its work in the home of the hi-fi fiend to its expert manipulations by professional broadcasters, recording companies, movie sound experts, and the like.

As does its opposite number, the loudspeaker, the microphone performs its sound-to-audio conversion through an intermediate mechanical step. The sound energy from the performer's vocal cords or musical instrument passes through the air in the form of sound waves—successive condensations and rarefactions of air particles. At some point in space between the performer and the microphone, the air particles are packed together under the influence of the sound energy; a moment later, the air particles at that same point are spread widely apart. The number of successive packings which occur per second at that point is the frequency of the sound wave; the extent to which the particles are packed together is the intensity of the sound wave. As these air disturbances strike the microphone, they cause the mechanical vibration of some device inside the instrument. This moving device, associated with a source of electrical or magnetic energy, then produces the audio signal.

The Carbon Microphone

Microphone types are usually named according to the moving devices they contain. In the carbon microphone, the moving device is a cluster of tiny carbon granules contained in a little metal pillbox called the *button*. Across the mouth of the button and insulated from it, is a thin steel diaphragm held tightly at its outer rim. As the diaphragm vibrates in response to sound waves striking it, the granules inside the button are alternately compressed or decompressed. If, now, a battery is

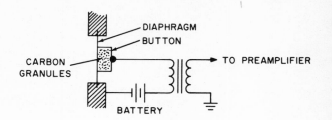

Fig. 13.2. *Carbon Microphone.* The microphone consists of a "button" filled with carbon granules. The alternate compression and rarefaction of the carbon granules when the diaphragm vibrates under the influence of sound energy causes an audio signal to flow through the primary winding of the audio transformer. The audio voltage appearing across the secondary terminals is fed to a preamplifier.

connected to the diaphragm and button in series with the primary winding of an iron core transformer, the current through the circuit will vary with the compression and decompression of the granules. At compression, the granules are compacted tightly to offer little resistance to the flow of current, and the current through the primary of the transformer is at its peak; at decompression, increased resistance is offered by the loosely packed granules, and the current is a minimum. Thus the current through the primary winding of the transformer is an audio current varying with the sound energy incident on the microphone. The audio voltage appearing across the terminals of the transformer secondary can then be fed to a preamplifier.

The carbon microphone is highly sensitive, which means that it has a relatively high output response to a sound of standard intensity. But it has several disadvantages, one of them its relatively poor frequency response, the other its tendency to emit a continuous hiss. The latter defect is the result of changes in the contact resistance of neighboring carbon particles. Its poor frequency response keeps it from being used much for music, an application demanding a microphone with fairly constant output for a broad range of audio frequencies. But its sensitivity makes it valuable for voice communication, in such systems as police and taxicab call networks.

The Dynamic Microphone

The poor frequency response, typical of the carbon microphone, is not at all characteristic of the *dynamic* microphone. This is one point of superiority for the latter. Another is that it needs no battery, no external voltage source for operation, as does the carbon instrument. The moving device in the dynamic microphone is a coil of wire attached mechanically to a

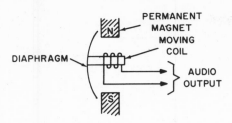

Fig. 13.3. *The Dynamic Microphone:* A corrugated circular diaphragm, moving freely, drives a coil back and forth in the field of a permanent magnet. An audio voltage then appears across the terminals of the moving coil.

diaphragm. As the diaphragm vibrates under the impact of sound, the moving coil vibrates between the poles of a permanent magnet and generates an audio voltage as it cuts the magnet's lines of force. The coil's motion in one direction produces a positive voltage across its terminals; its motion in the opposite direction produces a negative voltage. Thus the vibration of the diaphragm, stimulated by a train of sound waves, generates a train of audio waves. It is obvious, then, why the microphone needs no voltage source—it generates voltages of its own.

Although not quite as ruggedly built as the carbon mike, the dynamic microphone has a reputation for being able to stand up under fairly rough usage. This fact, together with its good frequency response, explains its popularity with the hi-fi clan.

The Crystal Microphone

Another favorite, in hi-fi circles, is the crystal microphone, a device which depends on the piezoelectric effect (Chapter 8). This instrument uses the Rochelle salt crystal. Two slices of the crystal are cemented together and held rigidly at one or both ends. When vibrated under the pressure of sound waves, the joined slices produce an audio signal. This type of microphone has excellent frequency response, but shows a tendency to alter its characteristics with change in temperature.

The Ribbon Microphone; Directivity

Probably the best of all is the ribbon microphone, in use by most broadcasting and recording studios. It is made of a very thin ribbon of aluminum suspended in a strong permanent magnetic field. Vibrating under sound pressure, the ribbon cuts the force field of the magnetic and produces an audio voltage across its terminals.

Each of the microphones mentioned, as well as a number of other types, has its own directional characteristics. Some are unidirectional, responding very well to sounds from one direction but showing poor or no response to sounds from any other; still others are attentive to sounds arriving from front and rear, but are deaf to sounds arriving laterally. And, of course, there are microphones or combinations of them which are sensitive to sounds from all directions. In choosing a microphone for a specific task, therefore, it is a good idea to check the instrument's directivity as well as its frequency response and general sensitivity.

It is best, for example, if the microphone used in a public address system is unidirectional, to turn its single direction of response toward the speaker's dais. While it is true that a two-directional microphone can pick up desirable audience reaction to the speaker's words, it can also contribute to the peculiar disease of PA systems known as *acoustical feedback.* In this plague of the lecture hall, some of the sound energy from the loudspeakers in the auditorium strikes the back of the microphone. Thus a feedback situation is created. The feedback, however, is regenerative; there is so little delay between the lecturer's sounds and those returning to the microphone from the loudspeakers that the two are practically in phase. With the returning sound energy continually aiding the input energy, the amplifier soon overloads, and a steady, ringing howl is the result. The unidirectional microphone, deaf to the loudspeaker return, is the cure for this situation. But if the lecturer is stuck with a microphone sensitive to two directions, his best bet is to turn the microphone away from the loudspeakers; or if that fails, to have the amplifier's volume control turned down.

The Tape Recorder

In the privacy of his own home, the hi-fi fan is apt to use his microphone for recording his voice, his own musical efforts, or whatever collection of sounds he wants to preserve for future reference. His recording apparatus is, of course, the tape recorder.

The system of recording sound on tape has so many advantages over the older system of phonograph recording that the latter may eventually be discarded altogether. Cutting a phonograph record requires a good deal of experience and amounts to a profession in itself. But any amateur with a good tape recording instrument at his disposal can, and does, turn out excellent reproductions. The process is almost automatic. And storage of the finished tape is much less a problem than stacking records; some four minutes of programming can be recorded on a reel three inches in diameter. A phonograph record which has come to be a bore through

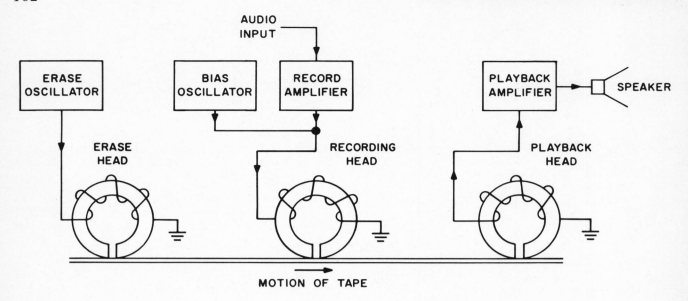

Fig. 13.4. *The Tape Recorder, Schematic:* **The better type of recorder has three heads: erase, record, and play back. The ultrasonic erase oscillator removes the magnetization of an old tape. Re-recording is made in the recording head** by an amplified audio signal input plus the ultrasonic bias voltage. The playback head converts the magnetization of the new program into audio and applies it to the speaker.

constant repetition winds up in the garbage dump, but the tape in the same situation can simply be erased and used to record something else.

The recording tape is a narrow strip of non-conducting material coated with iron oxide, a substance which can be magnetized. Under the influence of a strong magnetic field, the oxide is permeated with it, and retains its magnetism for quite some time if protected from mechanical and electrical disturbances. In the recording process, the tape is moved under the gap in an incomplete ring of metal. This ring is the recording head. Around it is wrapped a coil of wire conducting the input audio signal; the flow of audio current through the wire creates a magnetic field of varying intensity and direction in the gap. As the tape moves through the field, the iron oxide particles of its coating align themselves in the direction of the field, and the tape acquires a varying magnetic field of its own. Since the tape's magnetic strength has been impressed upon it by the audio signal working through the recording head, the strength of the field along the tape is a measure of the audio signal fed to the recorder.

To make certain that the magnetic field given to the tape is truly proportional to the audio signal, an a-c bias voltage is also supplied to the recording head coil. This voltage derives its name from its function: like the bias voltage in a vacuum tube amplifier, its purpose is to prevent distortion by guaranteeing that the magnetic field of the tape at any moment is accurately representa-

tive of the input audio signal at that moment. Supplied by a separate oscillator stage, the bias frequency is far beyond the audible range. It therefore cannot be heard when the tape is played back.

On playback, the process is reversed, with the tape as the active agent and the reproducing head as the passive one. As the tape runs past the reproducing head, it induces in the reproducing coil a voltage which varies with the magnetic field of the tape. This voltage is the audio signal. When amplified and applied to a speaker, it emerges as the recorded sound.

Like the recording and reproducing heads, the erase head is an electromagnet fed by an ultrasonic signal of about the same frequency as the bias voltage. The effect of this rapidly varying field is to throw the particles in the iron oxide coating of the tape into a confused and random orientation so that their total magnetic effect is practically zero. The tape is thus demagnetized and can produce no sound on playback. Having been restored to its original state, the erased tape can be put through the recorder to be re-impressed with a new program.

The less expensive recorders have a single head performing the three functions of erasure, recording, and playback, with a single ultrasonic oscillator doubling as bias voltage generator and as eraser. The better types provide three separate heads for the three different functions; thus the moving tape encounters successively the erase, record, and playback heads. This pretty arrangement permits erasing the recorded magnetic impressions

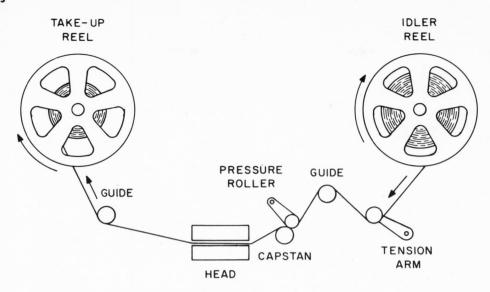

Fig. 13.5. *Tape Recorder Mechanical System:* **The purpose of this elaborate system is to keep the tape speed constant with minimum wear on the tape.**

on an old tape, re-recording a new program on it, and playing it back—all within an instant. Separate recording and playback amplifiers are, of course, required for this kind of quick-quick operation. While many recorders are equipped with amplifiers and speakers, there are models with neither to allow the hi-fi fan to do his own experimenting with microphone, amplifier, and speaker system.

Threading a tape into the mechanical system of the recorder is similar to but not nearly as complex as threading film on a movie projector. The tape has no sprocket holes. In the simpler recorders, little more is involved than slipping the tape through the recording head slot and securing its free end to the take-up reel. In more elaborate mechanical set-ups, the tape leads from the idler reel, goes under a tape tension arm which keeps the tape taut, rounds a tape guide, passes over a capstan to which it is held by a pressure roller to prevent slippage, runs through the head and under a second tape guide, and finally winds on the take-up reel. Both the capstan and take-up reel are driven by the motor inside the recorder. This rather involved system is necessary for keeping the rate of travel of the tape at as constant a pace as possible. Failure to do so will mar the recording with "wow" or "flutter," audible defects that appear when the tape is played back. Wow, a highly descriptive term, refers to the slow rise and fall of pitch in a faulty recording; flutter is a rapidly varying wow.

Professional recordings are usually made at the rate of 15 ips—inches per second of tape—while amateurs generally record at 7½ or 3¾ ips. There is an advantage to recording at a slow rate, the obvious one of being

able to get more of the program on a given tape length. The penalty paid, however, is the range of frequencies in which it is possible to record. A rapidly varying audio signal obviously cannot have much time to impress itself properly on a tape which is crawling. At low recording speeds, therefore, high frequency reproduction suffers. For speech recording, where fidelity is not too important, the operator can get more for his money by running his tape at the lowest speed.

Since tape speed is so important, it behooves the tape-recorder owner to keep a check on the mechanism of his equipment. Two devices can help him in this job: one is a test tape consisting of successive white and black squares; the other is a *strobe,* a lamp energized by an electronic circuit to flash on and off at a rapid rate. The first step in the procedure is to set the strobe at a flashing rate matching the speed the tape should have. Thus the time interval between successive flashes is equal to the time interval between the appearance of white squares on the tape as it moves past a fixed point. If the strobe is allowed to illuminate the tape in a darkened room, a white square will appear at the same spot for every wink of the light, and the tape will give the illusion of standing still. It will give this illusion, that is, if it is moving at its correct pace. If it is slower than it should be, it will appear to be moving backwards; if faster than normal, it will seem to be crawling slowly ahead. A wow will indicate itself by alternate backward and forward movements of the tape with motionless intervals in between. The same sort of phenomenon, incidentally, can be observed in the movies when the camera is focused on a rotating wagon wheel. Equality between the rate of rotation of the wheel spokes and the frame rate of the film is shown by the apparent freezing of the spokes in a fixed position.

Once the operator of the tape recorder is certain that his tape speed is as it should be, he can begin making his recording. The procedure takes care of itself, for the most part, but the operator has to take a hand in it by "riding gain." Most tape recorders have a panel indicator, usually in the form of a needle quivering over a db scale, which shows the amplitude of the input audio signal. With an eye on the indicator, the operator should be alert to turn down the amplifier volume control when the needle climbs beyond a certain maximum, and turn the control up when the needle drops to too low a level. The penalty for allowing too strong a signal to be recorded is the same as that for overdriving an amplifying tube— distortion; the penalty for recording too weak a signal is inaudibility. Riding gain is about the only recording procedure requiring an expert touch. The novice shows his inexperience by yanking the control hurriedly down or up at sudden jumps of the indicator needle. These abrupt breaks in the volume level are faithfully recorded and prove to be annoying when the tape is played back. An expert adjusts the gain with gradual shifts of the gain control. He may even acquire a sort of sixth sense and *anticipate* sudden rises and drops in the level of the program he is recording.

By clever handling of his equipment, the hi-fi fan can thoroughly exploit the entertainment value of the tape recorder. He can record his own musical or oratorical attempts by hooking the microphone to the recorder through the recorder's amplifier or a separate amplifier. He can tape off-the-air transcripts with an AM or FM tuner as the audio source. Or, he can transfer his disc records to tape.

The Phonograph

The hi-fi follower, enthusiast though he may be, is not likely to submit to the arduous discipline of learning to record on discs. Nor is he set on spending the small fortune disc-recording equipment requires. But the chances are that he owns a library of phonograph records and wants to get as much as possible out of them. A good amplifier and speaker are, of course, basic to that desire. So is a good record player.

Like the tape recorder, the phonograph is partly mechanical. Its major mechanical structure is the turntable. Rotated through different sets of pulleys by an electric motor, the turntable can run at one of the three popular speeds for phonograph records, 78, 45, and 33⅓ revolutions per minute. A switch sets the speed to be used.

The same basic rules followed in tape recording apply

with equal force to phonograph playbacks: the record must be played back at a speed as close as possible to the speed with which it was recorded; further, the speed at which the record is played back must be constant. A long-playing record originally cut at precisely 33⅓ rpm will sound just as good even to a carping ear if it is played back at, say, 32 rpm. But if there is an appreciable variation in that 32 rpm rate while playback is in progress, what is meant to be an awe-inspiring passage in the music can be distorted by the resultant wow into an occasion for hilarity. Strobe discs serving the same function as strobe tapes are useful for checking the rotary speed of the turntable.

Turntable trouble is also at the bottom of the churning sound perfectly described by the name of *rumble.* This affliction, which can mar the tone of even the best of records played on a faulty table, arises from mechanical vibration in the motor. This is transmitted to the record and thence to the pickup needle. The better— and higher-priced—tables are carefully suspended by spring arrangements to float them free of mechanical irregularities. As a further precaution, tables are generally weighted to provide them with sufficient inertia to resist small variations in rotating speed.

Lateral vs Hill-and-Dale

Although Thomas Edison is generally credited in this country with inventing the phonograph, the system he devised did not really come into prominence until recently. In Edison's scheme, the cutting stylus impressed the audio signal into the soft material of the master by an up-and-down movement. Recording engineers have applied the picturesque title of *hill-and-dale* to this method of cutting phonograph records.

The European lateral system is the most prevalent system in use today. In this recording process, the cutting stylus wiggles from side to side in response to the input audio signal. This motion of the stylus combined with its approximate linear motion as the master rotates under it gives the groove a wavy appearance, thus freezing the audio wave into the engraved master.

The hill-and-dale seems to be the superior method because it is immune from two defects which tend to make the lateral system difficult. One defect is the tendency of the cutting stylus, under the push of a strong audio signal, to overcut into an adjacent groove. The second is the increasing distortion as the cutting stylus progresses towards the center of the disc. Grooves cut close to the center spindle have a more pronounced curvature than those at the outside rim of the records. An identical audio signal will thus produce a wave of greater fidelity at the outside, where the grooves more nearly approximate a straight line, than towards the center of the record. Modern developments in equalization (see the preceding chapter) and other techniques have improved lateral recordings and thus insured the system's survival. The most important of these "other techniques" is the LP method in which the grooves are finely cut and the lands between them exceptionally narrow. This, together with its slow speed of 33⅓ rpm justifies the LP record's claim to "long playing."

The Pickup

The pickup is the other element, aside from the turntable, of the phonograph mechanism. Modern pickup arms are lightweight levers balanced evenly on a pivoting fulcrum. The balance is such as to permit the playback needle in the pickup head to rest lightly in the grooves of the record, without at the same time allowing it to be flung out of its groove when the record is played back. Towards the business end of the pickup, the arm angles off in the direction of a line tangent to the record grooves, an arrangement which allows the needle to ride more freely than it otherwise would.

The electrical system for the phonograph turntable consists simply of two rather thick wires which interconnect the turntable motor and the 110 volt a-c power obtained from the wall plug in most homes. More complex, however, is the electrical system concentrated in the pickup *cartridge*.

The Cartridge

The cartridge, fixed in the head of the pickup, contains the assembly of parts required to convert the motion of the playback needle into the audio signal of the original recorded program. Since the function of the cartridge is essentially the same as that of the microphone—conversion of mechanical into electrical energy—the structure of both instruments is similar. In the *dynamic* cartridge, the needle is fixed to a coil allowed to move in the field of a permanent magnet. As the needle rides the grooves of a lateral recording, the sidewise motion of the coil causes an audio voltage to be induced in its turns. A similar sequence of events takes place in the hill-and-dale cartridge; here the vertical motion of the coil in the permanent magnetic field generates the audio signal.

The variable reluctance cartridge also makes use of the movements of the pickup needle in a magnetic field. The needle is attached to a magnetized metal bar inside a coil and between the poles of a permanent magnet. Movements of the needle bring the bar nearer and farther from the permanent magnet poles, thus varying the reluctance in the magnetic loop formed by the bar and the pole pieces. The two quantities of reluctance and flux in magnetic circuits correspond respectively to resistance and current in electric circuits. And just as electrical current varies when the resistance in a circuit is changed, magnetic flux varies when a magnetic circuit's reluctance is changed. This variation in flux induces a voltage in the coil, and an audio signal appears across the coil terminals. Most reluctance cartridges contain twin coils with a magnetic bar in each, an arrangement which permits the cartridge to be used in an electrically balanced circuit with all the advantages balanced circuits afford.

The third of the popular styles in pickups is the crystal type, in which the audio voltage generator is usually a Rochelle salt crystal. As the cartridge needle vibrates in playback, the crystal is alternately squeezed and released to emit the varying voltage of the audio signal. This, of course, is the crystal's piezoelectric effect.

The one item in the cartridge which must endure a good deal of rough usage is the needle—or stylus, as the hi-fi fan will have it. In wiggling back and forth under the thrust of the record groove walls, the needle is badly abused and will, in time, become worn. The same is also true of the grooves in the record. Unless the phonograph user is insanely fond of a particular record, however, no one disc in his collection is likely to see as much action as the needle in his pickup cartridge. Consequently, that needle should be made of some good, hard material to be able to withstand the buffeting it gets. A good stylus, therefore, is tipped with sapphire, a tough mineral. An even better one is pointed with diamond, which is about the toughest substance found in nature. Neither of these is as prohibitively expensive as its name might suggest. Running a poor third is the osmium stylus, which has the endearing quality of being cheaper than the other two, but also wilts much quicker in harness. Since a crippled needle can be rough on records, it is best to use only the best.

Cartridges used in three-speed record changers are equipped with two styli, one for the old-fashioned and now rapidly disappearing 78 rpm discs, the other for the currently popular 45 and 33⅓ rpm's. A mechanical adjustment on the pickup head selects the stylus to be put into action. This substitution system is made necessary by the fact that grooves in the older recording are about three times as wide as those in the new.

Speakers

At the output of the amplifier are the speakers—the plural is necessary because no true hi-fi fan could be content with just one. This is more than mere swank. A single speaker is limited in its response; it favors one end of the audio frequency distribution to the detriment of the other. To use a single speaker with all its tonal limitations at the output of an expensive high-fidelity

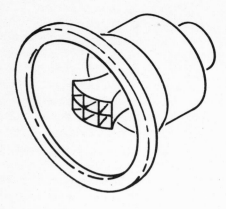

Fig. 13.6. *Combination Woofer and Tweeter:* **The woofer is the large circular cone; the tweeter is at the cone's center.**

amplifier is somewhat like presenting a beautiful heiress a necklace of glass beads.

The single speaker's inability to reproduce equally sounds of all frequencies arises from the basic principle that small devices are associated with high resonant frequencies, and large devices with low. This rule is just as applicable in the mechanical realm, of which the speaker is an inhabitant, as it is in the purely electronic. A speaker of small dimensions will respond more effectively to high frequencies than it will to low; a big speaker will do justice to the bassier tones where it will not to the treble. The names hi-fi fans apply to speakers of certain types show that they recognize the speakers' peculiarities: they call the small, shriller-toned ones "tweeters" and the larger, bassier speakers "woofers."

Obviously, tonal balance cannot be expected from a single large or small speaker. Adequate balance demands the use of both. Nor may these two be sufficient to the man with the sharp ear and the long purse; he may also want other speakers of intermediate size—the so-called "mid-range" type—to emphasize the middle frequencies. Hence the demand among the hi-fi fraternity for *speaker systems,* a battery of speakers which will reproduce with nearly equal intensity a large range of audible sounds.

Crossover Networks

Since the woofer and tweeter are specialists in different frequency ranges, it would be foolish to feed the entire output of the amplifier to both. Some attempt should be made to allot to each the frequencies it is best capable of handling. Realizing this, the hi-fi fan makes certain that his speaker system has a *crossover network.*

The network is an audio filter using coils and capacitors. A coil tends to oppose the rapidly varying currents of the audio highs, showing more tolerance to the low frequencies. Condensers give a reverse effect and favor

the high frequencies as against the low. The crossover network cleverly exploits these characteristics to separate the two frequency bands. The crossover frequency is reinforced by resonance effects of coil-condenser combinations. Systems with midrange speakers have three-way networks to accommodate these as well.

Enclosures and Baffles

Mounting the speakers with a view to getting the best out of them involves a problem in acoustics. When the cone of a working speaker pushes forward, it compresses the air just in front of it, but leaves a relative vacuum at its back. Such a compression and rarefaction are really opposite phases of the same sound impulse. Unless steps are taken to isolate the front of the speaker from its rear, the simultaneous compression and rarefaction will meet, cancel each other, and so deaden the speaker's output. What makes matters worse is that the deadening is most pronounced for the low frequencies; the treble tones are more directional by nature (Chapter 6) and are less likely to travel around the rim of the speaker cone.

One way to restore bass to the speaker is to mount it on a large board with a circular hole for the speaker mouth. An added refinement is a grille cloth covering the hole to keep dust out of the speaker. The board, however, is the important item in this ensemble. If it is big enough, it interposes a barrier between the front and rear of the speaker, and so satisfies the isolation requirement. For reasons easily imagined it is known as a *baffle.*

A simple arrangement like this is not really practical for a living room simply because the baffle, if it is to work properly, would have to be some ten feet square. This is going too far, even for the hi-fi fan. A cabinet, or enclosure, is a better idea. It is really little more than a large baffle with its wings folded back, so to speak. A

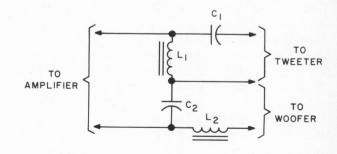

Fig. 13.7. *Two-Way Crossover Network:* **The high and low audio frequencies are separated, the highs going to the tweeter, the lows to the woofer. Coil L_1 and capacitor C_2, L_2 and C_1 are selected to resonate at the crossover frequency.**

better type of enclosure is a closed box with a port cut into the front to keep the mass of air inside from resisting the movements of the speaker cones by providing it with an outlet. If the dimensions of the enclosure are accurately calculated, the port will have the beneficial effect of permitting a rarefaction or compression at the rear of the speaker cone to emerge from the box in time to *aid* rather than cancel the action at the cone's front. Correct dimensioning of the box, that is to say, can delay a rarefaction emerging from the rear of the cone just long enough to meet a corresponding rarefaction in front of it. The same will be true of compressions. Such *bass reflex* enclosures, through this acoustical "push-pull" operation, can bring up the bass tones of the speakers wonderfully.

Monaural vs. Binaural Sound

In an ordinary broadcast or recording of a symphony orchestra concert, microphones are spotted at various points to pick up the playing of various sections. The audio signal outputs of the microphones are then piped through a single channel to amplifiers, and eventually reach the ears of the listener. Regardless of the number of microphones used, the listener is represented by one ear, so to speak, at the scene of the concert. The two ears Nature has given him are both working. They perceive the depth of tone in his living room. But the sensation of acoustical depth at the concert itself is missing.

Such is the nature of monaural sound reproduction. It is unsatisfactory to the sensitive hi-fi fan because he yearns for the illusion of sitting in the midst of a rich swirl of tonal colors. He demands binaural (two-eared) representation at musical events, and so collects stereophonic equipment. It is an expensive proposition, requiring two of everything: two amplifiers, two speaker enclosures, and a double audio source.

Stereo Tuners

Radio transmitters which now hold licenses for joint AM and FM operation are beginning to conduct stereo broadcasts. These require simultaneous AM and FM transmission of the same program. Each of two sets of studio microphones is piped into separate amplifiers. The audio signal emerging from each amplifier is then put on the air with one audio signal riding an AM carrier and the second an FM carrier. A similar doubling of facilities is needed by the listener at home. He must have an AM tuner for the AM carrier, an FM tuner for the FM carrier, one audio amplifier for each, and a set of speakers for each. In the works, however, is an FM multiplex system, a plan which permits twin stereo broadcasting to be done solely on FM. FM multiplexing will simplify things a bit for the listener, who can then get by with a single tuner; but he still must have the double amplifier and double speaker system.

Stereophonic phonograph and tape recording are very much with us. A very ingenious method of combining lateral and hill-and-dale operation permits just one phonograph to work as a double audio source. The record is cut by applying two audio signals, one from each set of microphones picking up the studio performance, to the cutting head. One of these signals stimulates side-to-side wiggling of the cutting stylus, the other an up and down movement. The stylus thus moves in three dimensions with respect to the master: forward, sidewise, and vertically.

On playback, the stylus of the pickup cartridge repeats this complex motion. Its lateral wiggling generates an audio signal which is conducted to the first of two audio amplifiers, its hill-and-dale ride contributes audio to the second. Each of these signals is separately amplified and reproduced as sound.

The tape recorder has also done its part in the stereo revolution. Stereophonic transcriptions are made on double-tracked tape—tape with twin layers of recordable iron oxide. The usual binaural equipment of two microphones, two amplifiers, and two recording heads prevails. Playback involves two reproducing heads, two amplifiers, and double speaker systems. No twin channeling is necessary for erasure, of course; the same high frequency a-c current which effectively scrambles the tiny magnets in the iron oxide coating can throw either track into magnetic confusion to destroy the recorded pattern. Hi-fi shops also feature four-track tapes for the economy-minded taping enthusiast. These permit transcriptions of twice the normal length by offering first one pair of tracks and then a second for impregnation by the audio signal.

The end product of the stereo system—the sound emitted by the two speaker systems—is the fly in the binaural ointment. Preservation of the illusion of tonal depth depends on the strict separation of the two audio channels. But how is it possible, when each speaker system is pouring its version into the same living room, to restrict the sound from each system to the corresponding ear of the listener? Short of dividing the room by a sound-proof partition and stationing the speaker enclosures at one end while the listener is glued to the other, little can be done. Purists insist that the only real solution is the stereophonic headset, in which one earphone receives the audio signal of one channel while the remaining phone gets the other. This device is unquestionably effective; its impact on the listener is so massive and stunning that he need only close his eyes to be transported to the conductor's podium—the best spot in the concert hall. But headphones are the height of selfishness. Only the listener can absorb the tonal feast while his family and guests go hungry.

Besides, headphones are a physical nuisance for all their foam rubber ear- and head-pads. For real comfort, however, nothing beats the loudspeaker. A man can loll at ease, sip soothing libations, show off his equipment to his friends—all without being wired for sound. But is it stereo?

GLOSSARY

A-c bias. An ultrasonic signal which reduces distortion in tape recorders.

Acoustical feedback. The return of sound from the loud-speakers to the microphone in public address systems.

Acoustics. The science of sound.

Baffle. A large board on which a speaker is mounted.

Bass reflex enclosure. A speaker enclosure so designed that the bass tones are reinforced.

Binaural. Two-eared; same as stereophonic.

Button. The capsule in a carbon microphone which contains the carbon particles.

Capstan. A rotating device in the tape recorder which assists the movement of the tape.

Carbon microphone. A microphone in which the variation in resistance of carbon particles produces the audio signal.

Cartridge. The electrical device in the phonograph pickup head.

Cathode follower. An electronic circuit used for matching the output of one piece of electronic equipment to the input of another.

Crossover frequency. The point of division between separated frequency bands of the crossover network.

Crossover network. The device between audio amplifier output and speakers which divides the high from the low audio frequencies.

Crystal cartridge. A cartridge containing Rochelle salt crystals.

Crystal microphone. A microphone containing Rochelle salt crystals.

Diamond stylus. A diamond-tipped record-player needle.

Dynamic cartridge. A cartridge in which the stylus moves a coil of wire through a permanent magnetic field.

Dynamic microphone. A microphone in which the diaphragm moves a coil of wire through a permanent magnetic field.

Enclosure. A cabinet containing speakers.

Erase head. The device in the tape recorder which removes the recorded sound from a used tape.

Flutter. A rapid wavering in pitch of a played-back phonograph or tape recording.

Flux. The lines of force of a magnetic field.

FM multiplex. A system of stereophonic broadcasting using FM.

Grille cloth. The cloth covering the mouth of the speaker in a baffle or cabinet.

Hill-and-dale. A method of disc recording in which the stylus moves up and down.

Idler. The supply reel in a tape recorder.

Ips. Inches per second; the speed of tape movement in a recorder.

Land. The flat surface between adjacent grooves in a phonograph record.

LP. Long-playing; a phonograph disc, finely cut, which is recorded and played back at a 33⅓ rpm speed.

Midrange speaker. A loudspeaker which best reproduces sounds in the medium audible range.

Monaural. One-eared; a single-channeled sound system.

Monitoring. Checking a newly made recording by listening to its playback.

Overcutting. Erratic cutting of a master disc in which adjacent grooves intersect.

Pickup arm. The pivoted arm, in a phonograph, which holds the cartridge and playback needle.

Port. A hole cut in the front of a bass reflex enclosure to permit air inside the enclosure to circulate to the front.

Recording head. The device, in tape or disc equipment, which contains the electrical recording device.

Reluctance. The opposition, in a magnetic circuit, to flux.

Reproducing head. The playback head in a tape recorder.

Ribbon microphone. A high fidelity microphone in which the vibration of a thin metal ribbon in a magnetic field generates the audio signal.

Riding gain. The process, in making a recording, of varying the volume control of the amplifier to keep the amplitude of the audio signal at a reasonable level.

Rpm. Revolutions per minute.

Rumble. A bassy, growling sound heard in a playback on a poor phonograph turntable.

Sapphire stylus. A sapphire-tipped record-player needle.

Stereophonic. Giving the illusion of three-dimensional sound.

Strobe. Short for stroboscope; a device containing a rapidly blinking light.

Take-up reel. The motor-driven reel in the tape recorder on which the tape winds.

Tape. A strip of nonconducting material with a coating of iron oxide used for magnetic recording.

Tape recorder. A device used for magnetic recording.

Test tape. A tape of alternating black and white squares used for testing the speed of travel of tape in a recorder.

Tuner. A radio receiver without an audio amplifier.

Turntable. The rotating metal base disc of a phonograph.

Tweeter. A small speaker which best reproduces treble tones.

Ultrasonic. Of a frequency higher than the audible range.

Variable reluctance cartridge. A phonograph pickup cartridge in which the varying reluctance in a magnetic circuit produces the audio signal.

Woofer. A large speaker which best reproduces bass tones.

Wow. The slow variation of tonal pitch in a poor recording.

Chapter Fourteen

THE TELEVISION RECEIVER

OF ALL THE stages in the television receiver, the video detector—the second detector of the TV superheterodyne—is perhaps the most versatile. Something of this was seen in Chapter 7, in which the general structure of the television receiver was discussed. Given the picture and sound i-f carriers, the detector selects the 4.5 mc signal representing the difference between the frequencies of the two carriers. At the same time, it develops the video signal carried by the picture i-f. And finally —a lesser but still important function—it extracts from the i-f picture carrier an agc voltage (Chapter 3) proportional to the strength of the carrier.

Having made these transformations, the video detector becomes the point of departure for the various signals it has formed. The 4.5 mc signal, carrying audio in its frequency modulations, is supplied to the sound channel, the series of stages terminating in the loudspeaker. Thus the sound portion of the TV program is produced. To provide the varying light values of the picture image, the video signal is brought to the control grid of the picture tube; and, to give the image coherence, the video signal is also furnished to the sync circuits ending in the deflection coils of the picture tube yoke. Finally, the agc control voltage, which helps

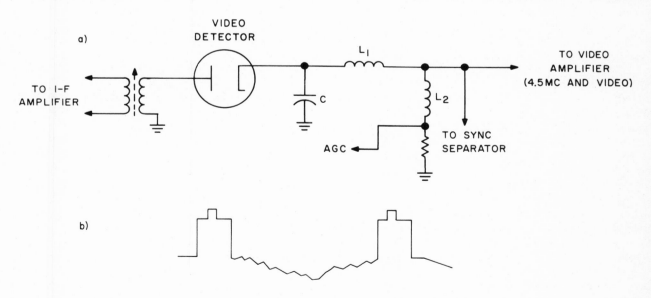

Fig. 14.1. *The Video Detector:* The circuit diagram is shown in (a). C is a bypass condenser for the i-f carrier. Coils L_1 and L_2 increase high frequency components of the video signal. The output video signal of this circuit (b) is positively phased.

smooth the operation of the front end and i-f amplifier stages, is supplied to the control grids of those tubes.

When the circuit diagram of the video detector is compared with that of the AM detector in Chapter 3, it becomes obvious that the two are birds of a feather. But the video detector must be a bit more elaborately arranged. The video signal covers so broad a band of frequencies—from as low as 30 cycles to as high as 4 million cycles (4 mc)—that special care must be taken to preserve that range. Hence there is usually an arrangement of coils at the output end of the circuit to strengthen the high frequency components. The bypass capacitor also works to emphasize the lows. While it effectively bypasses the extremely high frequencies of the two i-f carriers, it offers a good deal of opposition to the extremely low frequency elements in the video signal. The lows are therefore free to enter the next stage, the video amplifier.

The Video Amplifier

Both the video and the 4.5 mc intercarrier signals secured by the detector are amplified in the video amplifier stage. This latter circuit is usually built around a pentode tube, and would be just another amplifier except for one outstanding feature, the 4.5 mc trap. The trap is not really remarkable, but it has the virtue of separating the 4.5 mc intercarrier signal from the video signal at the output of the video amplifier.

Consisting of a coil and capacitor, resonant to the frequency of 4.5 mc, the trap is part of the plate circuit of the video amplifier. Since both the 4.5 mc intercarrier

and the video signals are fed to the control grid of this tube, current in the plate circuit contains both intercarrier and video components. But the trap is tuned to the frequency of the intercarrier signal; hence it absorbs—or traps—most of the 4.5 mc component, leaving only the video component to flow through the remainder of the plate load. Two separate voltages thus appear across the plate circuit of the video amplifier: one, a purely 4.5 mc voltage across the trap coil; a second, purely video, across the remaining portion of the circuit—usually a coil. If the trap coil is the primary winding of a transformer, the secondary winding will carry 4.5 mc, and can be connected to the first stage of the sound channel. The video signal is taken off *its* load, and brought to the control grid of the picture tube. Thus the two signals are separated.

Aside from its function of separating the 4.5 mc signal from the video, the trap excludes that signal from the resistor and coil in the remainder of the plate circuit. No intercarrier signal can therefore be fed to the control grid of the kinescope. This is precisely the desired effect; any 4.5 mc signal appearing on the kinescope grid would show up in the picture as interference.

The Sound Channel

The 4.5 mc signal is primarily an FM signal (Chapter 7), and is therefore furnished to the sound channel. In many types of receiver, the 4.5 mc signal obtained from the trap is applied first to an amplifier, and then to the FM detector. Most modern TV receivers use ratio detectors which are insensitive to amplitude modulations.

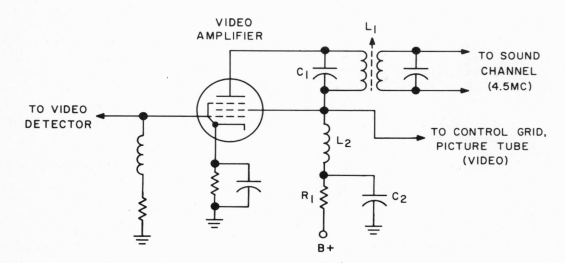

Fig. 14.2. *The Video Amplifier:* The 4.5 mc trap is the combination of L_1 and C, resonant to 4.5 mc. Since the trap absorbs the 4.5 mc intercarrier energy, only the video signal current flows through L_2. The voltage across this coil is

brought to the control grid of the picture tube. The signal voltage across R_1 is low frequency video owing to the action of the bypass capacitor C_2.

Responding only to the frequency modulations in the 4.5 mc signal, the ratio detector selects the audio signal contained in those modulations, and passes it to the audio amplifier. Audio amplifiers in all but custom-built TV receivers are most emphatically not hi-fi, with little more than a first audio triode, an output power ampli-ner, and a volume control to set the loudness level. They are adequate; nothing more. Nor is the speaker in the average TV receiver a marvel of acoustics; it, too, is merely adequate.

In older TV receiver models, the FM detector is of the discriminator type, which is sensitive to amplitude modulations. But the discriminator usually works with a limiter (Chapter 11). Hence the 4.5 mc amplifier stage just ahead of the discriminator will have the limiter design.

One noticeable difference between the FM receiver which is part of the television set and the simon-pure FM radio is the independence of the former of local oscillator wobbling. The 4.5 mc signal fed to the TV sound channel is the difference in frequency between the sound and picture carriers. This frequency separa-tion is solidly maintained by the TV transmitter. A slight shift in frequency by the local oscillator at the receiver front end, therefore, cannot vary the 4.5 mc FM signal. Should such a shift occur, both picture and sound i-f carriers will shift by the same amount; the frequency difference between the two will be unaffected. But there is no such guarantee for the FM radio set unless it happens to be equipped with an afc circuit (Chapter 11).

The Video Signal

While this FM activity is going on, the video signal at the output of the video amplifier is being fed to the control grid of the kinescope. At the same time, the sync circuits are doing their work of swinging the beam through its scanning maneuvers. The picture portion of the video signal paints its bright and dark elements in each scanned line to match the bright and dark elements of the original transmitted image. All these events occur simultaneously.

But, as was pointed out in Chapter 7, the video signal must be furnished to the kinescope control grid in its *negative* phase. This must be done, first, to enable the picture component of the signal to portray the image in its true light and dark shades, and second, to allow the blanking component of the signal to drive the grid so far negative that the beam will be shut off at the end of each scanned line. An engineering error through which a positive-phased video signal is given to the grid will have some laughable—and disastrous—consequences. First, the picture signal will be inverted, thus reversing the black and white values of the image. A man in a bright uniform standing against a dark background will show up on the receiver screen clothed in funereal black; a snow-covered ski jump will look like a coal chute. Second, the retrace path of the scanning beam, normally erased by the blanking signal, will show up as a bright streak across the picture. In fact there may be so many of these streaks as to obscure the image.

Evidently, the chain of stages between the video de-tector, where the video signal originates, and the kine-scope control grid must be such as to give the grid a negatively-phased video signal. The video detector cir-cuit shown earlier in this chapter provides a positively-phased signal. Before the signal is applied to the grid of the picture tube, its phase must be reversed. This is done in a single stage of video amplification between detector and kinescope. A positive half-cycle applied to the control grid of the video amplifier increases the plate current and so reduces the voltage at the plate of the tube; a positive peak is therefore inverted to a negative peak. The same inversion process turns a negative video peak at the input of the amplifier into a positive peak at the output. Thus, although the video signal at the detector is in its positive phase, the same signal applied to the kinescope is in its negative phase.

Contrast and Brightness

Most television receiver manufacturers prefer to keep the front panel of their sets looking simple by installing only the most necessary controls on it. Aside from the screen and the loudspeaker, only the channel selector and the fine tuning control face the viewer. Both of these are continually adjusted as the viewer searches for a program. But concealed at the rear of the set or under a hinged panel at the front are other manual controls. Every set owner can—and should—learn to use all these controls to get the best reception his set has to offer. He can find this information by reading the booklet the manufacturer supplies with the equipment.

Two of these less obtrusive controls are labeled CONTRAST and BRIGHTNESS. The first has the ef-fect, when turned up, of deepening the dark shadows in the televised scene and simultaneously heightening its brighter portions. Turned down, the control has the opposite effect, and provides less dramatic contrast between lights and darks. The control exerted by the BRIGHTNESS knob is similar but not quite identical. It brightens up the *overall* lighting of the scene when it is turned up, and dulls it when turned down. The chances are that once these controls are set satisfactorily for one channel, they are adjusted equally well for all others.

So much for the functions of these controls from the point of view of the confirmed knob-twiddler. But how

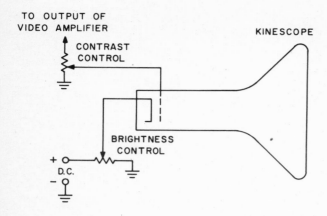

Fig. 14.3. *Contrast and Brightness Controls, Simplified Schematic:* **The contrast control is a variable resistor through which the video signal applied to the kinescope control grid is varied in amplitude. The brightness control changes the grid bias and so affects the overall lighting of the televised scene.**

do they work electronically? The contrast control in many receivers is a variable resistor, with its resistance element connected across the output of the video amplifier; its slider is connected to the control grid of the kinescope. A clockwise turn of the CONTRAST knob moves the slider away from the chassis end of the resistance element, thus increasing the video signal voltage applied to the kinescope grid. The positive peaks of the picture signal represent bright points in the televised image, and the negative peaks the dark points. The effect of increasing the picture voltage applied to the kinescope grid is to enlarge the voltage difference between these positive and negative peaks. With the grid of the kinescope at an increased positive voltage, the beam of electrons from the cathode is stronger, and the point it strikes on the screen is therefore brighter. Given a correspondingly stronger negative voltage, the beam is made less intense and produces a darker impact point. As a result, the contrast in the viewed image is deepened.

The voltage handled by the BRIGHTNESS control, on the other hand, is a constant d-c rather than a varying signal. Since the resistance element of this control is hooked across a d-c voltage source, the movement of the slider on the element as the knob is turned puts the cathode at a more or less positive potential, depending on how the knob is rotated. If the cathode is positive with respect to chassis, and the grid is at chassis potential for d-c, the grid must be negative with respect to cathode. The BRIGHTNESS control, in short, sets the grid bias of the kinescope. Turning the knob clockwise, for greater brightness, decreases the bias; turning the knob counterclockwise increases the bias.

An increased bias puts the grid at a steady, highly negative voltage. This, superimposed on the varying video signal, lowers the overall voltage level of the signal and so dims every scanned line of the image on the kinescope screen. Naturally, then, the whole image is dimmed. If the grid bias is decreased through an addition to the positive voltage of the kinescope cathode, every line of the image is intensified.

Vertical Blanking and Sync Pulses

At the end of every horizontally scanned line, as the beam makes its steady progress down the picture, a blanking pulse appears. When the last horizontal line of the field has been scanned, there must be a *vertical* blanking pulse. If the purpose of the horizontal blanking pulse is to cut off the beam in the interval between the end of one line and the beginning of another, the purpose of the vertical blanking pulse is to cut off the beam in the interval between the end of one field and the beginning of the second. It is to be expected that the vertical blanking pulse will last longer than the horizontal blanking pulse since the scanning beam takes much longer to maneuver downward through one field than it does to sweep through a single line.

Just as the horizontal blanking pulse has a sync pulse on top (Chapter 7), the vertical blanking pulse must be provided with a synchronization signal of some kind. Because the vertical blanking pulse is such a long one, the vertical sync should be correspondingly long. It is; but it is broken up into a succession of small pulses so arranged as to have the same effect as horizontal sync pulses. Through this ingenious method, horizontal synchronization is still maintained even while the beam is being brought back to the top of the screen.

The Basic Sync Circuit Arrangement

These vertical sync pulses, together with the horizontal sync pulses discussed in Chapters 6 and 7, are the signals sent out by the transmitter to control the sync circuits in the receiver. The picture cannot be properly scanned on the face of the receiver kinescope unless the sync circuits are in full operation and under the full control of the sync pulses.

We can construct a basic pattern of the stages in the television receiver sync circuits by using the information given in Chapters 6 and 7 as well as by doing some logical thinking. The scanning process, as described in those chapters, involves moving the kinescope beam rapidly from side-to-side, and simultaneously moving it downward at a much slower pace. The device which directly prompts these lateral and vertical scanning movements is the deflection yoke around the neck of the tube. In the yoke are two separate sets of coils. One set exerts a horizontal force on the beam when the proper current is passed through its wire turns. The second set exerts a vertical force on the beam in response to another current sent through its turns. Evidently, if there are two separate coil sets in the yoke, each with its own kind of current, there must be a double set of sync circuits—one for horizontal deflection, the other for vertical deflection. This is the exact skeletal pattern of the sync system arrangement in the receiver.

Some of the television information given in Chapter 6 can furnish us with other educated guesses about the set-up in the sync circuits. One of those statistics is the time taken for the scanning of a single horizontal line, given as 1/15,750 of a second. This fraction of a second is the time for one horizontal cycle—a cycle which begins at the start of one scanned line and ends at the instant the next line starts. If one cycle occupies 1/15,750 of a second, there must be 15,750 of these horizontal cycles in the space of one second. Thus, a signal of 15,750 cycles per second must be fed to the horizontal deflection coils of the kinescope yoke to drive the beam from side to side at that rate.

Since the beam makes its slow progression from the top of the screen to the bottom in 1/60 of a second, as another television statistic specifies, a signal of 60 cycles per second must be fed to the vertical deflection coils in the yoke. Both these signals, the 15,750 cycle per second horizontal and the 60 cps vertical, are generated by oscillators. And, since the current fed to the deflection coils must be strong enough to generate the magnetic field strength needed to deflect the beam, a power amplifier stage should be connected between each oscillator and its deflection coil set.

The two scanning oscillators are completely under the domination of the TV transmitter. This control is necessary if the received picture is to conform to the transmitted one. The signals which effect that control are the horizontal and vertical sync pulses transmitted as part of the video signal. A circuit called the sync separator—also known as the sync clipper—operates to remove the sync pulses from the video signal, hand those pulses on to the horizontal and vertical oscillators, and discard the remainder of the signal. But where does the sync separator get the video signal? From its source, the video detector.

Sync Circuit Action

The explanation just given helps us to discover the basic form of the sync circuit system and nail it down in the form of a block diagram, but it offers only a partial glimpse into the system's action. A clearer view of the overall work of the system can be obtained by tracing it from its beginning—the output of the video detector—to its end, at the deflection yoke around the neck of the picture tube.

The signal supplied by the detector is made up of the picture signal, blanking pulses, and sync pulses. The picture signal and the blanking pulses are primarily

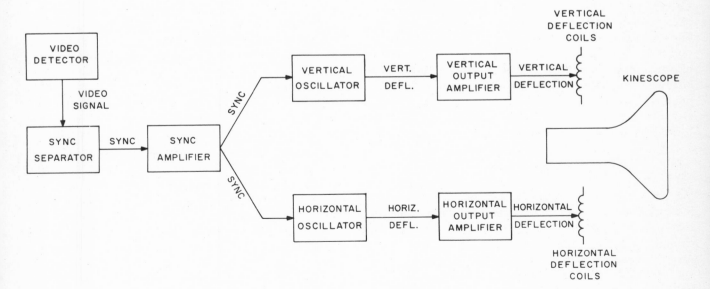

Fig. 14.4. TV Receiver Sync Circuits, Basic Block Diagram: The sync separator clips sync pulses from the video signal provided by the video detector; the picture signal is discarded. Sync signals obtained from the separator are ampli-fied, and are then used to trigger the vertical and horizontal oscillators. Deflection currents for the vertical and horizontal coils in the yoke are provided by the vertical and horizontal power amplifiers.

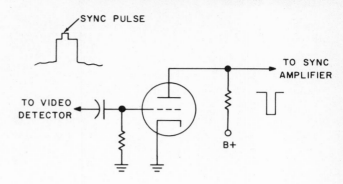

useful to the control grid of the picture tube: the former provide the light and dark elements of the final picture; the latter black out the tube beam at the end of each scanned line and each field. Sync pulses are also fed to the kinescope grid, but they have no effect on the action there one way or another.

The video signal from the detector is also given to the sync circuits. But here, neither the blanking pulses nor the picture signal are of any use. Only the horizontal and vertical sync pulses are needed. Hence the first circuit in the sync system is the sync separator. Its function is to get rid of the blanking pulses and picture signal and save the third component of the video signal, the sync pulses. The circuit therefore clips off the sync pulses—thus justifying the name "sync clipper" sometimes applied to it—and hands them on to the following circuits, the horizontal and vertical oscillators.

The sync pulses arriving at the end of every scanned line show up at the output of the sync separator at the rate of one every 1/15,750 of a second. But the separate pulses into which the vertical sync is broken arrive one on the heels of another, with much less time separation.

In the modern television receiver, the vertical and horizontal oscillators are free-running—they can operate independently. But they will not hold to their frequencies with the accuracy required for a good, steady picture. Hence they must be triggered by sync pulses.

The output of each oscillator is fed to a power amplifier. These latter circuits not only amplify the voltage of each oscillator, but the current output as well. The current is of primary interest here. If the output amplifier supplies a strong current to its set of deflection coils, the magnetic field in the coils will be powerful enough to do its work, moving the kinescope beam horizontally and vertically.

This, in brief, is the story of the television receiver sync system. As it has been presented here, it does not enlarge on the details of each stage, nor does it include all the stages present in the system. This information will be presented in the following paragraphs.

The Sync Separator

In Chapter 8, we came across a circuit known as the grid leak detector. As it was used in that chapter, it fulfilled the function of first detector in the receiver front end. But the same circuit is versatile enough to work also as a sync separator.

The video signal is applied to the grid of the tube in its positive phase. As a result of the flow of grid current on positive swings of the input signal, a bias approximately equal to the cutoff voltage appears on the grid. The bias voltage is also at about the same value of the blanking level of the video signal. Since, in the

Fig. 14.5. *The Sync Separator:* Only the sync pulse appears in the output circuit. The output pulse is in its negative phase.

video signal's positive phase, the sync pulses are more positive than the blanking level, plate current can flow only when sync pulses appear on the grid. Consequently, the output voltage of the tube consists only of sync pulses; the blanking and picture signal portions of the video signal are more negative than cutoff, and therefore cannot be reproduced.

In the grid leak variety of sync separator—there are several other types—the output sync pulses are in their negative phase due to the phase inversion occurring in a single stage. But if the sync separator is followed by a single-stage sync amplifier, the sync pulses can be re-inverted to the positive phase. As we shall see, both the vertical and horizontal oscillators require positive-phased signals.

Differentiators and Integrators

Since both horizontal and vertical sync pulses project beyond the blanking level, the output voltage of the separator and the amplifier following it will consist of both kinds of pulses. The job now is to use them to trigger the two oscillators properly.

Between the sync amplifier and the horizontal oscillator is a circuit known as the *differentiator,* made up of nothing more than a small capacitor in series with a resistor. This circuit, although important, is so simple that it is usually ignored in block diagrams of the television receiver. If a sync pulse in its positive phase is put into the differentiator, a large and almost instantaneous current flows through the resistor coincident with the initial rise of the pulse. But the capacitor in the circuit is small, consequently it cannot hold its charge for long, and the current drops to zero. However, coincident with the sharp fall in voltage at the trailing edge of the pulse, a large current flows through the resistor in the opposite direction and soon subsides. Thus the voltage

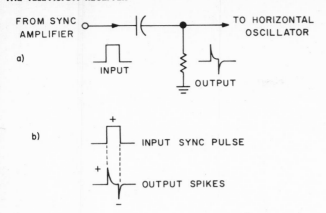

Fig. 14.6. *The Differentiator:* The schematic is shown in (a). In (b), the input sync pulse is compared with the output voltage spikes.

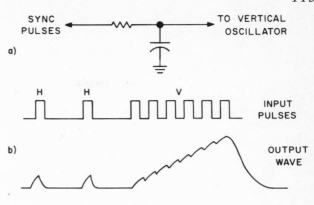

Fig. 14.7. *The Integrator:* The circuit is shown schematically in (a). In (b), the input horizontal and vertical pulses are compared with the output voltage.

across the differentiator resistor consists of two large voltage "spikes," one of which is positive and coincides with the leading edge of the sync pulse, the other negative and coincident with the trailing edge.

Since the differentiator responds with a positive spike for each sync pulse, there is one such spike every 1/15,750 of a second. Arriving at the horizontal oscillator, this spike triggers the oscillator into maintaining accurately its 15,750 cycle per second pace. The broken vertical sync pulses affect the differentiator the same way. Regardless of the type of pulse entering the differentiator, there is a positive spike fed every 1/15,750 of a second from the differentiator to the horizontal oscillator to keep the latter under control.

At the input to the vertical oscillator is another resistor-condenser circuit called the *integrator.* In this circuit, the input current enters a resistor and charges up a rather large condenser. Since the condenser has a large capacity, it holds the charge of an entering sync pulse for a fairly long time. If the pulses arrive at rather long intervals the condenser charge has time to leak off between pulses. The output of the circuit will then be negligibly small. But a pell-mell succession of pulses, one arriving almost directly after another, produces a pile-up of charges that can reach quite a strong peak. Before the charge due to the first pulse fades, the second one arrives and adds its bit to what remains of the first; the third pulse adds a little more, and so on. By the time the last of the pulses in this quick succession enters the integrator, the charge at the integrator's output has accumulated to the level at which it can trigger the vertical oscillator.

This is the reason that the horizontal sync pulses, which occur at relatively long intervals, have no effect on the vertical oscillator following the integrator circuit,

while the vertical sync pulses, arriving in rapid succession can pile up enough charge at the integrator's output to trigger the oscillator. Since the vertical pulses come at the end of every scanned field, the voltage at the output of the differentiator piles up to a triggering peak 60 times a second.

It is clear that vertical and horizontal separation involves more than a mere division of pulses into divergent paths. Both horizontal and vertical pulses are effective in keeping the horizontal oscillator in synchronization at all times, between as well as during field scans. Only the vertical pulses, however, keep the vertical oscillator in sync at its regular field rate of 60 cycles per second.

Vertical and Horizontal Oscillators; the Multivibrator

The schematic of a simple triode amplifier appeared in Chapter 4. There is nothing complex about this amplifier, consisting of merely a triode with a resistor between grid and chassis, and another resistor between plate and the B+ point of the power supply. Like most single stages of its type, it inverts the phase of an input signal. When a positive half-cycle is applied to the grid, a negative half-cycle appears at its plate; similarly, a negative half-cycle of input signal produces a positive half-cycle of output.

If a second, identical stage is joined to its output circuit, with a coupling capacitor between the plate of the first tube and the grid of the second, the second stage will re-invert the signal. The output voltage of the second stage will then be in phase with the input voltage at the grid of the first. Suppose a wire is now connected through a capacitor from the output of this system back

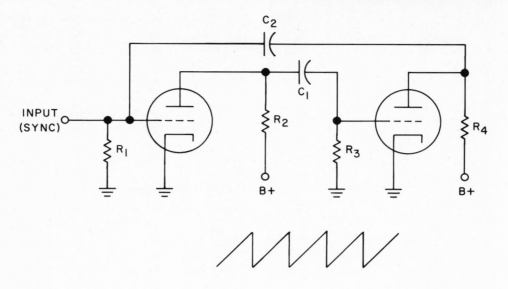

Fig. 14.8. *The Multivibrator:* The output voltage of this two-stage amplifier is in phase with the input voltage. When a feedback path is provided (through C₂), the amplifier becomes an oscillator. The natural frequency of vibration is determined by the values of the resistors and capacitors in the circuit. Accurate control of the frequency is forced by the sync input. The sawtooth wave appears below the schematic.

to its input, thus creating a feedback arrangement. Because the voltage fed back is in phase with the input signal, the feedback is regenerative; and because the feedback is regenerative, the circuit becomes an oscillator (Chapter 8). A *multivibrator* is created in this manner.

Like the oscillators in Chapter 8, the multivibrator is self-sufficient. As long as the heaters of its tubes are lit and the B+ voltages are continuously applied, the oscillations are kept going. No input signal is necessary. Unlike those other oscillators, however, the multivibrator has no resonant circuit, and so is rather peculiar. One of its peculiarities is that its rate of oscillation is unsteady. It has a natural frequency, determined by the values of resistance and capacitance in its circuit; but the frequency of its electrical vibrations at any moment display a tendency to shift above and below the natural rate.

A second peculiarity of the multivibrator is the shape of the voltage wave it generates, a wave which can easily be converted to a sawtooth form. The sawtooth voltage rises slowly and rather evenly to a peak, then drops sharply downward; it rises again slowly and evenly, and drops sharply to complete a second cycle, and so on. Its oddity in this respect makes the multivibrator a perfect candidate for the job of either horizontal or vertical oscillator in a television receiver. Such a sawtoothed current, passed through the kinescope's horizontal deflection coils will pull the beam steadily

across the tube screen and then yank it sharply back to start the scan of a new line. Put through the vertical deflection coils, a similar current will pull the beam downward steadily through one field and yank it sharply back to the top to begin a second field. It is only necessary that the multivibrator working as a vertical oscillator have a natural frequency of 60 cycles per second, and that the multivibrator as horizontal oscillator have a 15,750 cps frequency.

As for controlling the two oscillators to keep their frequencies from shifting, that can be done by applying positive spikes at the rate of 15,750 per second from the differentiator to the grid of the horizontal multivibrator, and pulse accumulation at the rate of 60 per second to the grid of the vertical multivibrator. And here we see the need for sync pulses in their *positive* phase. A positive pulse—or spike—put on the grid of the multivibrator at a particular moment causes an increase in current in the tube, and forces the oscillator to begin a cycle at that moment. The sync pulses supplied to the differentiator and integrator must therefore be positively phased to keep the oscillator running in step with their arrival.

The Blocking Oscillator

Another oscillator with similar characteristics is called the blocking oscillator. The distinguishing feature of this circuit is a transformer.

Both coils of the circuit transformer are wound around a common iron core. Since one winding is connected directly to the plate of a triode, while the other is applied to the grid through a bypass condenser, regenerative feedback from plate to grid occurs through the magnetic field shared by both plate and grid, therefore the circuit oscillates.

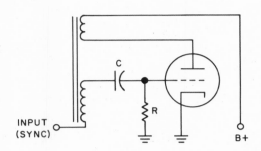

Fig. 14.9. *The Blocking Oscillator:* **The natural frequency of the oscillator is set by the values of the grid leak resistor (R) and the bypass capacitor (C). Positive-phase sync, applied to the grid through C, maintains control of oscillator frequency.**

Sharp-eyed readers will note that the blocking oscillator is almost identical in form with the Armstrong oscillator (Chapter 8). The major difference between the two is the frequency-determining system. In the blocking oscillator the natural frequency of oscillation is determined by the sizes of the grid leak resistor and the grid bypass capacitor. Regenerative feedback causes the grid to swing increasingly positive, and a strong d-c flow is drawn through the grid leak resistor. The grid thus assumes a growing d-c negative potential. In a very short time, the grid becomes so negative that it cuts off plate current in the tube. The tube then ceases to operate; in the slang of the electronics engineer, it *blocks*. With no plate current flowing, there is no feedback, and the action of the tube stops. It will not be resumed until the charge stored in the bypass capacitor leaks off—a comparatively slow, steady process. As the leakage progresses, the grid gradually loses its negative potential, the tube is unblocked, and the voltage of the grid is sent into cutoff once more. Thus a new cycle of oscillation is begun. Since the application of a positive voltage can bring the grid out of cutoff, a positively phased pulse can control the blocking oscillator's running rate.

It is the repeated slow, steady rise, and sudden sharp drop, in this process of the blocking oscillator, which marks it as the blood brother of the multivibrator. Both of these oscillators act like a frog trying to work his way out of a slippery well: he crawls with steady labor, inching his way upwards, then loses his footing and slides precipitously down the slimy wall. Once more he makes the patient, toiling climb, and yet again speeds backwards to the depths. Conceivably, the frog will give up after a while and resign himself to living his life at the bottom of a hole. But the oscillator, which behaves in the same way, keeps up the same unending grind and quits only when its power has been cut off or one of its components fails. Such frog-like circuits are called *relaxation* oscillators.

Oscillator Controls

Some of the less obvious television receiver hand controls are part of the vertical and horizontal oscillators in the set. One of these is the size control; there is a horizontal size control—sometimes called the *width* control—for the horizontal oscillator, and a vertical size control—the *height* control—for the vertical oscillator. These are almost always variable resistors. By varying the amplitude of the oscillators' outputs, the controls vary the strength of the deflection currents in the yoke. Thus a picture which is not wide enough to fit the screen and shows black borders on either side, can be corrected through an adjustment of the width control. A picture bounded on top and bottom by similar black borders demands a new setting of the height control knob.

A second pair of these controls is the *linearity* or *drive* knobs. If the slow rise of voltage in the oscillator is not quite even, but varies in its rate of increase, the picture is distorted. Such a fault in the horizontal oscillator may cause the scanning beam to move slowly at first and then speed up substantially towards the end of its run. If that should happen, a man standing at one side of the picture will appear considerably wider than his fellow actor at the other. A judicious adjustment of the horizontal linearity control is then required. Again, an actor directly in the middle of the picture may be quite normal from the waist down, but is abnormally stretched from the waist up. Resetting the vertical linearity knob will put him right.

A third pair of controls consists of the horizontal and vertical *hold* controls. The purpose of these variable resistors is to add to or subtract from the total circuit resistance in order to bring the oscillator's natural frequency closer to the sync rate. The hold controls, in the engineer's jargon, help keep the picture "in sync." A tendency of the picture to roll up or down the screen demands adjustment of the vertical hold to bring it back into sync. A tendency of the image to disintegrate into a number of near-horizontal bands of various shades of gray can be corrected by a touch on the horizontal hold knob.

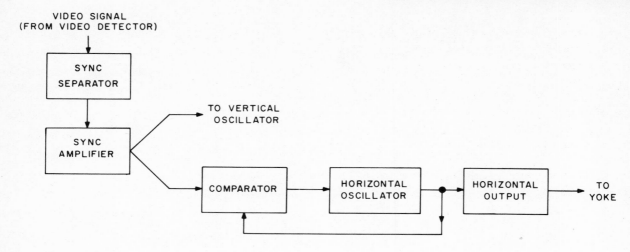

Fig. 14.10. *Horizontal AFC, Block Diagram:* **The comparator accepts sync pulses from the sync amplifier, and receives part of the horizontal oscillator output. If the comparator** detects an error in the oscillator signal, it applies a corrective signal to the oscillator.

Horizontal AFC Circuits

Pioneer television engineers found that while the frequency of the vertical oscillator generally stayed put, its companion oscillator needed exceptionally strong sync pulses to keep the correct frequency. They then devised an automatic frequency control circuit which would help maintain control of the horizontal oscillator. They succeeded so well that now the shoe is on the other foot: the horizontal hold control rarely has to be reset; but the vertical hold control, which has no afc circuit to aid it, may have to be adjusted from time to time.

Although the horizontal afc circuit operates at a frequency far lower than the afc circuit of the FM receiver (Chapter 11), the two systems are very similar. Like the FM system, the horizontal afc system makes a comparison of two signals, detects the difference in frequency between them, and adjusts an oscillator to keep the frequency of the two signals the same. And, like the FM system, the horizontal afc circuit operates in a closed loop.

The output signal of the sync amplifier, consisting of the horizontal and broken-up vertical sync pulses, is put into a circuit known variously as a comparator or horizontal control tube. The sync pulses pass through the comparator and are brought to the horizontal oscillator. In usual fashion, the pulses are converted to strongly positive spikes by the differentiator at the oscillator's input, and the spikes are fed to the oscillator to keep it in sync. Part of the oscillator's output, however, is fed back to the comparator to close the loop. The comparator—and this is the reason for its name—compares the frequencies of the two signals presented to it, the sync pulses and the oscillator output. The sync pulses are the reference signal; their frequency must be the correct one since they originate from the master source, the television transmitter. If the comparator finds the oscillator signal higher or lower in frequency than the rate of the sync pulses, it applies a corrective signal to the oscillator, and so brings it back to where it should be.

Like the discriminator in the FM afc system, the comparator is often a balanced circuit of two diodes. As a usual thing, however, the diodes are crystals rather than vacuum tubes—not the galena crystals of bygone days, but crystals of germanium or silicon. Other diodes in the modern television receiver, such as the video detector described earlier in this chapter, are also made of these semiconductor materials. This subject is reserved for a future chapter (Chapter 18).

The Output Amplifiers

Following the vertical and horizontal oscillators in the television receiver, the vertical and horizontal power amplifiers perform the final operation on the sync signals before they are fed to the deflection coils in the yoke. These amplifiers are similar to the power output stages in audio amplifier units (Chapter 10), and are built along similar lines. They have two distinguishing characteristics: the first is the type of tube used—a type designed for developing high plate current; the second is the output transformer. Since the frequencies handled by the vertical and horizontal output amplifiers are within the audio range—sounds of 15,750 cycles per second are audible to comparatively few people, and 60 cps can be heard by just about anybody—the output transformers for the vertical and horizontal stages are iron-cored, just as the audio output transformer is.

What enhances the resemblance between the sync circuit power amplifier and the corresponding stage in an audio system is the use to which the output transformer is put. In both types of circuit, the secondary of the transformer is connected to a coil. This coil, in the audio system, is the voice coil of the loudspeaker; in the television receiver sync circuits, it is the deflection coil of the yoke.

The Flyback Power Supply

In its pell-mell rush into the future, electronics frequently forgets its past. There was a time when the picture tube in television receivers had to be restricted to 12 inches because tubes any bigger were impractical. They demanded much too high a voltage.

The final accelerating anode of the television receiver kinescope (Chapter 6) needs an extraordinarily high positive voltage. To develop this voltage, early receiver models were equipped with power supplies of the conventional type—the full-wave supply described in Chapter 2 was the one most often used. With its primary connected to the 110 volt a-c line, the transformer had to be enormous to deliver the +10,000 volts a 12 inch tube required. The transformer was so immense that it took up most of the chassis space. But then a brilliant stroke of engineering sagacity, known as the *flyback power supply,* arrived in time to aid the infant television industry.

The flyback power supply depends on a familiar law of physics: the voltage across a coil of wire is proportional to the rate of change of the current flowing through the wire. Now, the current output of the horizontal oscillator falls, at the end of its cycle, from a very high level to quite a low one. Moreover, it does so in an exceedingly short time. Its rate of change is therefore extremely high. If such a current is passed through a coil, the voltage across the coil will be immense. And if that a-c voltage is then stepped up by a transformer, it will be still larger. Finally, when rectified and filtered, it can become a d-c voltage high enough to satisfy even a 23-inch picture tube.

Since the output of the horizontal oscillator feeds into the horizontal output tube, the plate current in this tube has the same characteristics, a slow steady rise and a precipitous drop. Consequently, the flow of this current through one of the output transformer's large coils (L_1 in the schematic) puts an enormous voltage across that coil. The a-c voltage across L_1 is the input

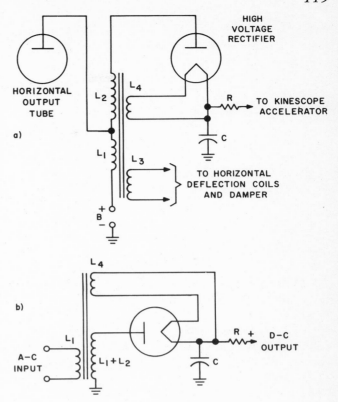

Fig. 14.11. *The Flyback Power Supply:* (a) The sharp drop in plate current of the horizontal output tube puts a high a-c voltage across transformer coil L_1. Total a-c voltage across L_1 and L_2 is very high. When this voltage is rectified by the tube diode and filtered by a resistor (R) and capacitor (C), the resulting positive d-c potential can be as much as +20,000 volts; (b) A simple half-wave rectifier power supply is shown for comparison. Corresponding parts in both schematics are correspondingly labeled.

voltage for the transformer, and so is analogous to the input voltage in the type of half-wave power supply we have seen in Chapter 2.

Connected in series with this first coil is a second large one (L_2). The turns of L_2 are wound about the same core as L_1. Quite a large a-c voltage is therefore induced in the second coil. Since both coils are connected in series, the voltage across both is equal to the sum of the voltages across each—a staggering total. The opposite end of L_2 is connected to the plate of a vacuum tube diode. And, at the other end of the L_1, L_2 combination, the terminal of L_1 is connected to chassis through the B supply of the receiver. The two series coils therefore correspond to the high voltage secondary of the conventional half-wave power supply transformer.

In the half-wave power supply of Chapter 2, the d-c voltage is developed at the heater of the rectifier, and is filtered by a circuit of two condensers and a choke. This same condition is reflected in the flyback power supply, except for the filtering. Since very little current is taken from the picture tube accelerator anyway, the filtering need not be so elaborate. A resistor in place of the choke, and a single condenser suffices. But that single condenser may be called upon to stand up under a voltage of 20,000 volts d-c!

The transformer of the flyback supply also fulfills the less startling but equally urgent need of an output transformer. Hence a third winding (L_3) is also part of the transformer. With the terminals L_3 connected to the horizontal deflection coils in the yoke, and L_1 joined to the horizontal output tube, the a-c path between the horizontal output stage and the deflection yoke is completed through the transformer.

But there is still one fault that needs correction, and that fault arises from the use of the transformer in two capacities at once—as a power supply transformer and as output transformer. The shock of the sudden drop of current in L_1 and the high voltage so created, cause winding L_3 to "ring" electrically—that is, to oscillate. The ringing does not last very long, but the initial surges of voltage it creates get into the horizontal deflection coils and affect the scanning beam of the picture tube, so that the image on the face of the screen is distorted. Ringing is easily cured by connecting a vacuum tube diode, known as the *damper,* directly across the terminals of L_3. The first surge of the ringing voltage puts the plate of the damper at a positive potential; the damper diode then conducts current, thus behaving like a low resistance to kill the ringing. In many receivers, the damper tube is also part of an auxiliary power supply which heightens still further the yield of the flyback supply.

A fourth winding of this versatile horizontal output transformer is a small one, used to furnish voltage to the heater of the high voltage rectifier. In this characteristic, too, the circuit of the flyback power supply conforms to the traditional half-wave power supply, in which electrical nourishment for the rectifier diode heater is tapped off the power transformer.

A circuit like the flyback power supply, which develops lethal voltages, is nothing for the part-time tinkerer to play with, certainly not while the set is alive. To protect their nosier customers, manufacturers of television receivers enclose the tubes and other components of the flyback power supply in a metal container, freely perforated with holes to permit air to circulate and carry off the heat. And, to make doubly certain that nobody will be hurt even if the high voltage "cage" is removed, the manufacturer frequently mounts on the rear wall of the set the socket into which the set's 110 volt a-c line cord is plugged. The

tinkerer who unscrews and dismounts that wall will then find that his set is completely inactive. This clever *interlock switch,* interrupting the path between the house current and the receiver's low voltage power supply, has saved many a bungler from a fate at least as bad as death.

The Low Voltage Supply

The flyback power supply is not an independent circuit. It derives its energy from the horizontal output stage, which in turn is dependent on the low voltage power supply for *its* energy. In fact, every circuit in the receiver depends on the low voltage supply for operation. But this fact does not make the low voltage supply especially remarkable; it is essentially the same full-wave power supply circuit first presented in Chapter 2.

As in practically every other piece of electronic equipment, the low voltage power supply furnishes the plates and screens of the tubes in the receiver with the d-c voltages they require. Those voltages are hardly "low" when compared with similar voltages in the ordinary radio receiver; but they are low when contrasted with the immense voltage available at the flyback circuit. So, to distinguish between the two power supplies in the television receiver, engineers apply the term "low" to the basic circuit. But nobody should be deceived by this innocuous title. A shock from the low voltage supply can be almost as nasty as one from the flyback supply. There are those who say that it is even worse. This is an issue from which the author, who has survived many an electrical jolt, wishes fervently to abstain.

Some Tips on Repair

In a sense, the television receiver is just as much a combination receiver as those described in Chapter 11. It has four fairly well-defined sections: sight, sound, horizontal sync, and vertical sync. Provided the technician can recognize the symptoms in a poorly operating TV receiver well enough to know which of the four sections is responsible for producing them, he can immediately go to the right section simply by observing the set. The tubes are the first components in a stage to be suspected. A careful examination of the symptoms should then provide a clue to the particular tubes to be checked.

Between the antenna and the video amplifier, there is a single channel of stages. These, as we discovered in Chapters 8 and 9, are devoted to both sound and video signals. A defective tube in one of these circuits, then, would cause a situation in which nothing—except, perhaps, a hum—would be heard from the speaker and no discernible picture could form on the screen, but the set would not be completely dead. The screen would be covered with a bright, white glow known to television engineers as the *raster*.

The raster is a product of the kinescope beam pushed horizontally and vertically by the deflection yoke. It is true that a bad tube between the antenna and the video detector can deprive the vertical and horizontal sync circuits of the sync pulse, but both the vertical and horizontal oscillators are free-running. Without the sync pulse to guide them, they may not run at their correct frequencies, but they will run nevertheless. Both the vertical and horizontal deflection coils in the yoke will then get their deflection currents, and the beam will scan. As for the beam itself, it will be perfectly healthy as long as the kinescope is good. The beam will also have all its intensity, because the accelerator of the kinescope gets its voltage from the flyback supply which, in turn, is stimulated by the horizontal oscillator. No picture will appear on the screen, but the face of the tube will be brilliantly lit just the same.

Consequently, in a receiver which shows a healthy raster but has neither picture nor sound, the tubes between antenna and video amplifier should be checked. But an exception to this rule should be made for sets manufactured before 1952 or thereabouts. In those older models, the sight and sound channels were divided after the first i-f stage. Similar symptoms in those sets therefore require a check of only the r-f amplifier, converter, and first i-f tubes.

What can be done about a set showing a good picture but no sound? A good picture indicates that the signal path from antenna to kinescope is freely available. The only departure from that path is the sound channel. Hence the trouble must be in those stages in the sound channel of the receiver. In the modern set, the purely sound stages are the 4.5 mc amplifier just ahead of the FM detector, the detector itself, and the two audio stages. The chances are that the detector diodes are crystals, which ordinarily have a longer life than tubes. This leaves only the 4.5 mc amplifier and two audio tubes to check. In the older TV models, all the stages between the first i-f and the speaker have to be examined.

Trouble in both sync channels is evidenced by these symptoms: the sound is good, and the screen shows black and white elements which indicate that there might be a coherent picture if they would only straighten out; there is both vertical rolling and a sort of horizontal zig-zag pattern, there is neither vertical nor horizontal sync. Since it is unlikely that two tubes, one in the vertical and one in horizontal sync channels, will simultaneously blow, the chances are that the trouble is in a stage devoted to *both* sync chan-

nels and to nothing else. Two stages answer this description: one is the sync separator; the other, the sync amplifier. Both these tubes should be checked and replaced if necessary. In some receivers a single duo-triode tube is used for the two stages, which reduces the number of suspicious tubes to one.

If everything is fine, except that the picture keeps rolling vertically in spite of all efforts to stop it with the vertical hold control, suspicion must center on the vertical sync stages—the vertical oscillator and output tubes. Again, these may be enclosed in a single tube. Trouble in only the horizontal sync circuits can take one of two forms, depending on the stage afflicted. If there is a picture of sorts which slants crazily to one side or the other, but can be kept from rolling vertically, the chances are that the horizontal afc circuit is not working properly. Then, the comparator—horizontal control tube, as some manufacturers call it—should be checked. The probability is that the horizontal oscillator is at least in some form of working order. If it is not, or if any of the tubes following it are bad, then the second possible symptom of horizontal sync trouble shows up—a dark screen. Failure of the horizontal oscillator tube means failure of the flyback supply, which it stimulates; and failure of the flyback circuit means no accelerator voltage for the kinescope. A bad vertical oscillator, on the other hand, usually cannot affect the flyback supply. If the tube works to some extent, the picture may keep rolling vertically, if it fails completely, the usual symptom is a single bright horizontal line in the middle of the screen. Since the kinescope beam cannot be moved in a vertical direction without the efforts of the vertical oscillator, it is doomed to swing eternally sideways.

A final word should be said about the flyback supply. In older models, receivers were equipped with small cartridge-type fuses in that circuit to protect against overload. These should be checked if the screen shows neither picture nor raster. Many newer receivers have their fuses in the low voltage power supply. If these fuses or the power supply rectifier blows, neither picture nor sound nor anything else can work since the low voltage supply is responsible for feeding all circuits in the set. Nor should it be forgotten that the line cord of the receiver must be firmly seated in its wall socket. Many a good set has been torn apart because its owner just forgot the set wasn't plugged in, or that the particular wall socket it was plugged into was not working.

Color Television

Under the present system of color television, an ordinary black-and-white television receiver can reproduce, without the slightest difficulty, a broadcast in color as a monochrome image. Conversely, a color television receiver can reproduce a black-and-white transmission as a black-and-white picture, in addition to performing the function for which it was designed. If this harmonious coexistence between the older "gray" and the newer color systems had not been devised, the resulting chaos might have thrown the industry into a disastrous turmoil. Owners of black-and-white sets, who only a few years before had spent small fortunes for their receivers, would have had to discard them as so much useless junk. The alternative would have meant the construction of two transmitter installations for each station on the air; one for black and white, the other for color. Either way, enormous amounts of money and effort would have been wasted.

But the problem of "compatibility" was solved. The transmitted TV color signal has, in addition to its usual carrier, two components. One of these, the *luminance* signal, is the equivalent of what in these past pages has been called the video signal; the other is the *color* signal, which reflects the hues in the televised image. Ordinary black-and-white receivers tuned to a color telecast respond to the luminance signal in the same way they respond to the usual video signal, thus providing the black-and-white image. But the color receiver is much more complex. It uses the luminance signal to give the black-and-white picture on ordinary telecasts, and processes the color signal to supply the image with its correct tints when a program in color is received.

The Color TV Picture Tube

In Chapter 6, a comparison was made between the television picture tube and the pointillist painter. Since a painter usually deals in colors, an even closer parallel can be drawn between his method of work and the operation of the picture tube in the color receiver. There is this difference, however: where the painter mixes the colors for each of his dots on a palette rather than on the canvas itself, the television tube mixes its tints directly on the picture—that is, on the screen of the tube. While the painter may use any number of shades as the ingredients for his mixture, the color TV tube uses only three basic tints.

The theory of color in the television system assumes that any color shade can be reproduced by mixing correct proportions of red, blue, and green. A purple costume, for example, might be duplicated by red and blue, plus a dash of green to match the image color precisely to the original. The correct proportions of all three colors can also produce white at maximum intensity and various shades of gray as the intensity of the mixture is diminished. Thus the TV color tube can produce the hues of the color transmission as well as

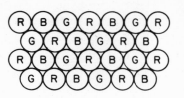

Fig. 14.12. *The Phosphor Dots:* **A section of the screen of the color television picture tube showing the arrangement of red (R), blue (B), and green (G) dots.**

the grays of the black-and-white telecast through the use of phosphors which glow in red, blue, and green.

The screen of the color television tube is made up of over a million phosphor dots which glow in the three primary colors when struck by the tube electron beam. Each dot always emits its color in an intensity proportional to the intensity of the beam striking it. In a portion of the picture which is predominantly green, for example, the green dots are most radiant, with the immediately neighboring reds and blues subdued. The smallest element of the image which has a blend of the three primary hues is therefore a cluster of three of these phosphor dots, each with its characteristic tint. At those times when the receiver is working on a black-and-white transmission, one of these *trio* elements will have the proper color intensity in each dot to give some shade of gray ranging from utter black to a brilliant white.

If each phosphor dot of the screen glows with some intensity in only one of the primary colors, it must be the target of a beam controlled by a signal devoted to one color only. Since there are three primary colors in the system, there must then be three scanning beams. No daring mental leap, then, is required to arrive at the conclusion that the picture tube in the color television receiver has three electron guns. Although the electrons which each gun directs at its particular phosphor dot is in no way different from the electrons shot from any of the other two guns, the three beams can be called the red, blue, and green beams. The red beam is responsible for the red component of each trio element of the image, the green beam for the green component, and the blue beam for the blue.

Quite a problem is involved in the last sentence of the preceding paragraph. Each beam must hit only its own phosphor dot and no other. If the red beam, for example, were to strike a blue dot, the amount of blue in that portion of the image would be either overexaggerated or underdone. Assuming similar contamination of other colors, the picture would be made up of completely false color values. The healthy pink of an actor's

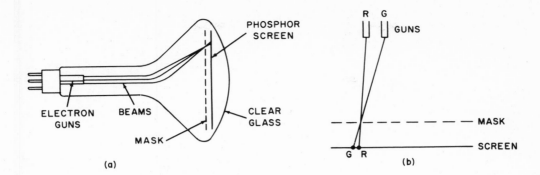

Fig. 14.13. *The Color Television Picture Tube:* A cross-section view of the tube is shown in (a). The diagram of (b) illustrates the use of the mask; in this two-dimensional view, only two guns, red (R) and green (G) are shown.

complexion could easily become a sickly blue-green under those conditions. What is called for, evidently, is marksmanship of a high order on the part of the red, blue, and green beams. To insure this marksmanship, there must be some device which can effectively restrict each of the three beams to the phosphor dots of its own color. In the color television tube, this device is called the *mask*.

Except for the fact that the holes in it are much smaller and are arranged in orderly fashion, the mask might be said to resemble a very thin slice of Swiss cheese. For every trio of phosphor dots there is one hole in the mask. Consequently, if there are more than a million phosphor dots on the tube screen, the mask must be perforated by something over a third of a million holes. In the operation of the tube, the three beams from the guns at the base end converge on one hole in the mask at a particular moment. The mask is just in front of the phosphor screen and parallel to it. Emerging from the screen side of the mask, then, the beams diverge. If the small distance between the mask and screen is precisely set, each beam will hit the phosphor dot it is meant to strike.

Since the beams diverge before hitting the screen, their points of impact obviously cannot coincide. But they are quite close to one another. The eye of the viewer, at some distance from the screen, cannot make out the individual color of each tiny dot in the trio. If he is able to distinguish the trio at all from the rest of the image, he sees it as a blend of its dot elements in a color shade matching the original object telecast. If the program is in black and white, of course, he will see the trio as a point shade of gray.

Chrominance and Luminance

Merely by following through with the logic of the system, we can unearth some more facts about the color television method. In a "colorcast," no one set of phosphor dots of a particular color can receive the same beam intensity from that color gun at all times. As long as the hue varies at different points in the image, the electron beam responsible for each color must also vary. In the single-gunned picture tube of black-and-white television (Chapter 6), the intensity of the one beam is controlled by the video signal applied to the control grid of the gun. It would seem logical, then, that the beams of the three guns in the color picture tube be controlled by a color signal plus a black-and-white luminance signal; the former to furnish the color, and the latter to brighten or darken the color as the image demands. Further, it is perfectly reasonable to assume that the *chrominance* signal, as the combination of color and luminance signals is called, contains red, blue, and green components, and that each of these component voltages be applied to the grid of its particular gun. That, in brief, states the method of operation of the three-gun color picture tube.

Color Receiver Stages

In the color TV receiver, the action at the front end is much like that in the black-and-white set. The signal is picked up from the transmitter by a dipole antenna and fed to an r-f amplifier stage. It is then conducted to a first detector where it is mixed with the signal from a local oscillator to produce the two i-f carriers for the sound and video signals. These carriers differ in frequency by 4.5 mc. After their production, both signals are amplified in as many as five i-f stages.

The last of the i-f stages serves as the point of departure for the sound strip. Both the i-f carriers are taken from this final i-f stage and brought to a 4.5 mc detector, usually a crystal diode circuit. The detector is the first of the sound strip stages. The 4.5 mc signal the circuit produces, like that in the black-and-white

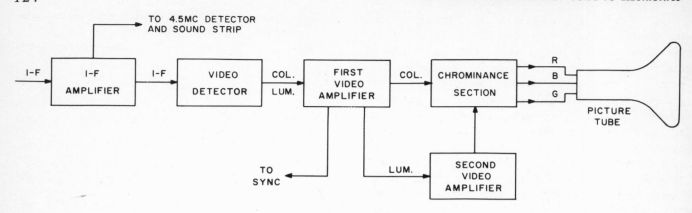

Fig. 14.14. *Section of Color TV Receiver, Simplified Block Diagram:* Separation of color (COL) and luminance (LUM)

signals takes place in the first video amplifier. The input to the sound channel is taken from the final i-f amplifier stage.

receiver, is to some extent amplitude modulated; but its desirable quality is its frequency modulations. After strengthening in a 4.5 mc amplifier circuit, the signal is brought to a ratio detector for conversion into audio, then to a simple two-stage audio amplifier, and finally to the speaker.

A second output of the last i-f stage feeds into the video detector. This latter circuit has the single function of discarding the picture i-f carrier and preserving its modulating signal composed of luminance and color signal components. Both these voltages are strengthened in the first video amplifier. The signals are parted, the luminance component enters the second video amplifier stage and the color component enters the chrominance section. After its separate amplification, the luminance signal rejoins the color signal.

The chrominance section is a fairly complex circuit composed of several stages. Its function can be simply expressed: it processes the primary color signals for application to their respective control grids in the three guns of the picture tube. Since the chrominance section supplies three different signals, its output stages are triple-branched, each branch devoted to one of the three primary colors. However, the section also handles the luminance signal required to provide each primary color with its correct brightness level. The luminance signal is fed to all three of the chrominance section branches.

Since the color television receiver must be adaptable for receiving either color or monochrome telecasts, some switching arrangement should be provided for that adaptation. The switching arrangement is an automatic one, and is found in the chrominance section in the form of a *color-killer* tube. When the receiver is tuned to a black-and-white transmission, no color signal can, of course, reach the chrominance section. The

absence of the signal triggers the color-killer into operation, and the tube operates to paralyze those circuits in the chrominance section responsible for the individual color voltages applied to the grids of the three picture tube guns. However, the luminance signal is still active. Its effect on the three grids of the tube guns is to keep the beam intensity of each at the proper proportion to produce some shade of gray. The proper proportion, roughly, is 60 per cent green, 30 per cent red, and 10 per cent blue. Under the influence of the luminance signal, these proportions are preserved. As the voltage of the luminance signal varies for different points of the scanned picture, the intensity of each color beam also varies, but the proportions are always maintained. Hence the picture appears in black and white— or, more accurately, in varying shades of gray. If the transmitter to which the receiver is tuned should now put on a color show, the color-killer tube is paralyzed, and the beam intensities of the three guns are free to adopt the proportion required to produce a particular hue.

Color Receiver Sync

Synchronization is as necessary in color television receivers as it is in black-and-white. The two systems are compatible, and their scanning techniques are consequently the same. Although there are three writing beams in the triple gun tube of color television, all of them converge at one point on the tube mask; and to remain converged throughout their scanning movement, they must be kept in step with one another and with the parallel scanning back at the transmitter. It can therefore be expected that the sync circuits in the color television receiver are, with some exceptions, the same as those in the black-and-white set.

One exception is to be found in the deflection system, the final component of the sync circuits. In the black-and-white receiver, the deflection yoke can manage to control the scanning movements of the single beam practically unaided; in the color receiver, however, the presence of three beams, each arriving from a different source, demands extra equipment in the form of *convergence coils*. It is the job of these coils and their magnetic fields to focus the three beams on the mask of the color tube. With the convergence of the beams thus taken care of, the deflection yoke can put the beams through their paces. Generally, the deflection yoke is positioned just back of the tube bell with the yoke containing the convergence coil seated just behind it.

The Future of Color TV

Color television is not quite as simple as this bird's eye view might suggest; the subject of color represents, in effect, an advanced course for the student of electronics. What complicates his study is the fact that color TV has not as yet reached the relatively static stage of radio and black-and-white television; it is still growing. While color sets now on the market can and do work beautifully, their design often differs radically from manufacturer to manufacturer; they have not as yet had a chance to settle down to uniformity. In any case, color TV definitely has a future. One of these days, that future will arrive.

GLOSSARY

Brightness. The overall lighting of a televised scene.

Blocking oscillator. A relaxation oscillator used in sync circuits of a television receiver.

Chrominance signal. The combined luminance and color signals.

Color-killer. A tube in the color TV receiver which prevents the appearance of color on the picture tube screen during black-and-white telecast reception.

Comparator. The control tube of a horizontal afc circuit.

Contrast. The comparative values of light and shade in the televised scene.

Convergence coils. The yoke just back of the deflection yoke on a three-gun color TV picture tube; the coils which focus the three beams on mask holes.

Damper. A diode in the flyback power supply which prevents ringing.

Differentiator. A resistor-condenser circuit at the input to the horizontal oscillator in a television receiver.

Flyback power supply. The high voltage circuit in a television set.

Height control. The TV receiver hand control which varies the height of the picture.

High voltage cage. The metal guard around the tubes and circuits of the flyback power supply.

Hold controls. A pair of TV receiver hand controls which help synchronize the picture horizontally and vertically.

Horizontal afc. The automatic frequency control in the horizontal sync circuit of a TV receiver.

Horizontal control tube. The comparator stage of the horizontal afc system.

Horizontal oscillator. The relaxation oscillator in the TV receiver's horizontal sync circuit.

Horizontal output stage. The power amplifier stage in the TV receiver's horizontal sync circuits.

Integrator. A resistor-condenser circuit at the input to the vertical oscillator.

Interlock switch. An automatic safety circuit breaker which cuts off the power.

Linearity controls. The TV receiver hand controls which help correct distortion in the picture.

Luminance signal. The signal controlling light values in the color TV receiver.

Mask. The device in the three-gun color TV picture tube which helps restrict each beam to the phosphor dots of its own color.

Multivibrator. A relaxation oscillator used in the sync circuits of a television receiver.

Phosphor dots. Elements in the screen of the color TV picture tube which glow in the three primary colors.

Primary colors. The basic tints of color television: red, green, blue.

Raster. The bright white glow which covers the television screen when no signal is received.

Relaxation oscillator. An oscillator whose output steadily rises and then quickly drops.

Sync clipper. The stage in the TV receiver sync circuits which removes sync pulses from the video signal; same as *sync separator*.

Trap, 4.5 mc. A coil-condenser circuit, resonant to 4.5 mc, which separates sound and sight signals in the TV receiver.

Trio. Neighboring red, blue, and green phosphor dots in the screen of the color TV picture tube.

Vertical blanking pulse. The pulse which cuts off the kinescope scanning beam when a field is completed.

Vertical oscillator. The relaxation oscillator in the vertical sync circuit of the TV receiver.

Vertical output stage. The power amplifier stage in the TV receiver's vertical sync circuit.

Vertical sync pulses. The series of pulses which controls the TV receiver's vertical and horizontal oscillators.

Width control. The TV receiver hand control which varies the width of the picture.

Chapter Fifteen

RADAR

SHORTLY AFTER the first engagements of World War II, Americans at home began to hear strange tales. A soldier's badly mutilated body was found on the streets; he had been an expert operator of a secret electronic weapon of immense military significance; he had been tortured by enemy agents in a vain effort to force him to reveal the mysteries he carried in his brain. The body had been found in Washington; in New York; in Louisville, Kentucky, in Corpus Christi, Texas. His name was anything the rumor-monger could think of at the moment, but everybody agreed on the name of the device he had mastered. It was called *radar*.

Radar is still a familiar word, to the student of electronics and the general public. But only the student has any notion of its real intricacies.

The student of this book has already discovered that the usual type of radar set is an entity in itself. It is not just a receiver operating under the control of a distant transmitter, but a combination of both receiver and transmitter. In the pulse radar system, the transmitter sends out r-f energy in the form of bursts of waves of constant amplitude and frequency. These waves strike a target that may or may not be specifically chosen for electronic investigation, and are returned to the single antenna which serves both the transmitter and receiver. As we shall see later, it is impossible to pinpoint the desired target so precisely with the transmitted r-f beam that echoes will be obtained only from that target and no other. At any rate, the reflections from the target and the objects in its vicinity return to the radar antenna, and are brought to the first of the receiver stages.

Most modern radar systems operate in the frequency range known as uhf. While uhf systems obey the same natural laws as other electronic devices, they cannot operate efficiently under the same conditions. Even such commonplace items as connecting wires cannot exist in uhf circuits, but must be redesigned as waveguides.

Aside from complicated plumbing, uhf radar must bear with another nuisance—electrical noise. Electronic equipment working at much lower frequencies can tolerate it, FM radio can get rid of it simply by clipping it away from the desired signal; but the high noise level at uhf is difficult to remove without affecting the shape of the precious echo burst. The signal energy returned from the target is usually so small that the radar receiver can use an r-f amplifier to strengthen it. But here the cure would be worse than the disease, because the amplifier itself would heighten the noise voltages.

Since most uhf radar receivers have no r-f amplifier, the first stage to which the returning echo is led is the mixer, a cavity containing a crystal diode. A second waveguide piped into the mixer cavity brings into it the output of a local oscillator, usually a klystron (Chapter 6). After the crystal first detector does its work of selecting the intermediate frequency, many of the difficulties associated with uhf disappear. At the relatively low i-f, wires can be used to interconnect components, and high-gain amplifier stages can be put to work without coming up against the noise barrier.

Following the crystal diode is the i-f amplifier strip, one of the items covered in Chapter 9. The signal strengthened in these amplifiers is the i-f version of the echo burst, consisting of a short train of waves substantially constant in frequency and amplitude. It is this signal which is brought into the second detector succeeding the final i-f stage. The detector's reaction to the beginning of the burst is to put out a steadily rising d-c voltage which increases as the first few cycles of the burst increase. The *rise time*, the interval in which the initial cycles of the burst grow from zero to maximum, is so extremely short that the voltage output of the video detector may be thought of as increasing in practically no time at all; yet it must be taken into account. Once the rise time is over, the burst settles down to a constant amplitude, and the output of the video detector is similarly constant. This situation lasts for a relatively long period—much longer than the rise time. At the end of that period, the amplitude of the burst drops to zero—again in an extremely short time. The output voltage of the video detector follows this drop precisely, then remains at zero until the next echo comes along.

The sum total of the video detector's work during the echo period is to put out the pulse shown in the drawing in Chapter 7. A pulse of this type is generally called "square," which is really more a convenient than an accurate term. Actually, it should be pictured with an upward slant in its leading edge and a downward slant in its trailing edge, since it neither rises nor falls instantaneously. But the time in which its constant state endures is so long compared to its rise and fall times that the pulse would still look square, even if it were drawn to scale.

The Video Amplifier

Most of the waves the electronic engineer deals with are odd-looking affairs deserving the term "complex." They owe their complexity to their harmonics, a phenomenon first mentioned in Chapter 11. A thorough investigation of the subject of harmonics would require a whole battery of mathematical methods, but it would all add up to this fact: the more complex the wave, the greater its number of component harmonics. At one extreme is the simple wave known as the fundamental—the type of wave, approximately, delivered by the power company on its 110 volt a-c line—which has no harmonics. At the other extreme is the perfectly square wave, which has an infinite number of harmonics. Since real life does not admit infinities, there can be no such thing as a perfectly square wave. But the pulse derived by the video detector in a radar receiver is almost square, and is consequently made up of a whole band of frequencies.

It is important for the accuracy of the radar set that the pulse developed at the output of the video detector pass through the following video amplifiers with its wave shape intact. The single stage of video amplification that is enough for most television receivers may

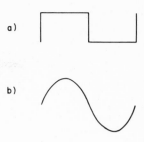

Fig. 15.1. *Square and Fundamental Waves:* **The square wave (a) and the fundamental wave (b) may have the same amplitude and frequency, but they differ in the number of harmonics in each. The perfectly square wave has an infinite number of harmonics; the fundamental wave has none.**

not be enough for a radar receiver. In its basic form, the radar video amplifier resembles the corresponding stage in the television set—but only in its basic form. The skeleton is fleshed out with networks whose purpose is to amplify to a proper degree each component harmonic of the square video pulse.

The end of the sight channel of the radar receiver is the radar tube, which was discussed in Chapter 6. As a general thing, the radar scope very closely parallels the picture tube of the television receiver. The basic construction of both is practically identical; the only difference, and that is slight, is the relative length of time in which the image persists on each: the television tube cannot be permitted to retain the picture of a single frame very long, since another will almost immediately succeed it; the radar scope screen may have a longer persistence.

But the subject of the similarity between these two types of tubes becomes a bit confusing if an attempt is made to pursue it too far. The television tube is limited in its application, and so varies little from one receiver to another. Radar, on the other hand, takes a bewildering variety of forms, and the use of its scopes changes with each. Some of these will be discussed in later pages of this chapter. In the meantime, we might expand our field of knowledge of the radar set's transmitter.

The Radar Transmitter

Timing is extremely important in radar. The master oscillator in the transmitter must deliver its r-f bursts to the antenna at definite intervals of time, and those bursts must last for an equally definite period. Working in close concert with the transmitter is the receiver, which is triggered into action the moment the r-f bursts begin. Since both major parts of the radar set are to be kept in coordination, it is logical that a single circuit

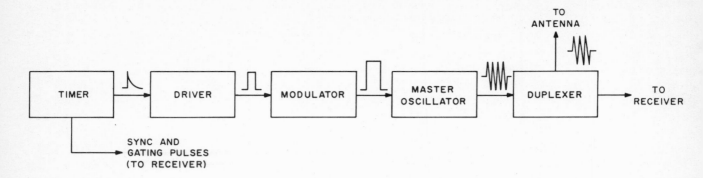

Fig. 15.2. *The Radar Transmitter, Block Diagram:* An oscillator in the timer furnishes square pulses which are differentiated to positive spikes. These trigger the driver to produce square pulses. The modulator amplifies the pulse and unblocks the oscillator which then produces an r-f burst for the duration of the input pulse. In addition to providing pulses for the transmitter, the timer furnishes pulses to the receiver for synchronization.

be responsible for the triggering signals for both. This circuit is appropriately called the *timer.*

If the timer is to be the timekeeper for the entire system, it must be accurate. Hence its most vital stage is an oscillator which can be depended upon to provide an unvarying frequency. In many radar timers, the oscillator is crystal-controlled, its circuit taking a form similar to the schematic of the crystal oscillator shown in Chapter 8. The quartz crystal, serving as the heart of this oscillator, furnishes a weaker voltage than the Rochelle salt crystal encountered so much in audio work; but it is a great deal more stable. When kept in a compartment strictly regulated for temperature and humidity, as it is in many radar transmitters, the crystal maintains a frequency of exceptional regularity.

The wave emerging from the crystal oscillator, however, is not quite ready to perform the triggering the radar set demands. Its frequency may be too high, for one thing; for another, it has substantially the shape of a sine wave, the same smooth-curving type of wave shown earlier in this chapter. Both of these faults can be corrected by a relaxation oscillator like the multivibrator of the preceding chapter. The multivibrator reduces the output frequency of the crystal oscillator by working as a frequency divider. If, for example, the multivibrator has a natural frequency one-fourth that of the crystal oscillator, it will be triggered into a cycle by every fifth peak of the oscillator's wave. Set into beginning one cycle by a first peak, the multivibrator ignores the second, third, and fourth which occur while its single cycle is still in progress, but responds to the fifth, which arrives at just about the end of the multivibrator's natural period. Thus the multivibrator output will have a frequency equal to one-fourth that of the crystal oscillator. Moreover, its output will have a

strictly regulated frequency since it remains under the oscillator's strict supervision.

The sine wave output of the crystal oscillator is not appropriate for triggering because it rises too gradually. What is needed is a sudden, decisive change in voltage, the type of waveform the multivibrator is capable of providing. When this pulse output of the multivibrator is fed into a differentiating circuit, like the one in the preceding chapter, it is converted into a large spike capable of triggering other relaxation oscillators in the timer. As we shall see, the timer must provide wave shapes of various types.

One of these relaxation oscillators, fitted with a differentiator, produces a voltage spike for the next of the line of stages in the radar transmitter, the modulator. The modulator is a circuit built around a tube normally at cutoff. In its normal state, then, the modulator is inactive. When a positive spike from the timer is applied to the modulator tube, the tube is immediately brought out of cutoff, and the circuit goes into action. It is so designed that a square pulse will appear at its output for every spike fed into its input. When amplified in a driver stage, the square pulse is strengthened to the level necessary to trigger the master oscillator.

In the uhf systems of modern radar, the master oscillator is a tube of the type discussed in Chapter 6. All of these tubes can be kept inactive until triggered by the proper pulse. If the radar transmitter is a powerful one, the chances are that its master oscillator will be a magnetron. This tube is essentially a diode, consisting of a heated cathode emitting electrons, and a plate to attract the electrons. The entire action takes place in a magnetic field. By and large, the tube is much different from the simpler diode discussed in Chapter 1. However, the two tubes have this much in common:

if the plate is kept at the same or a lower potential than the cathode, neither can work.

Normally, the plate of the magnetron is kept at a low voltage with respect to the cathode to prevent it from operating. The moment the driver just ahead of it releases its pulse, however, the plate of the magnetron is given a very high positive d-c voltage, the electrons hovering around its hot cathode are hurled in the plate's direction and begin traveling at high speed in their circular paths. The tube is then in oscillation. In effect, the driver is working as an electronic switch, turning the magnetron on almost instantaneously at the beginning of its pulse, and turning it off at the end of the pulse. In the interval between the pulse's leading and trailing edges, when the voltage is constant, the magnetron operates continuously to generate the radar transmitter's main bang.

The stages before the master oscillator handle pulse signals occurring at comparatively low rates, possibly around 200 per second. Although harmonics reaching quite high frequencies go into the makeup of each pulse, those frequencies are never so high as to intrude into the uhf range. Consequently, there is no need for waveguides to interconnect various points in these stages. The main bang output of the master oscillator, however, is a uhf wave, which means that a waveguide is needed to bring the output of the master oscillator into the following stage, the duplexer.

In most radar equipments, both the transmitter and the receiver use the same antenna (Chapter 8). For the transmitter, the antenna serves as a vehicle for propagating the r-f main bang in space; for the receiver, the antenna is used for conducting the returning r-f echoes. However, traffic between the receiver and transmitter on the one hand and the antenna on the other, must be so regulated as to prevent the transmitter main bang from entering the receiver through the latter's input waveguide. That traffic regulation is done electronically by a transmit-receive switch inside the cavity of the duplexer.

The transmit-receive switch is usually a tube partially filled with a chemically inert gas. Inside the tube are two metal electrodes separated by a narrow gap, the two electrodes facing each other across the receiver input waveguide. Under the influence of the master oscillator's main bang, the gas inside the t-r tube ionizes (Chapter 1), and a heavy short-circuiting current flows across the gap between the electrodes, thus sealing off the entrance to the receiver. While the main bang is in progress, then, none of its power can invade and destroy the relatively delicate components of the receiver's input circuits. At the same time, the path between the master oscillator and the antenna is clear. Once the main bang is completed and the t-r tube has had time to recover

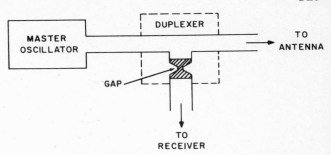

Fig. 15.3. *The Duplexer, Simplified View:* **The shaded area is a gas tube within the wave guide leading to the receiver. When the transmitter main bang goes off, the gas is ionized and a heavy current flows across the gap; the receiver input is therefore short-circuited.**

and revert to its original un-ionized state, the short-circuiting arc disappears, and the path between antenna and receiver is open for the reception of returning echoes.

Introducing Some Radar Terms

All radio waves, from the very lowest to the very highest frequencies, are electromagnetic waves. They thus resemble light, and travel through space at the same rate —approximately 186,000 miles per second. If a radar wave, then, were directed at a target 30 yards away from the transmitter, it would take about six-tenths of a millionth of a second to get to the target and come back as an echo. In radar terminology, the time of travel is six-tenths of a microsecond. This means that the duration of the r-f burst sent out by the transmitter must be *less* than 0.6 microseconds if it is to avoid overlapping the returning pulse. Should any such overlapping take place, the entire echo pulse could not appear on the radar scope. The reason becomes obvious when it is remembered that the receiver is shut off while the main bang is in progress. One cardinal rule can therefore be stated: the *pulse width* must be shorter than the time the radar wave takes to travel to and from the nearest target in the antenna's beam.

Actually, it is in the best interests of the radar transmitter to transmit a short main bang—that is, a narrow pulse—in relation to the time between pulses. Even if the waves sent out from the antenna are concentrated in a narrow-angled beam, the area covered by the beam broadens with increasing range. The target is usually very small compared to this area; even if it should absorb none of the radar energy striking it, as it often does, it will reflect little of that widespread energy back to the antenna. The radar transmitter attempts to balance out this handicap by packing its available

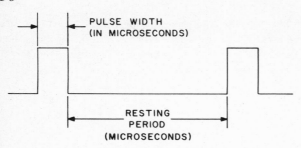

Fig. 15.4. *The Radar Pulse:* The pulse width is the length of time for which the main bang lasts. Ratio of the pulse width to the sum of the pulse width and the resting period is the duty cycle.

power into one swift, short burst, followed by a much longer interval to allow the return of echoes. The ratio of the pulse width, measured in microseconds, to the time between pulses, measured in the same units, is called the *duty cycle* of the transmitter. Since the duration of the main bang is usually quite small, the duty cycle is usually about 1 to 1,000.

The number of main bang pulses loosed by the transmitter in one second is called the pulse repetition frequency, usually abbreviated *prf*. Two things are to be noted about the prf. For one, it is unrelated to the pulse width even though it would seem, from the similarity of the two terms, that there might be some relationship between them. It is completely possible to broaden or narrow the pulse width and still maintain the same prf. And, conversely, it is possible for the radar operator to alter the prf of the transmitter without in the least affecting the pulse width. However, if he chooses to quicken the prf, he must realize that doing so shortens the resting period; and if the resting period is too short, distant echoes from one burst may be swallowed up in the next.

This last sentence indicates that the prf of a radar set is selected with an eye to the radar transmitter's range. If the area searched by the radar beam is a small one, in which the farthest objects within reach of the antenna are fairly close, the prf can be a rapid one. A high prf will mean a narrower resting period, and leave a shorter time for the collection of echoes. But since the echoing objects are not far off, the time of return is short anyway; there is little danger that the echoes for one burst will be drowned out by the following burst. For long range radar, however, care must be taken that the prf is not so high as to shorten the resting period to the point where echoes from distant objects will be choked off. One of the many control knobs in most radar equipments is the prf switch. This switch alters the circuit, and consequently the fre-

quency, of the timer oscillator responsible for triggering the master oscillator through the intervening stages.

The A-Scope

The description of radar equipment given so far in this chapter fits many types, for most radar is of the pulse variety. The real distinction between individuals in this general class is the kind of information each provides, and the kind of display seen on the face of its scope. Since radar scopes—at least, some of them—are designated by letters of the alphabet, we might begin with the type named for the first letter: the A-scope.

Some of the story of the A-scope has already been given in Chapter 6, in the discussion of the oscilloscope. In its ordinary form, the oscilloscope is a test instrument, used by engineers and technicians to observe wave forms. But with little trouble it could be converted into a first-class A-scope. If the oscilloscope can display the wave of an unknown signal, it can also display the blip representing the radar target. To convert the instrument to an A-scope, it is only necessary to connect the output of the radar receiver's video amplifier to the vertically-deflecting plates of the writing tube. Since the voltage applied to the horizontally-deflecting plates of the tube causes a steady movement of the beam across the tube's face, the blip will be written on the fluorescent screen; the practically vertical strokes of the blip in the radar receiver's video signal are drawn by the beam in its vertical movement, while the horizontal stroke marking the top of the blip is sketched by the beam's steady horizontal progression.

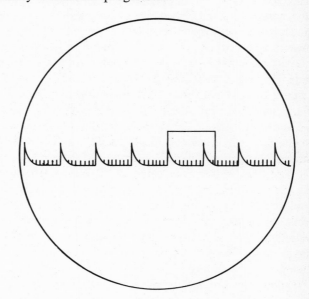

Fig. 15.5. *A-Scope Display:* The square pulse is the target blip, the tall, sharp spikes are cursor pips, and the smaller vertical projections are grass.

However, a blip so displayed can provide no information about the target it represents. It could provide a vital piece of information, if properly handled: the target's range. Since the blip represents the target, the distance measured across the face of the scope from the beginning of the horizontal line on which the blip stands to the blip's leading edge should be a measure of the target range. The display on the scope's face is thus a diagram, in miniature, of the true situation on the surface of the land or sea between the radar set and its target. But if that is true, then the point at the left-hand side of the tube screen—the point at which the beam begins its horizontal journey—should correspond to the position of the radar antenna, the point at which the radar main bang begins its journey to the target.

A-Scope Syncing

The problem, then, is one of synchronization—to start the horizontal sweep of the A-scope's beam at precisely the moment the main bang of the radar transmitter is set off. That problem is easily solved: the same pulse from the timer which is responsible for triggering the transmitter's main bang is also applied to the oscillator in the A-scope responsible for the constantly increasing voltage of the horizontal sweep. But if this horizontal oscillator is to generate its sweep voltage only when triggered by the timing pulse, it cannot be free-running. It must be of the one-shot variety. That is, it must begin its slow, steady climb and subsequent sharp drop only when ordered to do so by the synchronizing pulse, and then must wait patiently in an idle state until it is again commanded to go through the relaxation cycle.

The circuit of this *one-shot multivibrator* is the same as that given in the preceding chapter, with one important exception: the first grid is connected to a highly negative ˙potential rather than to chassis. With one tube thus kept cut off, the circuit is incapable of oscillating. But if a high-peaked spike pulse from a differentiator circuit in the timer should be applied to that first grid, the tube will immediately be brought out of cutoff, and the circuit can then go into its cycle. A similar scheme can be used to convert the blocking oscillator of the preceding chapter into a one-shot circuit. Both multivibrators and blocking oscillators, in one form or another, figure prominently in radar circuits.

Besides the voltages applied to the horizontal and vertical deflecting plates of the A-scope, a voltage is also applied to the control grid of its electron gun. When the beam of the A-scope finishes its horizontal sweep across the tube face, it swings quickly back to its starting point as the sweep oscillator relaxes. In its return, however, it will produce a trace on the scope screen unless it is cut off. This automatic shutdown of the writing beam is the function of the synchronizing *gating* pulse.

Gating

"Blanking" may serve well enough as a technical term for the television engineer. But the radar engineer prefers "gating" to describe the kind of pulsed voltage applied to the A-scope control grid. The gating pulse must also be synchronized with the other pulses in the equipment; it therefore originates in the timer. At the instant the scope beam reaches the end of its scan, a negative pulse from one of the oscillators in the timer is immediately clapped to the control grid of the scope. This gating pulse is negative enough to drive the tube into cutoff and throttle the beam. It will stay negative, furthermore, throughout the retrace time, and will not change until the sweep circuit is ready to drive the beam into a second left-to-right trace. When the beam begins that trace, the gating pulse turns into a positive-phased signal, allowing the scope beam to reach the screen once more in order to sketch the target blip. The reason for the "gating" term is now clear: the pulses of the gating signal swing an electronic gate open for the scope beam when the beam is in its blip-sketching phase, and slam the gate shut on the beam when its scan is, for the moment, finished.

All these pulses and gates must work in precise synchronization. The timer pulse, put through the various stages between the timer and the master oscillator, triggers the main bang. At the same instant, the sweep multivibrator is triggered to begin the sweep of the A-scope beam. And still at that very same instant, a positively-phased gating pulse is applied to the control grid of the scope. As the microseconds tick by, the target echo returns to the receiver, and the blip is traced by the A-scope scanning beam. When the scan is ended, the negative gating pulse snaps off the beam and the sweep oscillator returns to inactivity. There may then occur, for some fleeting interval, an instant of complete inertia. But at its end, the timer emits another pulse, and the whole simultaneous cycle of main bang, sweep trigger, and gating begins again.

The Cursor

With every part of the radar set working smoothly, its operator will observe a blip representing the target. The blip will move to or from the point at which the beam begins its horizontal sweep, depending on whether the target moves toward or away from the radar unit. The problem of determining how far, in actual units of distance, the target is from the radar antenna is worked out with the aid of a *cursor*, a transparent horizontal scale overlaying the face of the A-scope. Since the line of the horizontal sweep represents in miniature the actual distance outward from the antenna, the cursor is often subdivided into units of miles. This method allows the radar set operator to determine the target range by checking the cursor subdivision coinciding with the leading edge of the blip. Observing, for example, that the leading edge of the blip appears at the 5 mark on a cursor graded in miles, the operator knows that his target is five miles off.

But a mechanical cursor of this type has its limitations; a far superior and more accurate method is purely electronic. In this system, a marker voltage of equally spaced spikes is added to the video signal feeding the vertically-deflecting plates of the A-scope. Suppose, for example, that the frequency of the relaxation oscillator controlling the sweep of the A-scope is 1,000 cycles per second. A second oscillator of ten times that frequency will deliver 10 pulses for every one delivered by the sweep oscillator. If a differentiator is fitted to the output of this second oscillator, the circuit will deliver ten voltage spikes for every horizontal sweep of the A-scope beam. When the output of the differentiator is fed, along with the video signal, to the vertically-deflecting plates of the A-scope, the beam will have to hop vertically up and drop back to the sweep line ten times for every horizontal movement of the beam. Thus the horizontal trace, as seen on the scope, will show ten equally spaced spikes in addition to the target blip. These spikes, known as *marker pips*, serve nicely as a cursor.

If the width of the trace on the A-scope represents ten miles of actual distance, and there are ten equally spaced pips on the trace, then the distance between each pip corresponds to one mile. However, it is important that the first of the marker pips match exactly the point at which the sweep begins and so serve as a zero-range reference. A housewife uses this same procedure when she carefully matches the zero line of a yardstick to the end of a strip of cloth she wants to measure. But while the housewife makes that match without the aid of a scientific instrument, the radar set makes it accurately through an arrangement in which the signal triggering the sweep also triggers the marker oscillator. This triggering signal is also provided by the timer.

Ideally, the A-scope display should show only the target blip and the cursor pips. But this is an idle dream. Along with desired signals come undesired ones, such as noise generated in the receiver tubes and other parts of the circuits, which show up in the display as a kind of clipped fuzz stretching along the horizontally swept line. Because this noise manifestation looks like grass, it is called, appropriately enough, "grass." Radar units mounted on board a seagoing vessel also display another form of grassy-looking interference known as *sea return*, for the obvious reason that it is caused by echoes from waves.

Search and Tracking

There was a time when a naval commander followed enemy movements with his binoculars. It was a useful method, except that it could only be done if the enemy was fairly close and if visibility was at least average. Given these favorable conditions, the observing officer peered through his glasses, swept them back and forth over the horizon, and if he spotted any of the enemy ships in his vicinity, kept his gaze intently on them while he fed orders to his aides out of the corner of his mouth. The vessels under his command were then deployed accordingly.

In modern naval tactics, in which machine is pitted against machine, binoculars have given way to radar; but although the instrument of naval reconnaissance has changed, the method has not. The modern commander has his radar sweep the horizon in what is known as the *search mode*. When the enemy has been spotted, the radar set slips automatically into the *tracking mode* in which the radar antenna follows every movement of its prey with the keen eye of a predatory bird.

The automatic changeover from one mode to another can be electronically achieved through a sort of giant feedback loop in which part of the voltage output of the radar receiver agc circuit is fed back to an electromechanical device controlling the antenna. Like any agc or avc circuit, that in the radar receiver furnishes a d-c voltage proportional to the strength of the received signal. As long as the target remains in the focus of the antenna's r-f beam, the received signal is strong, and the system keeps the antenna where it is. An attempt on the part of the target to dodge the antenna's glare is reflected in reduced signal strength. Thus notified that the hunted prize may be lost, the system readjusts the antenna to keep it bearing full on the enemy. Regardless of the enemy ship's efforts to elude the radar-equipped attacking vessel, the radar antenna is always pointed in its direction. With the A-scope of the radar giving precise information on the enemy's range, the attacker now has all the information he needs—the direction and range of the target—and can lay his guns with precision. And this without regard to conditions of visibility, for the radar antenna sees just as well by night as it does by day, and is immune to fog.

Friend or Foe?

Radar can thus be a powerful weapon in time of war. But like all weapons it can be a means of self-destruction. The blip representing an enemy vessel is exactly like the blip of a friendly one. Obviously the commander of the radar-equipped ship cannot simply blaze away at every target his radar screen shows; he had better ask a few questions first, and he had better ask them discreetly.

He asks them through his radar. Instead of having the transmitter eject bursts of constant length, he sets it for a series of main bangs in a particular pattern—a code known to the other ships in his fleet. He may, to choose a simple example, send the letter G of the International Code (Chapter 7), which consists of a long burst, a second burst of equal length, and finally a short burst. It is true that the second or third burst may obliterate the echoes from the first, but the radar operator is not interested in echoes this time. He is waiting for a reply from the target.

He will get a reply if the target has a device known as a *transponder*, or radar beacon, on board, and if the transponder has been set to the G signal code. At the input to the transponder is a gating circuit; the gate may be nothing more than an amplifier with an integrator at its input. The amplifier is normally at cutoff; but with the two long and the single short pulses piled up on its grid as a positive voltage, the amplifier is brought out of cutoff and triggers the transmitter of the device. The transmitter, in an entirely automatic manner, returns the friendly G signal, which appears on the A-scope of the querying vessel's radar as two wide blips and a narrow one; both crews can then breathe sighs of relief. This is the famous IFF system—identification, friend or foe—which was developed in World War II and is still used.

Countermeasures

When the military sciences asked for the help of the natural sciences, they got it, but at the price of being swallowed up. Military strategy is no longer a match of wits between general staffs but a struggle in ingenuity between opposing groups of scientists. The process is a simple one: our side invents a gadget that may overpower their side; their side gets busy to invent an anti-gadget which will reduce ours to impotence; we get wind of their scheme and invent an anti-anti-gadget; and so on.

The progress of radar has been moving precisely along this pattern. When naval vessels began to fall prey to the searching and tracking radar, fleet admirals began to equip their dreadnoughts with countermeasure devices designed to thwart the spying electromagnetic waves. Most of these devices were themselves electronic in nature, and so were known as *electronic countermeasures*, or ECM equipment. A common type is simply a transmitter which sends out random pulses—electrical noise covering a large range of frequencies. A hostile radar unit trained on a ship with ECM equipment on board will have more pulses returned to it than it bargained for. In addition to the echoes, on which the hostile radar depends for its information, a whole host of utterly meaningless pulses swarm into the receiver. Its poor operator can make no sense of the stately procession of blips marching across his radar scope.

An even simpler countermeasures method is *chaff*. To a farmer, chaff is the featherweight, useless stuff that is the waste product of threshing. To the military tactician, chaff is a quantity of thin strips of aluminum foil which may be light in weight but is far from being useless. An aircraft under the eye of an enemy radar simply releases its store of chaff and flies safely off behind the curtain of the bright, shimmering flakes drifting slowly downward like so much confetti. The enemy radar gets its echoes, but not from the elusive craft. It will instead get as many echo pulses as there are chaff strips. A sophisticated type of chaff dispenser is controlled electronically. The first main bang of the enemy radar obligingly trips an electronic gate on the dispenser, the dispenser opens, and the chaff is released. This ingenious device literally tricks the enemy radar into throwing dust into its own eye.

The PPI Scope

Although the radar set using a PPI scope (Chapter 6) is not a search-track equipment, it is still pulse radar, and shares the family characteristics of that electronic clan. Whatever differences exist between PPI and A-type radar arise from the designs of the two scope tubes. Where the A-scope usually uses electrostatic deflection—the system of moving the writing beam by means of the electric field existing between parallel plates—the PPI scope uses electromagnetic deflection, in which the writing movements of the beam are guided by a magnetic field; where the video signal at the output of the receiver is fed to the vertical deflecting plates of the A-scope, the output video is fed to the control grid of the PPI tube.

In most radar equipments, there is some sort of

connecting link between the scope and the antenna. Consequently, the difference between the A-scope and the PPI should also be reflected in the actions of their antennas. This, as we have seen, is true. While the antenna of the former may make a circuit of the neighboring land, sea, or sky area in its search mode, it will settle down to perhaps even a motionless state once it has caught its target and begins tracking it. The PPI antenna, on the other hand, never varies from its constant rotation.

Aside from these head- and tail-end differences, however, the two systems are practically identical. The lineup of stages in both is the same, and the sync and gating signals through which the timer in each controls the operation of the systems are just about interchangeable.

In the PPI system, the triggering spike through which the timer sets off the main bang is also sent to the relaxation oscillator controlling the current through the deflection coils. The PPI scope beam thus sets out from the center of the scope to its outer rim at precisely the same instant the r-f of the main bang is radiated from the antenna. Returned echoes appear on the control grid of the PPI scope in the form of video pulses, and the intensity of the writing beam changes in accordance with these pulses. Thus the beam sketches the bright and dark elements of one small sector of the scanned area.

When the beam has ended its one-line trip, the relaxation oscillator controlling it goes into its abrupt decline. At that precise moment, a highly negative gating pulse is sent from the timer to the PPI scope control grid and the tube is cut off. And it should be; for the beam, in returning to its center position, will show an interfering trace on the scope face unless it is blotted

out. The gating pulse will not go into its positive phase until the beam is ready to start another scan. Then the gate opens, the beam is allowed to strike the PPI screen, and a second scan is made.

The problem of setting up a cursor for the measurement of range is solved for the PPI radar just as it is for the A-scope—by an oscillator which goes through several cycles in the time the sweep oscillator takes for one. There is an important difference, however. In the PPI system, the cursor spikes are applied to the control grid of the scope, and usually in their positive phase. For every spike which occurs as the writing beam begins its outward movement from the tube face center, the beam will brighten to produce brilliant and equally-spaced points. The next line it scans will also have similar points. Since every one of these cursor points is marked off equally from the center of the tube face for every scanned radius, a series of concentric rings will appear on the PPI face once the whole circular area is scanned. The radial distance between the circles represents some corresponding length in miles of the actual mapped surface. Thus the operator of the equipment can measure real distances on the mapped image at a glance.

This cursor oscillator also is triggered by the transmitter timer. It would have to be to make its first spike the zero reference point. The position of the radar antenna on the scope image is at the center of the display; thus the first cursor pip occurs at the point of zero range. Furthermore, it is precisely because the cursor oscillator is synchronized to the sweep oscillator that the bright cursor points can form perfect circles. If the cursor oscillator were allowed to run without synchronization, there would be little correspondence between points on successive scanned lines, and the symmetrical pattern of circles would degenerate into a drunken scrawl.

Antenna-Scope Correlation

The cursor is one improvement that can be made on the PPI scope as it was originally presented in Chapter 6. Another is the coordination of the antenna and the scope writing beam to give the map on the scope face a desired orientation. As we found in that chapter, the rotation of the antenna is kept in step with the rotation of the beam's radially scanned lines around the tube face. But, for any instant, how is one to be directed with respect to the other?

There are several ways to answer that question, depending on how the radar operator wants to see his PPI map. If he wants it to appear as any map would, with north at the top, east at the right, south at the bottom, and west to the left, both antenna and scanning

Fig. 15.6. *The PPI Display:* **The circles are cursor markings. Usually the cursor circles are brighter than the mapped area.**

beam will have to be set according to compass directions. Thus, at the very moment the antenna points north, the scanning beam moves towards the top of the screen; when the antenna has rotated to the east, the beam will have changed to a scan to the right; and so on.

But the radar operator may want to see the map in relation to the direction of movement of his ship, so that an imaginary vertical diameter on the PPI face will exactly coincide with the nose-to-tail line of his aircraft. Such a PPI display can facilitate navigation. Having spotted his point of destination on the PPI map, the pilot turns his aircraft until that point, rotating on the screen, assumes a position directly above the center. The pilot then holds his craft along that line. As the ship wings its way forward, his destination moves towards the center of the PPI screen until, when the landing is finally made, the two points coincide.

The PPI scope can be set up either way. For a compass-oriented display, the beam scans vertically upwards from the center of the tube face at the moment the antenna is pointed north; for a fore-and-aft display, the beam scans vertically upward at the moment the antenna points in the direction of the ship's nose.

Doppler Radar

The system of pulsed radar, to which we have confined ourselves so far, carries so many advantages that a non-professional might be deceived into thinking that it is the only kind of radar in existence. But in these days of airborne vehicles traveling at tremendous rates, a type of continuous wave radar suited to detecting high-speed objects has emerged. This system is known as Doppler radar, named for the discoverer of the physical principle on which it is based.

The observations made by Doppler which led to his principle have been repeated many times since the early day in which he worked. What motorist, for example, has not heard the horn of a car speeding by him in the opposite direction and noticed the drop in pitch of its tone from a cheery blast to a trailing snarl as the car shot by? This is the Doppler principle in action: the frequency of a wave motion decreases when the source moves away from the observer. Its converse is also true: when the source approaches a stationary point, an observer at that point detects an increase in the frequency. If the principle holds for sound waves, it is also holds for electromagnetic waves.

It is in the realm of electromagnetic waves that the Doppler radar is used. Here, as distinct from pulse radar in which there is just a single antenna, two antennas are the general rule. The transmitter radiates its continuous, unmodulated waves from one of the

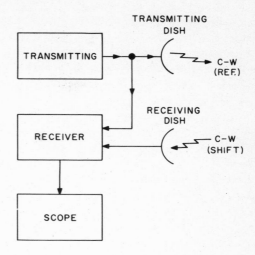

Fig. 15.7. Doppler C-W Radar, Basic Block Diagram: A continuous wave of constant frequency and amplitude is radiated. When reflected by a moving target, the echo wave is changed in frequency. The frequencies of the output and input waves are compared in the receiver, and an indication of the difference frequency is shown on the scope.

antennas, and at the same time sends part of its radiation to the receiver. Returning echoes of the wave from a target are picked up by the receiver antenna. If the target is speeding towards the installation, the frequency of the echo signal is higher than the frequency of the transmitted signal; or, if the target is moving away from the radar, the echo frequency is lower. An FM detector in the receiver solves for the frequency difference between the incident and reflected waves, and the result is shown on a scope display. The display informs the operator as to whether the target is moving towards or away from the radar installation—a piece of information determined by the frequency of the returned signal relative to the transmitted frequency— and just what the velocity of the moving target is.

Usually, the receiver and transmitter in the Doppler radar are situated some distance apart. With both antenna dishes focused on the target—usually by an automatic system—the operator can determine its position and range through the angles made by the antennas. Thus the Doppler radar rivals the pulse radar in acquiring target data.

The one disadvantage of the Doppler system, its inability to respond to a stationary target, is oddly enough a definite asset. Pulse radar shows a blip for the target, but it also shows blips for unmoving objects between the target and itself. These false blips, known as *clutter*, can be understandably annoying. For the Doppler radar, however, clutter is no problem. As long as the interfering object stands still, it has no existence for the Doppler unit; the frequency of the wave it reflects is exactly equal to the frequency of the wave which strikes it. The Doppler receiver then detects a zero frequency difference and the scope cannot respond.

GLOSSARY

A-scope.   A radar scope giving target range information.

Chaff.   Strips of aluminum foil used as camouflage against tracking radar.

Clutter.   False blips on an A-scope.

Cursor.   An electronic device for measuring range.

Doppler radar.   A type of radar used for the detection of rapidly moving objects.

Duty cycle.   The ratio of pulse width to the period between pulses in radar equipment.

ECM.   Electronic countermeasures; electronic equipment for jamming enemy radar.

Frequency divider.   A circuit which reduces the frequency of an oscillator.

Gating pulse.   A pulse which permits the operation of a circuit.

Grass.   The visible evidence of electrical noise in an A-scope display.

IFF.   Identification, friend or foe; a method of challenge and identification through radar.

Marker pips.   The pulses produced by a cursor oscillator.

Microsecond.   A millionth of a second; a time interval often used in electronics.

Modulator.   The stage in a transmitter which varies the wave shape of the master oscillator output.

One-shot multivibrator.   A multivibrator which goes through only one cycle when triggered.

Prf.   Pulse repetition frequency; the number of pulses made by the radar transmitter per second.

Prf switch.   The switch in the radar set which governs the pulse rate frequency.

Pulse width.   The time duration in microseconds, of the pulse.

Quartz crystal.   A piezoëlectric crystal which regulates an oscillator frequency.

Radar beacon.   A radar transmitter which automatically responds to a transmitted radar pulse.

Rise time.   The time, in microseconds, taken by a pulse to rise from zero to its maximum level.

Sea return.   Interference on the scope of a sea-going radar set caused by reflections from waves.

Search mode.   The operation of a radar set scouting for enemy craft.

Sine wave.   A perfectly formed electromagnetic wave with no harmonics.

Square wave.   A wave of rectangular shape.

Timer.   The stages in the radar transmitter which control the synchronization function.

Tracking mode.   The operation of a radar set following the progress of an enemy ship.

Transponder.   Same as radar beacon.

Chapter Sixteen

TRANSMITTERS

COMMUNICATION AT a distance has been practiced for just about as long as the human race has existed on earth. Some of the methods used by ancient man are still relied upon in isolated corners of the globe when one tribesman wants to communicate with a comrade out of the reach of his voice. He may, in the fashion of our own plains Indians, use smoke signalling—in the language of modern electronics, a method of communication through smoke pulsing. Or, if visibility is obscured, he may try beating a drum in a coded rhythm —communication through sound pulsing. Both these systems have the dual advantages of ease of operation and low cost, in terms of labor if not money. If it weren't for their severe limitations, we might be using them yet.

The telegraph and telephone—both electrical devices, incidentally—were effective in removing those limitations; but they were still unsatisfactory. Laying cable was a troublesome and expensive procedure; a system of communication without wires between the sender of the message and its recipient would have been ideal. But how was such a wireless method possible? Guglielmo Marconi provided the answer with a fantastic experiment, performed shortly after the start of the present century. He successfully transmitted a wireless message across the Atlantic Ocean. And it *was* a fantastic experiment for those times. Even from our present vantage point, with the atomic and space age in full swing, the boldness of the attempt is still breathtaking.

Marconi's amazing breakthrough proved that wireless transmission across long distances was possible. But the telegraphic form of the messages transmitted was far from the dreams the experiment had stirred, and engineers began looking for the next breakthrough—

the wireless transmission of the human voice. Nothing could be done in that direction, however, with the materials then available. Above all, what was needed was an amplifier. When, some five years after the transatlantic experiment, Lee de Forest presented his triode to the world, the dream was on its way to reality. It was not long afterwards that the first experimental AM transmitter was set up.

Transmitters in General

In this day of efficient electronic communicating systems, equipment has become so stabilized that only minor improvements are necessary. Every transmitter, for example, has the same basic structure; and this is true regardless of the system involved.

The first requirement is generating a carrier wave of so high a frequency that it can be efficiently handled by small components and can span large distances. But no mechanical generator can be entrusted with that task. The generators used in modern power stations can rotate comfortably at the rate of 60 revolutions per second to create an alternating voltage of 60 cycles per second. But those same generators could not possibly be used to produce even the lowest of practical radio frequencies; they could never survive the fantastic spin rate of some 600,000 revolutions every second. Only an electronic device which has no moving parts can do the job. That electronic device—we have seen some samples of it in Chapter 8—is the oscillator. Because it enjoys a commanding position in the transmitter, the oscillator which generates the carrier is termed the *master oscillator*.

Although the master oscillator can supply an a-c

voltage of the required frequency, it cannot be depended upon to supply it in sufficient strength. To give its signal the required power, then, it must be followed by a series of amplifiers. The last of these stages is called the *final*, for the obvious reason that it is the ultimate electronic circuit before the antenna. In a sense, the final stage of the transmitter is like those "last chance" gasoline stations the Western travelers sees on desert roads; it furnishes the last powerful push to the carrier before it is applied to the antenna for its long journey into space.

The master oscillator, its subsequent amplifiers, and the final are the necessary stages for a powerful carrier, but they contribute nothing to the meaningful signal the carrier is meant to transport. That meaningful signal—some engineers refer to it as the *intelligence* —is impressed on the carrier by the modulator stage. The design of the modulator depends on the system of transmission. For the interrupted continuous wave transmitter, in which intelligence is introduced by chopping the carrier up into short dots or longer dashes (Chapter 7), the modulator is little more than a switch —a telegraph key usually controlled by the operator's fingers, and sometimes controlled by automatic means. In the pulsed radar transmitter, where the intelligence is more subtle, the modulator is still a switch, but it is

more sophisticated, as the preceding chapter shows.

Such simple on-off switching modulators, however, are of no use in the three major communications systems everybody knows—AM radio, FM radio, and television. In these systems, the intelligence is a complex audio signal or a much more complex video signal. AM radio demands that the audio intelligence be impressed on the carrier by varying the carrier peaks without at the same time altering its frequency; FM radio reverses the procedure by having the audio signal change the frequency of the carrier without disturbing the carrier's amplitude. These are the activities which the modulators in each type of transmitter performs. Working in the AM transmitter, the modulator is given an audio signal, and operates on the carrier to change its amplitude accordingly. The FM modulator is furnished with the same type of audio signal, but uses it to vary the carrier's frequency. And in the TV transmitter, which broadcasts two carriers, there is a video modulator to convert the picture carrier to an amplitude-modulated wave, and an audio modulator to convert the sound carrier to a frequency-modulated wave.

The modulators in these familiar broadcasting systems must be supplied with the proper signal materials. Sound is the desired energy form in AM and FM radio, but sound itself cannot be used to operate in an electrical

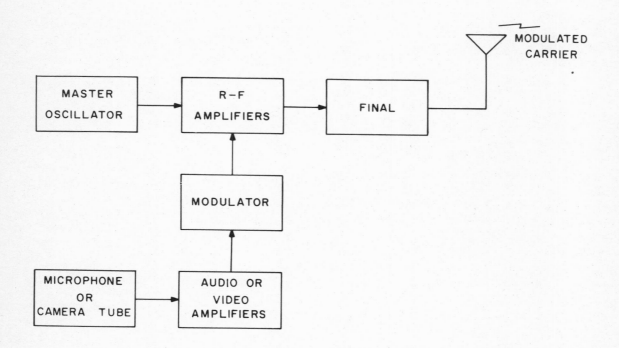

Fig. 16.1. *General Block Diagram of the Transmitter:* Audio or video signals from the microphone or camera tube are amplified and impressed by the modulator on the carrier generated by the oscillator. The modulator carrier is amplified in the final stages and is put on the antenna for transmission.

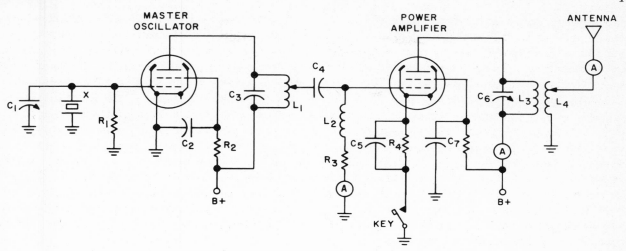

Fig. 16.2. *MOPA:* The master oscillator is regulated by a quartz crystal (X), C_1 is a fine-tuning capacitor, and R_1 the grid leak. Resonant circuits L_1-C_3, L_3-C_6, are tuned to the crystal frequency. The circles labeled "A" represent tuning ammeters. The key breaks the cathode circuit of the power amplifier. Schematic diagrams are usually laid out to indicate a left-to-right movement of the signal; thus, in this diagram, the oscillator circuit originating the signal is at the left, and the antenna is at the right.

system. It must first be transformed to its electrical audio equivalent by a microphone. Emerging from the microphone in rather a weak form—certainly too weak to drive the modulator—the audio signal is put through several stages of audio amplification; the first may actually be in the microphone housing. It is now strong enough to operate the modulator properly and be impressed upon the carrier.

This same setup of microphone plus audio amplifiers is the rule in the sound part of the television transmitter. For the picture part, in which light is the desired form of energy, a different sequence of events takes place. The light reflected from the objects to be televised must first be converted to electrical form by the image orthicon. This vacuum tube, first encountered in Chapter 6, is the prime occupant of a TV camera housing which also contains a preamplifier. Although the electron multiplier system in the image orthicon furnishes a good picture signal, that signal is still not strong enough to do much work. Hence the preamplifier. As a result of its operation, the signal conducted out of the camera along the camera's cables is a strong one which varies in intensity with the dark and bright elements of the televised image.

But the picture signal is only one of the three elements that make up the television video signal. The second and third elements, the blanking and sync pulses, must be added before the whole ensemble can be brought to the video modulator. Timing is of utmost importance in TV work; the blanking and synchronizing pulses are therefore shaped in accurately controlled pulse generators, and are inserted in their correct places in the picture signal. The completed video signal is conducted to the modulator, and the latter varies the amplitude of the picture carrier accordingly.

With the exception of radar, covered in the preceding chapter, these transmitters will be given closer scrutiny in the paragraphs that follow.

The CW Transmitter

The term "continuous wave" applied to the communications transmitter is not as accurate as it might be. True, the wave put out by the transmitter is unchanged in amplitude and frequency; in that sense it is continuous. But when a meaningful signal is introduced the output wave from the equipment's antenna is interrupted at intervals demanded by the letter groups of the International Code. "Interrupted continuous wave" would be a more precise description of the system's operation mode.

With no modulation to worry about, the designer of the CW transmitter has a relatively easy task. Quite a serviceable though simple transmitter can be built of only two stages plus, of course, a power supply. The first stage is a master oscillator, and the second a power amplifier, usually abbreviated MO and PA respectively. The whole, consequently, is known to radio amateurs —and professionals—as a MOPA transmitter.

The MOPA shown here in schematic form has a

crystal-controlled master oscillator of almost exactly the same form as that shown in Chapter 8. In the plate circuit of the MO is a resonant circuit (C_3, L_1) in which the capacitor is fixed, but the coil tuned, as the arrowhead at the schematic representation of the coil indicates. When this resonant circuit is properly set, the resonant frequency of the circuit is almost the same as the crystal frequency. The operator uses the available meters to determine this setting. In tuning the transmitter, he tries to squeeze the ultimate in power out of the oscillator—a task in which he is aided by a d-c ammeter connected in the grid circuit of the PA.

In the PA grid circuit is a grid leak (R_3) and an air-core choke (L_2). The positive peaks of the oscillator output r-f drive the grid of the power amplifier positive, and current is drawn in the grid circuit. The choke opposes the high frequency a-c current drawn, but has no effect on the d-c current. As the coil in the plate circuit of the master oscillator is tuned to resonance, the grid current increases, and the ammeter reflects this increase by a greater reading. When the ammeter needle has risen to its maximum and the operator can get no more out of it, the plate circuit of the MO is properly tuned. However, this tuning cannot be accomplished if the key in the cathode circuit of the PA is left open. With the cathode circuit incomplete, the PA circuit won't work, and the d-c ammeter will show a reading of zero. Hence the key is kept closed during the tuning process.

The d-c current flowing through the grid leak resistor of the power amplifier puts a negative bias across the resistor. With the circuit working normally, this bias voltage is more negative than cutoff, which means that the power amplifier is operating class C (Chapter 4), and is thus given the advantage of superior efficiency which this type of operation affords. The varying component of the plate current in the tube consists only of pulses rather than complete cycles. But the resonant circuit in the power amplifier (C_6, L_3) takes care of that through its flywheel effect. As we have noted at several points in this book, a tank circuit—the informal term often given to such coil-capacitor combinations—converts powerful electrical pulses into complete cycles of alternating voltage, just as a heavy flywheel will go through several complete rotations under the influence of a single push.

To get the best performance from the transmitter, the PA plate circuit tank must be correctly tuned. The ammeter, a d-c instrument, is helpful in determining the resonant point of the circuit. As resonance is approached by the variable capacitor in the circuit, the d-c component of the plate current drops off. Theoretically, this current should be equal to zero at resonance; the best the operator can hope for, however, is a very low reading. He therefore rotates the capacitor knob

slowly, watching the meter all the while, and releases the knob at the point at which the meter reading is a minimum.

The final step in the transmitter tuning procedure is a tune-up of the antenna. Transformer coupling (L_3, L_4) links the output of the power amplifier with the antenna to carry the r-f energy out into space. This r-f output transformer, between the final stage of the transmitter and the radiating antenna, has its parallel in the audio output transformer between the last stage of a receiver and the radiating speaker. If one of the functions of the audio output transformer is to match the final receiver audio stage to the loudspeaker, the r-f output transformer in the transmitter has the comparable function of matching the PA stage to the antenna. Since different frequencies will demand a different type of match, the secondary of the antenna transformer (L_4) is tunable. A third ammeter is placed in the antenna circuit to aid in the tuning process. This ammeter, however, is an a-c type since the current surging through the antenna is an a-c current of high frequency; its reading is a measure of the generative power of the transmitter. In setting the L_4 tap—represented in the schematic by the arrowhead—the operator keeps a hopeful eye on the antenna meter, and quits his tuning when the ammeter needle is at its maximum point. He then knows that his antenna is radiating r-f at its healthiest.

In this part of the tuning process, as in the others, the key is held down to keep the PA in operation. Once the tuning procedure is over with, the key is in its normal broken-contact position, and ready for use. Communication begins when the operator starts his rhythmic pressure and release of the key to make or break the cathode circuit of the PA. During the interval in which the key is depressed, the cathode circuit is complete, the PA can work, and a train of waves goes out over the air. The moment the key is released, the power amplifier stage is deadened, and no transmission can take place.

The AM Transmitter

By operating to change the carrier, even if that change is the elementary one of switching the carrier on and off, the key in the CW transmitter fulfils the definition of modulator. The change in the carrier involved in ampliture modulation, however, is a more difficult one. Here, the function of the modulator is to increase and decrease the peaks of the carrier to comply with the dictates of an audio signal.

One common method is that of plate modulation, in which the secondary winding of an iron-core transformer is connected between the plate of one of the r-f amplifiers and its B+ feed point of the transmitter power

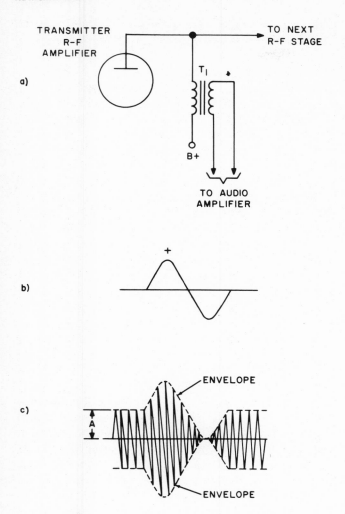

a)

b)

c)

Fig. 16.3. *Amplitude Modulation:* **The simplified schematic of plate modulation is shown in (a). One cycle of modulating audio is shown in (b). The resulting modulated r-f appears in (C); A is the amplitude of the unmodulated wave.**

tude of the carrier also hits its largest peak. As the amplitude of the audio signal falls off, the peaks of the carrier also fall off.

The process continues while the audio signal enters its negative phase. Before reaching its negative peak, however, the audio voltage is still smaller than the B+ supply. Hence the net voltage at the plate is still positive, and the r-f amplifier is still capable of operating. If we make a further assumption that the amplitude of the audio signal is equal to the B+ voltage, we have a situation in which the audio signal, at its negative peak, is exactly equal to the B+ voltage. Then the audio voltage is equal and opposite to the B+ level, and the net voltage on the plate of the r-f amplifier is zero. Under this condition, the r-f amplifier cannot work, and the carrier output vanishes. Such a situation is referred to as 100 percent modulation.

Finally, as the audio signal pulls out of its negative peak and begins once more to rise, the net voltage on the plate of the r-f amplifier becomes increasingly positive, and the carrier peaks begin to grow. This system, in which the audio is introduced at the plate of an r-f amplifier in the transmitter, is sometimes known as Heising modulation, after its inventor. There is a similar method of modulation in which the audio signal is introduced at the grid of the transmitter's r-f amplifier. In either case, the result is the same. The carrier is molded so that its envelope—the curve formed by its wave peaks—is the same shape as the audio signal. This is precisely the way the AM wave was shown when it was first introduced in Chapter 3.

The FM Transmitter

In commercial AM transmitters, the master oscillator is almost always a quartz crystal oscillator of the type shown earlier in this chapter. The crystal assures the carrier's adherence to its assigned frequency. Hence it is usually kept in a sealed box, uniformly heated so that it will remain on frequency with as little error as possible.

This same method is used for FM transmitters, which may seem a bit odd since the very nature of FM demands that its carrier be varied in frequency, and a crystal oscillator's frequency remains fixed. Yet the fact is that the first of the practical FM transmitters, designed by Armstrong, used a master oscillator which was crystal-controlled. The scheme of this transmitter was a complicated one. It did not attempt to change the frequency of the master oscillator directly, but changed the *phase* of the wave so that one cycle would occur a little earlier or later than it should under the influence of the audio signal. Thus, if one of the cycles in the wave train is caused by the modulating audio signal to

supply. The primary of the transformer is connected to the output of the last stage of audio amplification. To keep the explanation of the process simple, we assume that the studio microphone of the transmitter picks up a tone consisting of a perfect sine wave of one cycle. If we assume also that the audio amplifier of the transmitter is without distortion, the wave emerging from the last audio stage will have this perfect form, and the wave coupled into the secondary will be similarly blessed. Now, as the audio signal in the secondary of the transformer rises toward its positive peak, it adds to the B+ voltage fed to the plate of the transmitter r-f amplifier. With an added plate voltage, the amplifying ability of the r-f amplifier tube increases, and the amplitude of the carrier grows correspondingly greater. When the audio signal is at its most positive, the ampli-

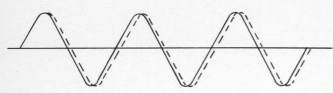

Fig. 16.4. *Phase Modulation:* **The peaks of the phase-modulated signal (solid line) occur earlier than they would if the wave were unmodulated (dashed line). Hence they are compressed, and the frequency of the wave is increased—there are more cycles per unit of time.**

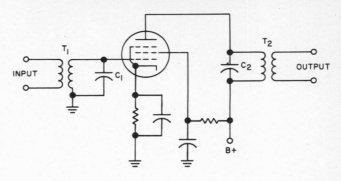

Fig. 16.5. *The Frequency Multiplier:* **The resonant circuit of C_1 and the secondary winding of transformer T_1 is resonant to the frequency of the input signal; the plate circuit of C_2 and the primary winding of T_2 are resonant to a harmonic of the input signal.**

follow the preceding one after a shorter interval of time than the crystal oscillator calls for, the two cycles are compressed together. By the same token, if a cycle is slightly delayed in following the cycle ahead of it, the two are spread further apart. The final effect of this phase advance or delay of one cycle with respect to the next is to produce a wave which is compressed at one part of its train and is spread apart at another. This, as shown in Chapter 7, is typical of an FM wave.

The one difficulty which faced the Armstrong system is that the phase modulation—the variation of the carrier phase through the audio signal—could not be made too large if distortion were to be avoided. That, in turn, meant that the modulating audio signal had to be kept low; the receiver, at the other end of the communication system, would then have to have a large number of audio amplifier stages to rebuild the audio to its normal strength. To get around this difficulty, Armstrong had his phase-modulated wave feed into *frequency multipliers*. These circuits, essentially amplifiers, multiply the frequency of the modulated signal by as much as 36 times, thus providing several advantages. First, they permit the use of a master oscillator of low frequency; the signal from an oscillator of 3 mc, for example, would emerge after this kind of multiplication with a frequency of 108 mc. But a second and even more important advantage of the multiplier stages is that the weak frequency deviations in the modulated signal are also multiplied by the same amount. Thus, as the r-f signal finally leaves the transmitter's antenna, the impress of the audio signal on it is a powerful one.

The Frequency Multiplier

Modern FM transmitters are equipped with a simpler setup than the Armstrong system. The newer method varies the frequency of the master oscillator wave *directly* rather than through the roundabout system of phase modulation. This newer arrangement also involves the use of frequency multipliers; an explanation of the frequency multiplier circuit is therefore in order.

The wave put out by an oscillator is not perfectly shaped. As a result, it has harmonics, the frequency of each a multiple of the frequency of the oscillator. Consequently, an oscillator with a fundamental frequency of, say, 3 mc will also put out second and third harmonics of 6 and 9 mc. Now, if the amplifier stage which follows the oscillator has at its output a coil-capacitor circuit resonant to the second harmonic of the oscillator signal, that resonant circuit will respond strongly to the 6 mc frequency but only weakly, if at all, to any other. Consequently the output of this amplifier will be a signal with twice the frequency of its input. Such a circuit is called a *doubler,* for obvious reasons. A *tripler* can be built in the same fashion, by giving its output circuit a coil-capacitor arrangement which responds to the third harmonic of the input signal. Usually, however, harmonics beyond the third are quite weak, so that multipliers beyond triplers—quadruplers or quintuplers—are rather rare.

Direct FM Transmitters

Now we can take a look at what this direct method of FM transmission involves. Since, in such a system, the frequency of the master oscillator will be varied by the audio signal, some electronic device will have to be installed between the source of audio and the oscillator. This device will have the responsibility of influencing the oscillator's frequency to respond to the demands of the audio signal. Such a device, called the *reactance modulator,* was discussed in Chapter 11.

Connected to the oscillator—which, in the direct FM method is not crystal-controlled—the reactance modulator acts as if it were part of the oscillator's frequency-determining resonant circuit. If a positive voltage is applied to the reactance modulator input, the circuit

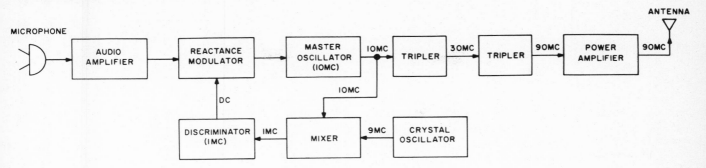

Fig. 16.6. *Basic Block Diagram of Direct FM Transmitter:* The master oscillator is assumed to put out a frequency of 10 mc. The first frequency tripler stage produces a frequency of 30 mc, the second triples this frequency to 90 mc. Part of the master oscillator output is fed to a heterodyne detec-tor (mixer) to which a 9 mc signal from a crystal-controlled oscillator is also given. The discriminator detects errors in the resulting 1 mc signal, and corrects the oscillator through the reactance modulator.

raises the frequency of the oscillator by a proportionate amount; a negative voltage applied to the reactance modulator causes the oscillator frequency to drop below its normal figure. Since the audio signal furnished to the reactance modulator is an alternating voltage, it can drive the oscillator's frequency above and below the normal resting frequency in the same way it varies. Thus the oscillator's output, through its frequency changes, is made to carry the audio signal.

The lineup of stages in the direct FM system would appear to be a simple one. It begins with the microphone, which collects the sound to be broadcast, and converts it into the corresponding electrical audio signal. A system of audio amplifier stages then follows. The audio signal provided by the last of these stages is applied to the reactance modulator for variation of the frequency of the master oscillator. From the master oscillator, the modulated signal is brought to a succession of multipliers which not only multiply the frequency of the oscillator but also multiply its variations above and below the resting value. At the end of the process is the power amplifier and the antenna, the former to build up the power of the FM wave and the latter to speed it on its way through space.

This system, however, has one flaw: there is no guarantee that the frequency of the signal transmitted will return to its normal resting value once modulation ceases. The master oscillator producing the carrier is not strictly controlled and so is not strictly trustworthy. But this deficiency can be repaired by a feedback system of automatic control similar to the afc system described in Chapter 11. Part of the oscillator output is diverted into a heterodyne detector. The output of a crystal-controlled oscillator, having a slightly different frequency from that of the master, is also fed to the detector, which then produces a signal equal in frequency to the difference between the two input fre-quencies. This heterodyne frequency is then given to a discriminator whose resonant circuit is tuned to that signal. If the master oscillator is at its correct resting frequency, the heterodyne signal matches the frequency to which the discriminator is set, the discriminator d-c output is zero, and there is no resultant effect either on the reactance modulator or on the master oscillator. Should the master oscillator tend to rise above its normal resting frequency, the heterodyne signal frequency similarly rises, the discriminator puts out a correcting signal, and the reactance modulator operates to pull the master oscillator frequency down to normal. An opposite activity takes place if the master oscillator frequency should drop to an abnormally low level. While this arrangement is not absolutely foolproof, it is basic to the frequency control systems used in many newer FM transmitters.

The afc system just described must be delayed in some way. If it goes into action too quickly it will tend to cancel out even the normal changes in the master oscillator frequency that the modulating audio signal demands. An electronic delay device to keep the system from working too quickly might take the form of a resistor-capacitor network similar to the integrating circuit shown in Chapter 14. This little arrangement, connected between the discriminator output and the reactance modulator, would keep the reactance modulator from getting the full correction voltage until enough time elapses for the full voltage to accumulate. With this electronic rein on the afc system, the master oscillator is allowed to go through its necessary frequency changes and yet is kept from drifting.

The Television Transmitter

What has just been said about the FM transmitter applies with equal force to one part of the television

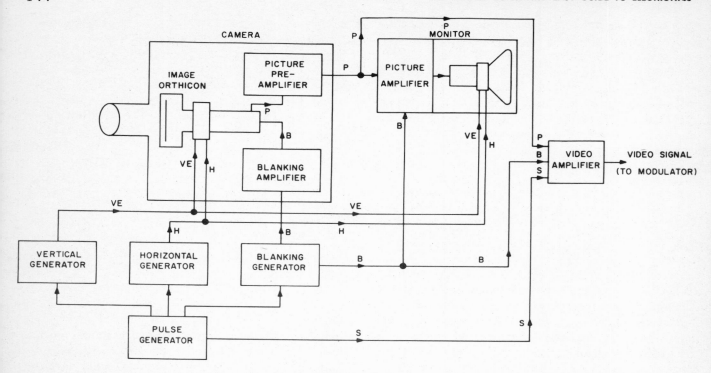

Fig. 16.7. *Generating the Video Signal:* All pulsing orig- inates in the pulse generator. The vertical and horizontal generators supply current controlling the vertical (VE) and horizontal (H) movements of the image orthicon and moni- tor kinescope beams. Blanking pulses (B) are furnished to the image orthicon and monitor kinescope, and to the video amplifier. Sync pulses are provided directly to the video amplifier by the pulse generator. Picture signals (P) orig- inating in the image orthicon are amplified within the cam- era housing, and are fed to the monitor kinescope and the video amplifier. Thus the output of the video amplifier is comprised of picture signal, blanking, and sync.

transmitter—that part which is devoted to the trans- mission of the program's sound. Television transmission involves two carriers, one frequency modulated, the other amplitude modulated. Except for possibly a com- mon power supply, designed to furnish the necessary operating voltages to the tubes generating both carriers, the two systems are practically independent of each other. It is only at the final point in the transmission process, the antenna, that their signals unite. As far as the sound system is concerned, there is little to differen- tiate it from the purely audio FM transmitter: it is either the Armstrong system of phase modulation or the direct one employing a reactance modulator. Since both systems have already been discussed, nothing further need be said about the FM part of the television transmitter. But the AM part of it contains a great deal that is new.

The AM part of television involves the complex video signal as the modulating electrical wave. This video signal, as we know, is made up of three elements: the picture signal, which may be described as the electrical equivalent of the lights and darks in the televised image; the blanking signal, a square pulse with the responsi- bility of cutting off the receiver kinescope scanning beam at the end of each line and each field; and finally the sync pulse, also square in shape, which keeps the vertical and horizontal oscillators of the receiver under control. All these components of the video signal—also known as the composite video signal—are generated, shaped, and put together in the transmitter.

Along with the equipment generating the composite video signal are several monitors. These are television receivers much like those in living rooms all over the country; the only way they differ from the consumer's set is that they are fed the video signal directly through cables. There is a monitor for every camera in action during a particular program, thus giving the program director an opportunity to see exactly what scenes the working cameras are trained on, and to choose the one he wants to send to the viewing audience.

We have already discovered, in Chapter 6, that the picture signal originates in the image orthicon. Although the electron multipliers inside the tube build up the pic- ture signal to some extent, it still requires amplification. This is provided by a preamplifier built right into the camera, thus avoiding a long cable and the weakening of the signal long wires would cause. From the preamplifier, the picture signal is fed to the control grid of the kinescope in the monitor through the monitor's own amplifier. This signal must also be furnished to the transmitter's video amplifier, for here the three components of the composite video signal are put together.

The scanning beams of the image orthicon inside the camera, the kinescope inside the monitor, and the kinescope inside the set of the viewer at home, all have to be synchronized. Consequently, the signals controlling the movements of those beams must arise from a single source in the transmitter. This single source is the *pulse generator,* the basic control unit of the entire system. Under the pulse generator's control are the horizontal and vertical generators, which work in similar fashion to the horizontal and vertical oscillators in the home receiver: they supply the beam-deflecting currents for the camera's image orthicon and the monitor's kinescope. The currents these generators supply circulate through the deflection coils of both these tubes, and through the magnetic fields they set up, drive the beams of the tubes through their horizontal and vertical movements.

Blanking is also important. When the scanning beams of the image orthicon, monitor kinescope, and home kinescope reach the end of their horizontal lines and vertical fields, they must be switched off. The blanking pulses responsible for that switching are shaped in the blanking generator, which is also controlled by the pulse generator. Blanking pulses are fed to the control grids of the image orthicon in the camera and the kinescope in the monitor. For the benefit of the kinescopes in home receivers, they are fed also to the video amplifier,

and are strung between each line of picture signal and each field of picture signal lines.

The third element of the composite video signal, the sync pulses, are required neither by the image orthicon nor the monitor kinescope; the horizontal and vertical generators controlling the beams in these tubes are already being synchronized through cables from the pulse generator. However, the sync pulses are needed by home receivers for controlling the horizontal and vertical oscillators which, in turn, control the movements of the home kinescope beams. Consequently, the pulses are supplied directly by the pulse generator to the video amplifier. Thus the third and last of the video signal elements is added to the others. The video signal emerging from the video amplifier is now ready to modulate the picture carrier generated by the sight portion of the television transmitter.

Picture Carrier Modulation

Since the television picture carrier is amplitude modulated, the lineup of stages generating that signal parallels the AM lineup given earlier in this chapter. The first of these stages is the master oscillator, in which the carrier originates. For the sake of a stabilized frequency, the master oscillator is crystal-controlled; the quartz heart of the oscillator is kept in a chamber maintained at uniform temperature by a thermostat to make certain that the carrier frequency remains stable.

Television transmitters, however, work in the vhf range. In accordance with the rule that high frequencies generally require smaller components, the crystal governing the master oscillator would have to be an ex-

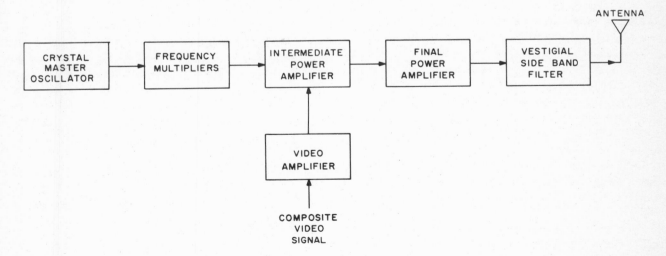

Fig. 16.8. *The TV Sight Channel Transmitter:* Frequency multipliers raise the master oscillator output to a high frequency r-f. Modulation by the video signal is accomplished at the intermediate power amplifier. Before the finally am-

plified modulated signal is applied to the antenna, it is put through the vestigial side band filter to remove 2 mc. from one of the signal side bands.

tremely thin section. To avoid this necessity, the master oscillator is designed to operate at a frequency of about 5 mc, with a controlling crystal cut to this frequency. A series of multiplier stages following the master oscillator builds the frequency up to the value required for the station by the Federal Communications Commission.

The stage following the last of the multiplier circuits is an intermediate power amplifier. It is at this point that the composite video signal, created in the transmitter room, is applied to the carrier wave for modulation. For this purpose, the video signal may be applied to the grid of the intermediate power amplifier tube or to its plate. As the carrier leaves this stage, the peaks of its wave are molded to outline the video signal's complex waveform (Chapter 7). This is the form in which the signal is strengthened in the final power amplifier stage of the transmitter.

However, the signal issuing from the final cannot immediately be transmitted by the antenna. As we found in Chapter 8, the full, uncut band width of the television signal is 8 mc, a figure which the FCC regards as excessive. The method followed by all television transmitters is to cut part of one of the side bands, thus limiting the television band to an overall 6 mc spread. To put this system of vestigial side band transmission into effect, a filter is inserted between the output of the final power amplifier and the antenna. Thus the video portion of the TV signal is completed.

Transmitter Antennas

Transmitting antennas are designed with an eye to the function of the transmitter. In commercial AM, FM, and TV work, the transmitter aims at bringing the station's programs to as many listeners as possible; the station depends on the number of advertising contracts it has, and its advertising efficiency depends on the number of people who pick up its messages. Consequently, the commercial transmitter's antenna is omnidirectional to radiate the carrier to every point of the compass. The commercial AM station, operating in the broadcast band, is in this category. Its antenna is usually a vertical mast of structural steel raised high above the surrounding territory.

The distribution of an antenna's signal strength can be represented by a drawing called the *directivity pattern*. Since the vertical mast antenna radiates its signal equally in all directions, its directivity pattern is a circle with the antenna as the center. Any point on the circumference of a circle is as far from the center as any other circumferential point; the circular pattern thus reflects the fact that two receivers at equal distances but different directions from the transmitting mast will receive its signal with equal strength.

Since AM broadcast band carriers are low in fre-

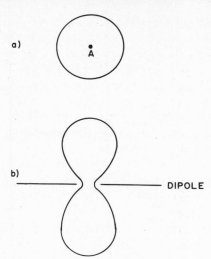

Fig. 16.9. *Directivity Patterns:* **The pattern at (a) represents the directivity of a vertical mast antenna. A straight line drawn from the antenna (A) to the periphery of the pattern is the same regardless of the direction of the line, thus indicating that the antenna is equally effective from all directions. The pattern of (b) is for a single dipole. Here a straight line drawn from the center of the dipole to the periphery of the pattern is longest when it is at right angles to the antenna, indicating that the antenna broadcasts best in the perpendicular direction.**

quency, the antenna of a transmitter operating in that band is bound to be large. FM transmitters need not face that problem. At the high frequencies of FM carriers, the antennas required are much smaller than their AM counterparts, measuring approximately five feet. They usually take the form of dipoles—the same as the receiver antenna (Chapter 11)—the line of the dipole being parallel to the ground. A single dipole, however, has directional characteristics, favoring the line at right angles to its alignment. Thus an FM transmitter dipole oriented in the east-west direction transmits best to the north and south. To give the transmitting antenna a more nearly circular pattern, the engineers of the commercial FM transmitter set up a *turnstile* antenna, a double dipole in the shape its name suggests.

Television transmitting antennas are similarly formed. But these present rather a special problem since they are the junction points of two carriers, picture and sound. Precautions must therefore be taken to keep the sound signal from getting into the picture stages and vice versa.

Ground and Sky Waves

The transmitted wave behaves differently at different frequencies. At the broadcast frequencies, which range roughly from 600 to 1600 kc, the wave from the transmitting antenna generally takes two paths, one along the ground, the other through the sky. During the day, the ground wave predominates, the sky wave being almost completely absorbed—which explains why AM broadcast band receivers cannot usually pick up distant stations at those times. At night, however, the sky wave is strong. Moreover, lines of wave propagation angling upwards from the surface of the earth are bent back to the earth by the *ionosphere,* a layer at the outer fringes of the earth's atmosphere in which the rarefied air particles are ionized by the sun's radiation to produce quantities of free electrons. These electrons refract radio waves at the broadcast frequencies, much as water refracts rays of light.

At the higher frequencies of the so-called short waves (Chapter 10), the ground wave is of little importance, dropping to zero only a short distance from the transmitting antenna. The sky wave is the notable vehicle of communication. For rays emitted at the same angle to the earth's surface, the refractive effect of the ionosphere is considerably less for the higher frequencies than it is for the lower frequencies. The sky waves of broadcast band transmitters bend sharply back to earth, but the angle of bend is broader for the higher frequency short waves. Hence the long skip distance permitting communication over immense distances.

Rays of vhf and uhf transmissions are hardly affected by the ionosphere, and so head out to space if they are directed that way. This fact explains why vhf and uhf are limited to line-of-sight operations. Skip distances enable a transmitter working in the short wave bands to reach a receiver hidden from it by the bulge of the earth. Because there is no skip distance in either vhf or uhf, receivers can only be reached by the direct ray —a straight line between transmitter and receiver. If the transmitter antenna cannot "see" the receiving antenna, it cannot communicate with it. The same fact also explains why *telemetering,* the transmission of radio signals between earth stations and space satellites, is conducted at uhf—frequencies of as much as 2000 mc.

The ray-bending ability of the ionosphere varies with its density, just as the refraction of light in water varies with the density of water. Great conflagrations pockmark the face of the sun from time to time, and intense radiation accompanies these disturbances. Under this heavy *sunspot* bombardment, more and more of the air particles in the earth's atmosphere are ionized, and the density of free electrons is multiplied. Radio communication begins to behave peculiarly, and may be halted altogether. But this phenomenon, in which the earth's magnetic field and possibly its gravitational field play a part, is a mystery still a long way from being thoroughly probed.

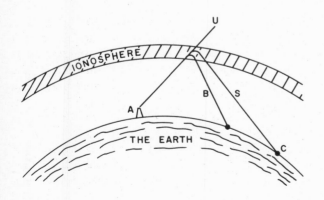

Fig. 16.10. *Ionosphere Refraction:* **Waves emitted from a transmitter (A) are refracted to a different extent, depending on the frequency. Broadcast band rays (B) are bent sharply; short waves (S) are bent to a lesser extent, thus providing a long skip distance (A to C); uhf waves are not bent at all, but pierce the ionosphere to soar off into space. The last explains why transmissions at vhf and uhf are limited to line-of-sight.**

GLOSSARY

Composite video signal. The video signal of TV, consisting of picture signal, blanking pulses, and sync pulses.

Direct FM. The system of FM transmission in which the audio modulates the frequency of the master oscillator through a reactance modulator.

Directivity pattern. A geometrical representation of the output strength in various directions of a transmitting antenna.

Doubler. A frequency multiplier which multiplies the frequency of an input signal by two.

Frequency multiplier. A circuit which multiplies the frequency of an input signal by a whole number.

Grid modulation. A system of modulation in an AM transmitter in which the modulating audio is applied to the grid circuit of an r-f amplifier.

Ground wave. The earth-bound wave from a low frequency transmitter antenna.

Heising modulation. A system of modulation in an AM transmitter in which the modulating audio is applied to the plate circuit of an r-f amplifier.

Intelligence. The meaningful signal impressed on a transmitted carrier wave.

Intermediate power amplifier. An r-f amplifier just ahead of the final power amplifier in a transmitter.

Ionosphere. The charged layer in the upper reaches of the earth's atmosphere.

Monitor. A TV receiver in the control room of a TV transmitter studio.

MOPA. Master oscillator-power amplifier; a two-stage CW transmitter.

Phase modulation. An indirect method of FM transmission in which the phase of the carrier is changed in accordance with the audio signal.

Plate modulation. Same as Heising modulation.

Pulse generator. The circuit in a TV transmitter which generates the basic timing pulses for blanking and sync.

Sky wave. A radio wave which travels through space rather than along the ground.

Sunspots. Electrical disturbances in the sun which affect the ionosphere and so affect radio communication.

Tank circuit. A resonant circuit of coil and capacitor.

Telemetering. The exchange of guidance and other informational signals between earth stations and satellites or guided missiles.

Tripler. A circuit which multiplies the frequency of an input signal by three.

Turnstile antenna. The antenna, consisting of crossed dipoles, of a TV or FM transmitter.

Vestigial side band filter. The filter in a TV transmitter which cuts a 2-mc portion from the band width of the transmitted picture carrier.

Chapter Seventeen

ELECTRONICS IN NAVIGATION

THE ELECTRONIC equipments we have discussed in past chapters can be divided, at least as far as function is concerned, into two categories: communications systems, embracing AM radio, short waves, FM, and television; and non-communications systems such as hi-fi and radar. The distinctive feature of the first category is the exchange of intelligence between a transmitter and a receiver, each unit often widely separated from the other. In the second category, some intelligence (no pun is intended) is also involved, but the transmitter and receiver are operated as a single unit.

But these are not the only ways in which electronics is used. There are systems which involve transmitters and receivers at widely separated distances on the face of the globe but are not primarily communications devices. Their purpose is to satisfy a need brought about by an apparently compulsive human activity—the incessant gadding about the world by sea, air, and land.

The Radio Direction Finder

One of the commoner types of electronic navigating devices, found on many craft, is the radio direction finder. This instrument is really nothing more than a radio receiver whose antenna is especially sensitive to signals arriving from a particular direction. As a matter of fact, a radio direction finder of a rather crude sort can be found in almost every American home. The AM radio receiver of the tabletop variety, with a built-in loop antenna, has some direction-finding ability and might even be converted to a serviceable navigation instrument if its owner is electronically adept.

We found, in the last chapter, that a transmitter's antenna has a directivity pattern of one shape or another, depending on the antenna's construction. The same is true also of the receiver's antenna. A long vertical wire, if connected to the input circuit of a receiver, will be equally sensitive to signals from all directions. Hence its directivity pattern is a circle. If the antenna is a dipole—assuming that the receiver is FM or TV—it will have the same directivity pattern as that shown in the preceding chapter. For a receiver antenna in the form of a loop, however, the directivity pattern is like a figure 8, with each circle of the 8 centered around a vertical member of the loop wires. This pattern indicates that the loop antenna is most sensitive to signals arriving from a direction along its plane, and least sensitive to signals at right angles to it. Without touching the volume control, the owner of such a set can get better reception simply by turning the cabinet to point the loop in the proper direction.

The factor that accounts for this antenna's peculiar directivity is the distance between its two vertical wire members. If the loop plane coincides with the line from transmitter to receiver, unequal voltages are induced in those members. Suppose, for example, that the transmitted wave is at its peak at one set of vertical wires. At that same instant, its strength at the other set is somewhat less; the wave, being alternating, varies in intensity at different points along its wavelength. Because of this difference in induced voltage, a current circulates through the loop, and the antenna delivers an appreciable signal to the receiver's input circuits. If, however, the loop is turned to direct its plane at right angles to the line between transmitter and receiver, both vertical members are equidistant from the transmitter, and the distance between members is no longer a factor. Approximately equal and opposite voltages are then produced; little current can flow in the loop and the result is poor reception.

Such a receiver can therefore be used to locate the direction of a transmitter, and is, in effect, a direction finder of sorts. However, its loop cannot sense the true direction since it responds to both ends of its plane. For example, if its owner finds that he gets best reception by aligning the plane of the loop in the east-west direction, he knows that the transmitter is somewhere along the east-west line; but he has no way of finding out whether the transmitter lies to the east or west. To give the loop maximum sensitivity in one direction and one direction only, a sensing device is necessary.

The sensing device is merely a vertical wire. We have found that an antenna consisting of a vertical conductor has the directivity pattern of a circle. When such a conductor is combined with a loop, its circular pattern is completely in phase with one of the loop's figure 8 circles, and completely out of phase with the other. Thus the sensing antenna aids the loop's response in one direction but opposes it in the other. The final pattern of the combination is a heart-shaped figure known as the *cardioid*. Note that the largest protuberance—lobe, as engineers call it—of the cardioid is in one particular direction.

In older types of ship board radio direction finders employing the antenna combination of loop and sensing device, the loop was rotated by hand until the signal

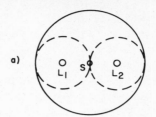
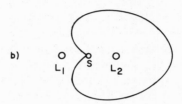

Fig. 17.2. The Cardioid: The directivity patterns of the loop (L_1, L_2) and the sensing device (S) are shown in (a); dotted lines are the loop pattern, the solid line is the sensing pattern. The resulting cardioid is shown in (b). Since the lobe of L_2 is in phase with that of the sensing device and aids it, the major lobe of the cardioid protrudes to the right. The lobe of L_1 opposes the sensing device pattern, however, and the cardioid therefore has no lobe immediately to the left of S. It is obvious from this drawing that a receiver with this combination antenna will respond best to signals coming from the right.

received provided the correct direction of the tuned-in transmitter with respect to the ship. The operator, picking up the identifying call letters of the transmitter, located its shore position on his charts, and drew a straight line through the dot representing it on the map in the direction his instrument provided for him. He knew, then, that the position of his ship had to be somewhere along that line. To pin it down to one particular point, he tuned the direction finder receiver to a second transmitter, rotated the antenna once more to find this new transmitter's direction, and drew a second line accordingly. The point at which the two lines crossed was therefore the ship's position. This is the so-called triangulation method of obtaining a "fix."

Small craft still use this type of direction finder for locating their positions offshore, and to good effect. But there are more sophisticated instruments using the same basic idea, many of them employed by the military, to locate a friendly or enemy aircraft. Since the direction finder is essentially a receiver, relying only on the transmitted signals of the object it senses, it has the tactical advantage of radio silence—no small advantage for a landbased installation in what may be a hostile area.

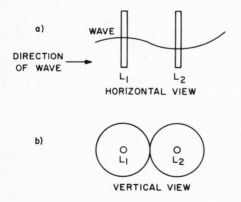

Fig. 17.1. Loop Antenna Directivity: The drawing of (a) demonstrates the difference in voltage induced in the two vertical strands of the loop (L_1, L_2). The wave at L_1 is at its maximum, but is less intense at L_2. For a wave at right angles to the line between L_1 and L_2, the voltages induced in both strands are equal and opposite. The resultant figure 8 pattern of the loop shows that it is sensitive to signals arriving from left or right, but insensitive to signals arriving from top or bottom of the page.

The Military D-F

The military d-f equipment—the Army, in its penchant for initials, prefers "d-f" to "direction finding"—uses the same antenna combination of two vertical conductors with a sensing conductor between them to produce the cardioid. But the military instrument differs from its civilian counterpart by having the cardioid pattern rotate continuously at the rate of 30 revolutions per second. When the receiver is tuned to an airborne transmitter, the level of the received signal depends on the direction in which the cardioid is pointed at any given moment. At the instant the major lobe of the cardioid is aimed directly at the transmitter, the received signal is a maximum. When the opposite end of the cardioid—representing minimum sensitivity of the antenna—points at the transmitter, the amplitude of the received signal is at its lowest. For any direction of the cardioid between these two extremes, the reception level is somewhere between maximum and minimum. Since the cardioid rotates at 30 revolutions per second, the level of the receiver's output varies at this same rate. Thus, the received carrier contains a 30 cycle per second component known as the *d-f signal*.

What is interesting about this d-f signal is its phase. When measured by a phasemeter, the phase of the signal indicates the direction of the transmitter which caused it. This is best shown in the test runs performed on a newly constructed d-f equipment, which begin when an oscillator is placed due north of the direction finder. The d-f signal then obtained from the receiver reaches a maximum when the cardioid is pointed due north; the phasemeter reads zero degrees in response to this direction of the test oscillator. In the second step, the oscillator is moved to a point due south of the direction finder. For this setup, the d-f signal is a minimum when the cardioid is pointed due north. If the d-f equipment is working properly, the phasemeter should show a reading of 180 degrees—the opposite end of the dial—indicating that the phase of the new signal is exactly inverted with respect to that found in the first step of the testing process.

This method of measuring the direction of the transmitter accords exactly with the azimuth method of compass scaling, in which the circle of the compass is divided equally into 360 degrees of azimuth. North then becomes zero degrees of azimuth; east, 90 degrees; south, 180 degrees; and west, 270 degrees. When the phasemeter of a military d-f responding to an airborne transmitter reads 45 degrees, for example, the man operating the equipment knows that the transmitter is to the northeast of the installation, at an azimuth of 45 degrees.

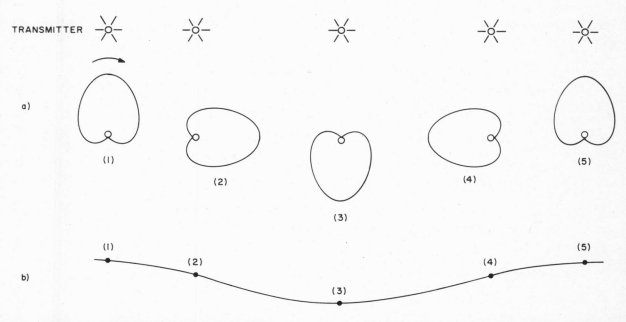

Fig. 17.3. *The D-F Signal:* Rotation of the cardioid is shown in (a). When the major lobe is directed at the transmitter, the received carried is maximum (1). The strength of the carrier decreases gradually as the cardioid rotates, becoming a minimum when the major lobe is pointed directly away from the transmitter, and returns to maximum when a full rotation is completed. The resultant d-f signal is shown at (b). Since the cardioid rotates at a 30 revolution-per-second rate, the d-f signal has a frequency of 30 cps.

The VOR System

The rotating cardioid idea is also at the bottom of a system known as VOR—another ingredient for the alphabet soup of electronics—which stands for "very high frequency omnidirectional radio range." This long-winded title immediately provides some clues about the features of the system. First, the system operates in the very high frequency band; second, the term "omnidirectional" indicates that the radio transmissions involved range through every point of the compass. This latter feature is fairly obvious since the rotating cardioid covers every sector of the azimuth scale.

The function of the system is to guide aircraft into the home base. Instead of the land installation looking for the aircraft, typical of the radio direction finder, the aircraft looks for the land installation. We can therefore expect that in the VOR system, as opposed to the direction-finding system, the aircraft and the base installation exchange roles; here the base installation is a transmitter equipped with the cardioid-creating antenna we have already seen, and the aircraft seeking it is the receiver. The aircraft pilot then gets his 30 cycle signal which, measured by his VOR receiver phasemeter, informs him of the direction in which the base lies.

Shoran

Another aid to aircraft navigation is the system known as shoran, a manufactured word assembled from the capitalized letters in SHOrt RAnge Navigation. Beacons (Chapter 15) are involved, which indicates that shoran is a pulse radar system. There is a strong parallel between this method through which an aircraft can fix its position, and the triangulation method described earlier in this chapter through which a ship offshore can obtain its "fix."

The apparatus of the shoran system involves radar equipment in the aircraft seeking the fix and two radar beacons located at known points on the ground. While the aircraft navigator knows the positions of the beacons —he can locate them on his maps—he has no idea how he is located with respect to them. Consequently, he operates his radar to send out a triggering signal, and the beacons automatically respond with an identifying pattern of pulse widths. The scope of his radar receiver furnishes him the range of each of the beacons. With his compass—the instrument schoolboys use for drawing circles, not the magnetic needle device—the navigator draws an arc centered at the map position of one beacon, with the radius of the arc measured to the map's scale of the actual distance between beacon and aircraft. He repeats the process for the other beacon, and

finds that the two arcs intersect. That point of intersection must be his position.

The range within which shoran is effective is necessarily limited by the relatively weak beacon signal. But there is a system of a somewhat similar kind which works over much longer distances. Naturally enough, this system is known as loran, a handy abbreviation for LOng RAnge Navigation.

Loran

Loran basically involves two transmitters, both of which assist the aircraft navigator to obtain his fix. The range factor which gives the system its name is a consequence of the high power of both transmitters. One of them emits r-f pulses which are picked up not only by the pilot seeking the fix, but also by the second transmitter, which is thereby triggered into action a small fraction of a second later. The first of these two transmitters is therefore the master, while the second is its slave.

The aircraft navigator receives the signals of both transmitters. He notices that there is a time difference between the arrivals of the two transmissions, a natural consequence of the fact that he is usually closer to one of them. With the equipment he has on board, he can measure this time difference; but such a measurement will not give him his precise position since there are many points between the two transmitters at which this same time difference would be noted. All of these points are located along a curved line known as a hyperbola— the reason, incidentally, why such navigation systems as loran are said to be *hyperbolic*.

To fix the position his ship is occupying on that hyperbola, the navigator needs a second curve which will intersect the first at a particular point, that point

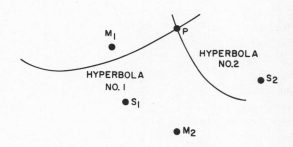

Fig. 17.4. *Loran:* Hyperbola #1 is the path along which the time difference between signals from a master (M₁) and slave station (S₁) is always the same. Hyperbola #2 is a similar path for master and slave transmitters M₂ and S₂. The location of the aircraft receiving the proper time differences from each pair of transmitters is at the intersection of the curves (P).

being his precise location. This second curve is provided by another master-slave transmitter pair. Between
the transmitters of this second pair exists another hyperbola, each point on which represents the same time-
difference in signal reception as any other point on
the line. Thus the aircraft navigator, measuring a particular time-difference for one pair of transmitters and
another time-difference for the second pair, can pinpoint
the position of his ship.

The keystone of the loran structure is the principle
on which many similar electronic devices are based—
the principle that the speed of any electromagnetic wave
is constant. Since the radio wave covers equal distances
for equal units of time, the time difference for one of
the hyperbolic paths of the Loran system can easily
be translated into the difference between the distances
from the aircraft to the master-slave transmitter pair.

Altimeters

For a surface vessel on the high seas, the navigation
problem is comparatively simple. Its medium is two-
dimensional; it neither rises above the surface of the
water nor sinks below it. For the aircraft or submarine,
however, altitude or depth is part of the problem of
navigation. An aircraft is not precisely located in space
if only its position in the plane of the navigator's map
is known. Its altitude must also be determined.

Hence the need, in an aircraft, for the *altimeter*, a
device which measures the height of the aircraft above
the ground. Many of the altimeters now in use are
pressure instruments; they determine the altitude by
measuring the air pressure at the point occupied by
the aircraft carrying them. The basic principle of these
instruments is the variation of air pressure with altitude.
At sea level, at the very bottom of the ocean of air
in which we live, the pressure is naturally greatest; as
the altitude above sea level increases, the air pressure
diminishes.

These pressure altimeters work well, but they can
be misleading. An aircraft flying over a mountain range
may be only 20 feet above the peak of one of the moun-
tains, practically scraping the surface, but its altimeter
actually registers 10,000 feet. Should the airplane
crash it would not be entirely the fault of the pilot,
who must be guided by his instruments. Nor is it the
fault of the altimeter, which is working well; the air
directly above the mountain peak *is* at the density to
be expected at a 10,000 foot height.

Obviously, it is preferable to measure the altitude of
the aircraft by determining the height of the aircraft
underbelly above the ground over which it is flying.
This more reliable method is afforded by the radio
altimeter. In this electronic system, a transmitter and

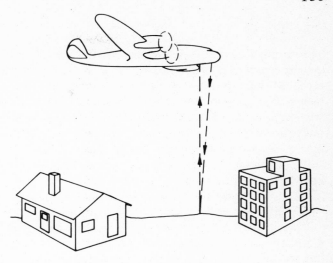

Fig. 17.5. *The Radio Altimeter:* **The FM wave reflected from
the ground back to the aircraft is compared in frequency
with the originally transmitted wave to determine the altitude of the aircraft.**

receiver, each with its own antenna, is slung under
the aircraft fuselage. The antennas of both are oriented
downward, but in such fashion that a small quantity
of the transmitted signal reaches the receiver antenna.
In this way, the receiver antenna obtains both the directly transmitted signal and the reflected signal from
the ground. The receiver then compares the direct signal
with the reflected one and so determines the height of
the aircraft off the ground.

The important feature of the system is that it is
frequency modulated. The straight-line distance between
the two antennas is only a matter of a few feet; consequently, the time taken by the direct wave, traveling
with the speed of light, to get directly from the transmitter to the receiving antenna is so small as to be
negligible. But the wave reaching the receiver antenna
by way of reflection from the ground has a much longer
distance to travel, and so spends much more time in
covering it. Thus, the frequency of the signal has
changed by the time the reflected wave returns. A
comparison of this changed frequency with the frequency of the direct signal gives the altitude of the
aircraft. Of course, the path traveled by the reflected
wave is actually twice the altitude, but the equipment
compensates for that in its calculations.

Aircraft Autopilots

When the aircraft pilot has determined his position and
the direction he must follow to get to his destination,
there is nothing much left for him to do except stay

at the controls and make sure his craft follows a more or less straight line. Guiding a cruising aircraft is a tedious and exacting job; however, an automatic system taking care of the details would free the pilot for the other important duties he must perform. There is such an automatic piloting device, and it is called, appropriately enough, the *autopilot*.

Once it is switched on, the autopilot must be able to duplicate every maneuver of its human counterpart. An aircraft in flight can be put through a good many paces, but all of them can be resolved into rotations of the body of the aircraft around one or more of three axes. The first of these is the longitudinal axis, the line through its fuselage from nose to tail. A rotation of the aircraft around this axis, which involves dipping one wing while raising the other, is called rolling; the longitudinal axis is therefore often called the *roll axis*. Perpendicular to this axis and in the horizontal plane is the *pitch axis*, so called because it is the axis around which the aircraft rotates when its nose rises and its tail drops, or vice versa—an action known as pitching. Finally, there is the *yaw axis,* a vertical line perpendicular to both the roll and pitch axes. The yaw axis is the line around which the aircraft rotates when it veers—or yaws—to the right or left in the horizontal plane. All these terms were at one time the sole property of seamen; they are now part of the lexicon of airmen as well.

In putting the aircraft through its rotations around these axes, the pilot—human or auto—operates the movable portions of the aircraft which execute them. The aircraft's roll is brought about through the ailerons, movable flaps in the aircraft's wings. Pitch is controlled by the elevator, a horizontal flap in the aircraft's tail assembly which can be rotated either up or down. As for yaw, that is the province of the rudder, a vertical flap in the tail assembly capable of swiveling to the right or left—or, in air terms, to starboard or port. In the vocabulary of sea and air, everything to the right as one looks towards the nose of the ship is starboard, everything to the left is port; everything straight ahead is forward, and everything to the rear is aft.

The Autopilot Loop

The autopilot system guiding the aircraft in flight is pretty much self-contained. There are neither transmitters nor receivers involved, at least in the sense of equipment exchanging electromagnetic signals through space. Nor can the system be said to be either purely electronic or purely electrical, since mechanical connections exist between some of the system components. Consequently, it is known as an electromechanical system. Since the aircraft is capable of maneuvering around three axes, the autopilot system breaks down

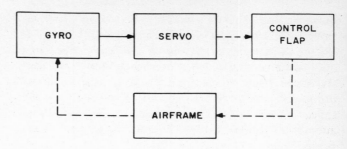

Fig. 17.6. *Autopilot Loop, Basic Block Diagram:* **This general block diagram is the pattern for autopilot control of roll, pitch, and yaw. Solid lines between blocks represent electrical connections; dotted lines, mechanical connections.**

into three channels; roll, pitch, and yaw. The purpose of these channels is to steady the aircraft against disturbances tending to rotate it around these axes.

Since the system is corrective, the chances are that it has the closed-loop, feedback form typical of corrective circuits we have seen in past chapters. That this is true is proved by the simplified block diagram of a typical channel. The three channels are just about alike and follow the general pattern the diagram presents: the airframe—the body of the aircraft—is mechanically connected to a gyroscope; the gyroscope is a mechanical device capable of emitting an electrical signal, a signal which is fed to a servomechanism; the servo, a self-correcting electromechanical device, contains a motor whose shaft is linked through a system of gears to the aircraft control flap to be stabilized; finally, through the aerodynamic system of flap and airframe, the latter is restored to its normal position. The flap in question is the one appropriate to the channel: if it is the roll channel, the flaps to be corrected are the ailerons in the

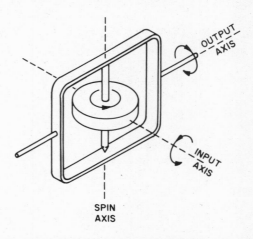

Fig. 17.7. *The Gyroscope:* **The rotating disc turns counterclockwise, as shown. If an attempt is made to rotate the assembly around the input axis, the whole rotates around the output axis as indicated, thereby producing an electrical signal.**

wing; for the pitch channel, the flap is the elevator; and for the yaw channel, it is the rudder.

Like the toy variety offered for sale in novelty shops, the gyroscope consists of a disc rotating at high speed and pivoted in a frame. Unlike the toy, the gyroscope in the autopilot system is whirled by an electric motor supplied by the generator on board the aircraft. If any attempt is made to rotate the gyroscope around an axis perpendicular to the axis around which the disc spins, the gyroscope responds by tending to rotate around a third axis at right angles to both the axis of spin and the axis of attempted rotation. In more technical terms: a forced rotation of the gyroscope assembly about its input axis causes the assembly to precess about its output axis. Connected mechanically to the output axis is a synchro generator (Chapter 6) which puts out an electrical signal when its shaft is rotated. Thus an input torque applied to the gyroscope results in a signal which is passed on to the servomechanism. As for this latter device, we shall have much more to say about it in the final chapter; for the moment, however, we shall consider it merely as a device which converts a mechanical rotation into an electrical signal.

With this information in mind, we can now turn to an explanation of the autopilot system, using the block diagram as an aid. Let us suppose that a sudden updraft on one of the wings of the aircraft causes the airframe to roll. In response to this torque on its input axis, the roll gyroscope precesses and puts out an electrical signal to the servomechanism. The servo responds by a rotation of its motor which adjusts the aircraft ailerons in such fashion as to oppose the original roll of the ship; the airframe is then righted until the wings of the craft are once more in the horizontal plane. With the roll torque thus removed from the gyroscope, the latter no longer puts out a signal, and the circuit is restored to balance to await another disturbance. A similar loop circuit employing a pitch gyro, a servo, and the elevator as control flap operates in the same way to restore the aircraft to its correct flying posture in the event of a disturbing pitch. And, finally, a third such loop corrects any tendency of the aircraft to yaw.

Instrument Landing System

The autopilot just described cares for the guidance of the aircraft in level flight, and so might be called a cruising system. But there are equally reliable autopilots for maneuvering the aircraft as it comes in for a landing. These, however, are not completely self-contained as is the cruising system; they depend on guidance signals furnished by airport transmitters. Thus the autopilot which brings the aircraft into port is the slave of transmitters at the landing strip, and obtains its command signals through the aircraft's receiver.

An effective guidance apparatus for either human or

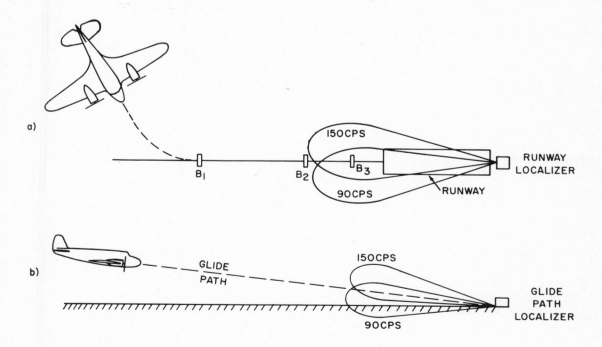

Fig. 17.8. *The ILS:* (a) A vertical view of the air field. B$_1$, B$_2$, B$_3$ are the marker beacons. The overlapping patterns of the runway localizer patterns mark the runway approach;

(b) A horizontal view. The aircraft follows the glide path set by the two patterns of the glide path localizer.

robot pilots is the instrument landing system, known familiarly as ILS. Any aircraft coming in for a landing changes position fairly rapidly in all three dimensions: vertically, it descends from a sizeable altitude to an altitude of zero when its landing gear hits the ground; in the horizontal plane, it may approach the landing strip from the side and require sharp banking—a combination of roll and yaw—to bring it into line with the runway. The function of the landing system transmitters, therefore, is to mark out a three-dimensional zone through which the aircraft must come for a safe touchdown.

Guidance in the horizontal plane is provided by *runway localizer* transmitters. The transmitters put out two signals, both of the same carrier frequency, with one carrier modulated by a 90 cps signal and the other by a 150 cps signal. Their antennas' directivity patterns are so distributed that one of these signals predominates on one side of the landing strip while the other signal covers the opposite side. In the center, both signals overlap and are consequently of equal strength. One or both of these signals is picked up by the aircraft receiver and is detected to provide the 90 and 150 cps modulating signal. Thus, from the relative strengths of the two signals, the man—or robot—in charge of piloting the aircraft is aware of the ship's deviation from the course it should follow to fly true to the landing runway. If either the 90 or 150 cps signal predominates, the ship is off to one side. It is only when the two signals are of equal strength that the aircraft is literally and figuratively on the beam.

Once the aircraft is guided along the line of the strip by the runway localizer, it encounters the signals of three successive low-powered transmitters known as marker beacons. The antennas of the beacons, planted at specified intervals along the line of approach to the runway, are arranged to throw up a pattern fanning out on either side of the center of the runway localizer pattern. These beacons are the modern version of the roadside milestones that once mutely informed the traveler of the distance to his destination.

Additional transmitters are required to guide the aircraft vertically. Here, ILS takes no chances, for it specifies a particular glide path for the incoming aircraft. The glide path, as the angle of descent for the aircraft, should neither be so close to the perpendicular that the ship has to be wrenched out of a dive, nor so small that the ship runs the risk of overshooting. The same system of signals, one with 90, the other with 150 cps modulation, is used to mark the upper and lower limits of the aircraft's glide path; one set of transmitter antennas angles up a directivity pattern to put a roof on the descent angle, another set provides the floor. With both the runway and glide path localizers

outlining an invisible corridor, the aircraft can safely complete its flight.

Sonar

From the three-dimensionl medium of the air, we go now to the three-dimensional medium beneath the sea's surface. The electromagnetic exploratory methods of light and electronics, so practical above the surface, are of not much use below it. They are too easily absorbed, too limited in their penetration. The best form of energy for undersea navigation, oddly enough, is sound, the kind of energy man knew best how to handle before he began gingerly to sail the first boat. Sound can travel faster and further through water than it can through air. While it is not an electromagnetic wave, it is a wave nevertheless, and can be exploited for underwater navigation and exploration just as radar is on land or in the air. The submariner's version of radar is called *sonar*, a word formed from the initial letters of SOund Navigation And Range.

Sonar may be active or passive. The active system is much like radar, working both as a transmitter and as a receiver of the sound signal. Passive sonar, on the other hand, is simply a listening station in the depths of the sea which samples the sounds arriving at it from different sources to obtain whatever information it is designed to obtain; it is, in short, a receiver of sound.

Active Sonar

In a sense, the transmitter in an active sonar system is the reverse of the radio transmitter. Where the radio transmitter begins with sound energy and ends in electrical energy, the sonar transmitter uses electricity as the raw material and produces sound as the finished product.

One of the ways in which this electricity-to-sound process can be accomplished is through the physical phenomenon of *magnetostriction*. Briefly, magnetostriction is the alternating elongation and contraction which takes place in the iron core of a transformer under the influence of the alternating current passing through the transformer's coils. If an iron core is inserted in the coils of the Armstrong oscillator of Chapter 8, for example, the core will vibrate mechanically along its length at the oscillator frequency. Now, if this magnetostriction oscillator were immersed in water—or any other fluid, for that matter—the iron core would compress and decompress the water particles in its immediate vicinity, thus propagating a train of sound waves through the fluid.

As a practical sonar transmitter, however, the magnetostriction oscillator will simply not do. Its output

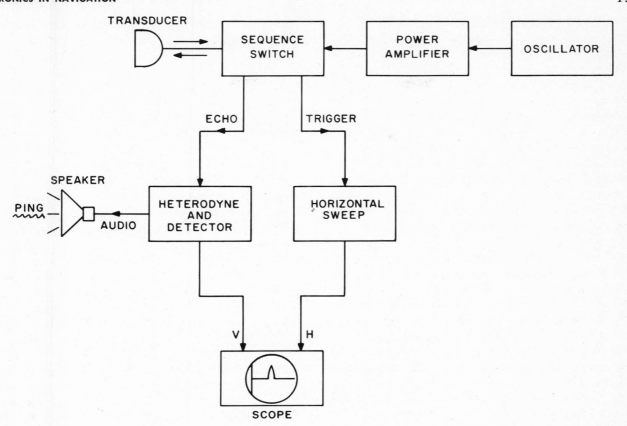

Fig. 17.9. *Active A-Scan Sonar:* **The arrangement is similar to radar. The seqence switch directs signal traffic, carrying transmitted pulses of a-c at ultrasonic frequencies from the power amplifier to the transducer and bringing received** **pulses from the transducer to the heterodyne amplifier. H and V are the signal voltages applied to the horizontal and vertical deflecting plates of the scope tube.**

is too weak. A much stronger system consists of an electrical oscillator to begin with, followed by a power amplifier which enormously strengthens the oscillator's output. The final step is to add a *transducer* capable of transforming the electrical energy of the power amplifier output into sound. These three stages—oscillator, power amplifier, and transducer—are the basic components of the sonar transmitter. The oscillator is usually crystal-controlled, working at a frequency in the ultrasonic range. The reason for so high a frequency is the same as that instinctive reason which motivates the bat in his use of ultrasonic tones to explore the depths of his cave (Chapter 6). The power amplifier of the transmitter is similar to amplifier circuits we have already seen. As for the transducer, it is simply a more sophisticated version of the speaker in the home radio set: through an intermediate mechanical process, it converts the electrical energy of the power amplifier into sound energy.

The transducer, however, has the added virtue of

being reversible. Not only can it convert electricity to sound, it can also perform the reverse process of converting sound into electricity. The latter capability permits it to work as the first stage in the sonar receiver. After the transmitter has sent out its ultrasonic wave and the wave has been reflected by some submerged object, the transducer picks up the reflection. What the single transmit-receive antenna is to radar, the single transmit-receive transducer is to sonar.

But this is not the only point of resemblance between radar and sonar. Some sort of switching control is needed to maintain proper signal traffic to and from the transducer. Furthermore, the continuous wave output of the oscillator, obtained via the power amplifier, must be chopped up into pulses equivalent to the ultrasonic cries emitted by the cave-exploring bat. Both functions are exercised by a sequence switch stage, a circuit which in many ways is similar to the duplexer of radar.

A- and PPI-Scan Sonar

We can now see how the A-scan sonar, analogous to the A-scope radar, operates. The crystal-controlled oscillator generates an a-c signal varying at the ultrasonic rate. This signal is strengthened by the power amplifier, and is then switched into and out of the transducer at a regular prf by the sequence switch. The connection between the power amplifier and transducer is maintained for only a short period. For this short interval, then, the transducer emits its ultrasonic burst into the surrounding water.

At a moment coinciding with the beginning of each pulse, the sequence switch also generates a trigger pulse which is communicated to the horizontal sweep circuit. The constantly rising voltage the circuit supplies appears across the horizontally deflecting plates of the scope tube. Thus the horizontal sweep of the scope tube writing beam begins at the same instant the transducer sends an ultrasonic pulse through the water medium.

After an interval of time, depending on the distance of the submerged target from the transducer, an ultrasonic echo is returned. The transducer converts this echo—an echo in the literal sense of the word—into an electrical signal which varies at the ultrasonic rate. The next step is to convert this ultrasonic pulse into a square pulse, a step undertaken by a detector circuit. This pulse is then applied to the vertical deflecting plates of the scope tube, thus becoming the blip representing the position of the target. Since the horizontal sweep of the scope writing beam begins at the instant the ultrasonic pulse is sent through the water, the distance of the blip from the beginning of the sweep is a measure of the distance between the transducer and the target. Thus the range of the target is determined. As for the target's direction with respect to the transducer, that can be found from the direction in which the transducer is trained as it keeps the target under surveillance.

The work of the A-scan sonar, in fact, almost precisely parallels the operation of the A-scope radar as described in Chapter 15. But there is an extra feature in sonar which gives its operator a method of judging aurally the information which the A-scope gives him visually. A portion of the electrical signal fed from the power amplifier to the sequence switch is brought to a heterodyne circuit which contains an oscillator. As a result of the heterodyning between the inaudible ultrasonic signal and the heterodyne oscillator signal, an audio beat note is created which, when put through a loudspeaker, emerges as a "ping" tone. This tone, of course, represents the transmitted pulse. When the echo returns to the transducer, it is conducted by the sequence switch to the heterodyne circuit and comes through the loudspeaker as a fainter ping. Thus the time interval between the strong and weak pings is an indication of the distance between the transducer and the target.

In the A-scan system, the transducer is kept focused on the target by a mechanical system similar to that which keeps the A-scope radar antenna trained on its target. But a sonar system using a PPI scope can be set up in which the transducer rotates continuously to plot a map of the ocean floor just as the antenna in the radar PPI system rotates to map the surface of the ground. A system of this kind is designed along the same lines as the PPI radar, with a similar method of synchronization between the rotating transducer and a rotating scope tube deflection coil (Chapter 6).

Sonar in War and Peace

The application to which sonar can be put in times of war is obvious: anti-submarine warfare; or, as the Navy puts it, ASW. Usually it is the task of the "tin can"—the destroyer—to seek out and exterminate enemy submarines. Most destroyers, therefore, are equipped with active sonar systems in which the transducer is slung under the keel in a submerged, water-filled dome. For the submarine itself, however, active sonar is hazardous since it may give away the vessel's position to a hunting destroyer. The submarine commander uses the active sonar system with extreme caution, employing it as a navigation device when he is sure nobody is within listening range. He usually depends on the more discreet passive sonar, which consists of little more than a transducer, an audio amplifier, and a loudspeaker. With this, he can detect the churning engines of his mortal enemy as well as those of possible victims.

A byproduct of sonar, in World War II, was the demonstration that sea creatures can talk—or at least produce a weird conglomeration of grunts, whistles, and barks. And more than once, dense schools of fish have caused the rapid ping-ping, ping-ping to drive a ship's crew to battle stations. But even these practical jokes of wartime sonar bore fruits in the peace that followed. Fishermen now use sonar to track down such schools, and a scientist is even trying to teach porpoises to talk.

GLOSSARY

Aileron. The hinged flap in either wing of an aircraft.
Altimeter. A device which measures the altitude of an aircraft.
Autopilot. An automatic piloting system for aircraft.
Azimuth. The circle of the compass marked off in 360

degrees, with the zero mark at north.

Cardioid. The heart-shaped directivity pattern of a loop and sensing antenna.

D-f signal. The 30 cps signal of a military direction finder.

Elevator. The horizontal hinged flap in the tail assembly of an aircraft.

Fix. The position, in latitude and longitude, of a ship.

Glide path. The downward path followed by an aircraft in landing.

Glide path localizer. The transmitter, in the ILS, which sets the glide path for the homing aircraft.

Gyroscope. A steadying device consisting of a rapidly rotating disc pivoted in a frame; same as *gyro*.

Hyperbola. A curve drawn between two fixed points such that the difference between the distances from any point on the curve to the two fixed points is the same.

Hyperbolic navigation. A system of radio navigation based on the hyperbola.

ILS. Instrument landing system; a navigational device for aircraft.

Loran. Abbreviation for "long range navigation," a hyperbolic system.

Magnetostriction. The expansion and contraction in length of the iron core of a coil through which an a-c current is passed.

Phasemeter. A device which measures the phase of an a-c signal.

Pitch axis. The straight line joining the wing tips of an aircraft.

Precession. The rotation of a gyro around its output axis as the result of an applied torque about its input axis.

Radio direction finder. A radio receiver with a special antenna capable of locating the direction of a transmitter; a navigation device.

Roll axis. The straight line joining the nose and tail of an aircraft.

Rudder. The vertical hinged flap in the tail assembly of an aircraft.

Runway localizer. The transmitter, in the ILS, which sets the runway path for the homing aircraft.

Sensing antenna. A vertical conductor which, together with the loop antenna, forms the cardioid.

Sequence switch. The stage in an active sonar system which controls transmitted and received signals.

Servomechanism. A self-correcting device which converts an electrical signal into a mechanical shaft rotation.

Shoran. Abbreviation for "short range navigation," a triangulation navigational device.

Sonar. Abbreviation for "sound navigation and range," an instrument for undersea navigation and detection.

Torque. A force exerted on a rigid body which results in the rotation of that body around one of its axes.

Transducer. In general, a device which converts one kind of energy into another.

VOR. Very high frequency omnidirectional radio range; a device to aid aircraft in locating their home base.

Yaw axis. A vertical line through the fuselage of an aircraft, and perpendicular to the plane of the pitch and roll axes.

Chapter Eighteen

SEMICONDUCTORS

UP UNTIL recently, as the history of science is reckoned, electronic engineers have tended to think of different materials as either conductors or insulators. Conductors are metals which contain so many free electrons that only a small voltage applied across the metal is needed to set an appreciable current flowing; insulators are non-metallic materials in which the electrons are so tightly bound to their atoms that a very large voltage is required before a measurable current can flow. While metals like copper, aluminum, and silver are excellent conductors of electricity, non-metals like rubber, glass, and dry wood are not.

Few people, however, gave much thought to the class of materials lying between these two extremes—materials which are neither conductors nor insulators, and so are given the rather vague title of *semiconductors*. But with the discovery that such semiconductors as germanium and silicon possess valuable electrical properties if properly treated, the course of electronics took a sharp turn in the direction of solid state physics —the science of semiconductors—which has been called part physics, part chemistry, and part instinct.

Doping

Germanium is a gray-white metal which, as used in electronics, takes a crystalline form. As a metal, germanium should be an excellent conductor, but it actually is not. The reason for this odd behavior is that the four extra electrons of the germanium atom form a strong bond with the four extra electrons of a neighboring atom in the crystal, and consequently are not free to move easily. To get an appreciable current

through the material, a heavy voltage would have to be connected across the crystal—a process which might destroy the crystal's regular structure. Pure germanium is therefore a difficult material in electronics. If it is tinged with small quantities of an impurity, however, it can be tremendously useful. This process of *doping* is an important one in the manufacture of semiconductors.

If the germanium crystal is doped with tiny amounts of arsenic, a metal whose atom has five extra electrons, the crystal will accept an arsenic atom into its structure. But only four of the arsenic atom's extra electrons will form a bond with a germanium atom in the crystal, thus leaving one electron free to roam. The arsenic atom now becomes a positive ion (Chapter 1) since it has lost an electron; it is called a *donor* because it has given an electron to the germanium. Crystals doped to obtain free electrons are said to be N-type, the "N" indicating that unbound negative charges are present.

By a similar but reverse process, pure germanium can be converted to a P or positive type of crystal in which there is not only a lack of free electrons, but actually less than a lack, strange as it may seem. If the pure germanium crystal is doped by a substance like aluminum, which has three extra electrons, the aluminum atom will form a bond with a germanium atom; but since the aluminum atom can offer only three electrons, an electron is missing from the bond. The missing electron is called, for lack of a better name, a *hole*. Since the aluminum-germanium bond is minus a minus electron, the hole is equivalent to a positive charge. Normally, if the aluminum atom were just another germanium atom, the hole would be occupied by an

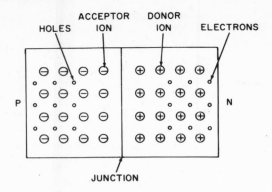

HOLES   ACCEPTOR   DONOR
         ION   ION   ELECTRONS

P   N

JUNCTION

Fig. 18.1. *The P-N Junction:* **At the time of union between P and N type germanium crystals, the electrons in N nearest the junction combine with corresponding holes across division, leaving positive donor and negative acceptor ions to face each other across the junction. The electric field between these oppositely charged ions cannot extend into the depth of the crystals, hence no further movement of charges takes place.**

electron. The aluminum atom can thus be considered as having taken an electron, and so is called an *acceptor* ion, an ion with a negative charge.

The hole is capable of behaving as if it were a positively charged electron. Like an electron, it may move from point to point within the crystal. If, for example, an electron moves from atom A in the crystal to fill a hole in atom B, atom A now possesses the hole left behind by the roving electron, while the hole formerly belonging to atom B has vanished. In effect, the hole in atom B has moved to atom A.

The P-N Junction

When a thin slab of N germanium is held in close contact with a thin slab of P germanium, a small momentary current flows even though no voltage is connected across the two. The electrons in the N slab nearest the contacting surfaces feel the attraction of the holes just beyond the junction. Both the electrons and holes migrate towards each other and an initial current flows across the boundary. Once these neighboring electrons and holes have canceled each other, the particles left facing one other across the junction are the negative donor ions on the P side and the positive acceptor ions on the N side. The electric field between these two sets of immobilized ions terminates on the ions themselves, and the electrons and holes in the depths of the crystals feel no forces and therefore remain where they are. After the first flow of current, then, interaction between the N and P crystals ceases.

If a battery is now connected across the N-P combination with the negative pole connected to P and the positive to N, only a very little continuous flow of current will take place. The negative terminal of the battery exerts an attractive force on the holes in the P section, pulling the holes to that end of the combination, while the positive terminal pulls the electrons of the N section to itself. As a consequence, there is no appreciable movement of charges across the junction. The small current that does flow is mostly the result of the vibration of atoms in the crystal stimulated by the heat the crystals contain. Because this vibration tends to shake some electrons out of their places, a few holes form on the N side of the junction and move across the boundary under the attraction of the negative acceptor ions on the P side. A P-N crystal connected to a battery in this fashion is said to be under *reverse bias*.

When the P-N crystal is given a *forward bias*—that is, when the battery connections are reversed so that the positive pole is wired to P while the negative is wired to N—matters take an entirely different turn. Under the electromotive force of the battery's voltage, the holes in the P section are repelled away from the positive battery terminal and driven toward the junction border. Similarly, electrons in the N portion rush to the border to meet and neutralize the holes. Since the march of holes from P to N is equivalent to a movement of electrons from N to P, a strong current flows through the circuit of the battery and the P-N unit. Moreover, if the forward bias voltage should be increased, the current in the circuit will increase correspondingly.

The account of the P-N junction just given is closely analogous to the discussion of the vacuum tube diode of Chapter 2. If a P-N crystal is substituted for the diode in any of the circuits in that chapter, the circuit will operate in precisely the same way; the N crystal replaces the cathode of the diode and the P crystal the plate.

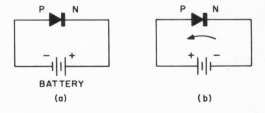

P   N   P   N

− + | + − |
BATTERY
(a)   (b)

Fig. 18.2. *Schematic Diagram of Diode Action of P-N Junction:* **In (a), only a small leakage current flows under reverse bias voltage. With forward bias (b), heavy current flows. The arrowhead in the schematic symbol of the P-N junction conventionally points in the direction of hole flow; the arrow in (b) indicates the direction of electron current.**

The Zener Diode

When the P-N combination is operated under a forward bias voltage, a fairly large current pushed by a relatively small voltage passes through the crystal. Thus the crystal is, in effect, a low resistance element. Under a reverse bias, the current produced is small even though the bias voltage is raised to a fairly high level. The crystal then becomes a high resistance element. Many high resistances, subjected to a high voltage, may generate enough heat to damage themselves. A similar effect occurs if the reverse bias voltage across the P-N junction is raised to higher and higher levels; but a second interesting phenomenon also takes place.

Reverse biasing, as we have seen, means connecting the P section of the crystal diode to the negative terminal of the biasing battery while the N section is connected to the positive terminal. As the bias voltage is raised, the bonded electrons in the P region feel the pull of the battery's electric field and strain towards the positive terminal. With a further increase in voltage, a point is reached at which the bonded electrons break away and, in heading across the junction, smash into the ions in their path to release additional electrons. Thus reverse bias can achieve a breakdown value at which a powerful current flows through a P-N diode in a direction opposite to the normal forward flow. This breakdown situation, accompanied by high temperatures, is capable of destroying the crystalline structure.

It is possible, however, to dope the diode in such fashion that the heavy reverse current flowing at breakdown leaves the crystal completely unharmed. Such a diode is known as the *zener,* after a pioneer investigator of the semiconductor breakdown phenomenon.

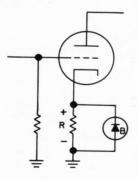

Fig. 18.3. *The Zener Diode as Voltage Stabilizer:* **The zener diode can be used in place of the capacitor in a cathode biasing circuit if the voltage across the cathode resistor is at least equal to the zener breakdown voltage. To distinguish the zener symbol from that of the ordinary crystal diode, it is surrounded by a circle and labeled "B."**

Some Notes on the Zener

If the ordinary P-N diode can duplicate its vacuum tube namesake, the zener diode can duplicate the gas tube diode discussed in Chapter 6. That this is true is obvious from the preceding description of the breakdown process in semiconductors, which is practically identical with the explanation of gas breakdown as presented in that chapter.

When breakdown occurs, the voltage across the diode remains constant while the current through it is permitted to vary. Thus the zener diode can be—and often is—used as a voltage regulator. In this function, it is connected across a power supply bleeder resistor in reverse bias fashion, with the P end of the diode connected to the negative terminal of the supply and the N end to the positive terminal. This same knack of the zener for stabilizing voltage is also applicable in the cathode biasing circuit of a vacuum tube amplifier (Chapter 4). The purpose of the capacitor in that circuit is to keep the voltage across the cathode resistor constant. The same effect can be achieved if the condenser is replaced by a zener.

Just as the firing current in the gas tube can be halted by reduction of the voltage across the tube, an end can be made to the breakdown regime of the zener if the voltage across the diode is reduced below the breakdown level. After the cessation of breakdown, the zener is in as healthy a condition as it was before. In fact, the zener diode is often used as a safety device for bypassing excessive currents resulting from high voltages, an application calling for repeated breakdowns of the crystal.

P-N-P Transistors

If diodes were the only contribution of semiconductors to the electronic art, they would still be worth the effort. But the semiconductor is much more versatile. The addition of a second P crystal to the *P-N* combination can turn a diode into an amplifying triode. The *transistor* thus formed not only rivals the vacuum tube triode but is superior to it in so many ways that the latter seems destined for obsolescence.

Two P-type germanium or silicon crystals separated by a narrow layer of N-type make up the P-N-P transistor. In the usual operation of the transistor, an external voltage is applied between one of the P sections and the N layer in a forward bias connection; that is, with the positive terminal of the voltage at P and the negative at N. The same activity that takes place in the P-N diode then takes place between these two sections of the triode: a current of holes passes from the P to

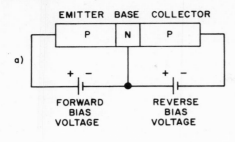

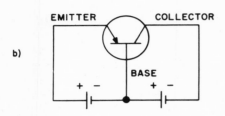

Fig. 18.4. *The P-N-P Transistor:* **(a) The transistor is formed by sandwiching a narrow block of N type between two larger blocks of P type germanium. In normal operation, the emitter-base junction is forward-biased while the base-collector junction is reverse-biased. The schematic symbol of P-N-P transistor is shown in (b). The arrowhead of the schematic indicates the direction of hole flow.**

the N section. Because it emits holes under the stimulation of forward biasing, this P section is known as the *emitter.* The function of the other P section is to collect these holes; this second P section is therefore called the *collector.* The N section serves as reference point for both P's, and is consequently known as the *base.* Normal amplifier application of the transistor calls for reverse biasing between base and collector for reasons which will shortly become evident.

The riddle of transistor operation can best be unraveled by thinking of the device as a combination of two semiconductor diodes. The first of these diodes is the P-N of emitter and base; the second is the N-P of base and collector. Suppose we begin by considering the base-collector diode, reverse biased, with no biasing voltage applied to the other diode. Because of the reversed bias, the holes in the collector P region are repelled toward the negative battery terminal, leaving the negative acceptor ions in the P region to face the base-collector junction. As long as no biasing voltage is applied between emitter and collector, no current—other than a tiny, unimportant leakage flow—can traverse the junction between base and collector.

Suppose, however, that a forward bias is now connected between the emitter and the base. Since the biasing here is in the forward direction, a fairly heavy flow of holes from the emitter floods into the base. If the

precaution has been taken, in the fabrication of the transistor, of doping the emitter section more heavily than the base, few holes entering the base will encounter electrons with which to combine. The base region is then filled with moving holes. These, being positively charged, are attracted to the negative acceptor ions just over the junction and flow through the collector into the external circuit.

The secret of the transistor's success lies in two facts: first, that a small increase in forward bias across the emitter-base diode produces a large current flow between emitter and base; second, that practically all the holes injected into the base reach the collector. Consequently, if an a-c signal source is connected between the emitter and the positive terminal of the emitter bias battery, the rise and fall of the signal voltage will cause a large corresponding rise and fall of emitter-base hole current. This hole current will then pass almost unaltered in intensity to the collector. If a load resistor is wired between the collector and its bias battery, a large signal voltage will appear across the resistor. Thus the transistor circuit becomes an amplifier: its output voltage, appearing across the collector load resistor, varies in much the same manner as the input signal source, but swings to much stronger extremes.

This explanation sheds a glimmer of light on the reason for the transistor's name. The term "transistor" is a telescoped version of the two words "transfer" and "resistor." The forward-biased emitter and base diode permits an easy *transfer* of current; the reverse-biased base and collector diode offers a high *resistance* junction which is overcome when the transfer is made.

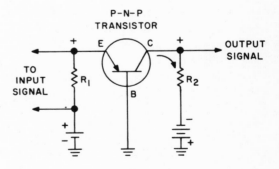

Fig. 18.5. *The Transistor Amplifier:* R_1 **is the emitter load resistor and** R_2 **the collector load resistor. When the input signal is positive, as shown, hole current through** R_2 **is maximum, giving the top of** R_2 **a highly positive potential with respect to the bottom end; when the input signal is negative, hole current through** R_2 **is minimum, putting a low voltage on the same polarity across** R_2**. Since holes are positive charges, the terminal of** R_2 **at which they enter is positive with respect to the opposite terminal. E, C, and B stand for emitter, collector, and base.**

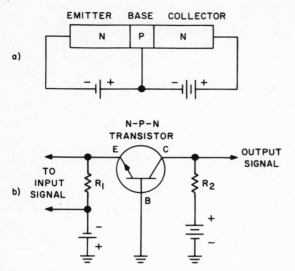

Fig. 18.6. *The N-P-N Transistor:* The construction of the N-P-N transistor is shown in (a); a schematic diagram of an N-P-N amplifier circuit is shown in (b), with R₁ and R₂ as emitter and collector load resistors. The arrow in the transistor symbol is in the direction of the hole current flow, according to the convention. In this circuit, the output signal is in phase with the input signal: when the input signal swings positive, the output signal is also in its positive phase.

N-P-N Transistor

The miracle of the P-N-P sandwich can be duplicated in reverse. When two large blocks of N-type germanium are separated by a narrow block of P crystal, an N-P-N arrangement is produced. In the construction of the N-P-N transistor, measures are taken to insure that the flow of current from emitter to base is not reduced by much when it continues on to the collector. These measures are the same as those which apply to the P-N-P type: the base material is only slightly doped,

and is much narrower than the crystals on either side of it. The biasing method is also the same, with the emitter-base diode biased forward, and the base-collector diode biased reversed.

Discussion of the N-P-N transistor amplifier circuit is best carried on in terms of electrons, however, rather than holes. When the input signal swings negative, its voltage is added to the bias voltage to stimulate the heavy flow of electrons from emitter to base. The collector picks up these electrons in quantity, and a large negative voltage appears across the collector load resistor. On the positive swing of the input signal, many fewer electrons seep into the collector region, and the voltage across the collector load is at a low negative value—equivalent, that is, to a high positive value. Thus the output signal reflects the variations of the input signal, but in an amplified version. In short, the action of the N-P-N transistor closely follows that of the P-N-P.

Common Base, Emitter, and Collector

The transistor circuits discussed so far have all had the same arrangement, the base of the transistor connected in common with the input and output circuits. But the transistor is versatile enough to be connected in other ways as well. Perhaps the most popular arrangement is the common emitter circuit, in which the input signal is coupled to the base of the transistor, and the output is taken off the collector. Regardless of the set-up of the circuit, however, the biasing of the transistor elements remain the same: forward between emitter and base, reversed between base and collector.

When the signal fed to the base of the P-N-P transistor is in its positive phase, the net voltage between emitter and base is slightly negative. This is true as long as the peak voltage of the input a-c signal is less than the bias voltage. With only a small forward voltage, then, the collector hole current is small, and the

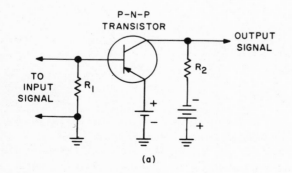

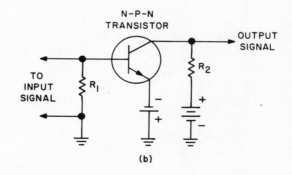

Fig. 18.7. *Common Emitter Connection:* The effect of the P-N-P circuit (a) and the N-P-N circuit (b) is the same. The signal output of both circuits is out of phase with the input signal.

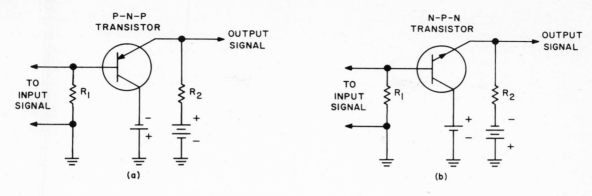

Fig. 18.8. *Common Collector Circuit:* In both circuits, the output signal is in phase with the input signal.

output voltage of the collector load resistor is at a low positive level—equivalent to a high negative level. Thus a positive swing of the input voltage produces a negative swing in voltage at the output of the circuit.

If the common emitter circuit is that of an N-P-N transistor, the effect is exactly the same. A positive swing of the input signal at the base adds to the forward emitter-base bias, and an intense current of *electrons* flows from the emitter to the base. These electrons are picked up by the collector. Since the point at which electrons enter a resistor is negative, the output voltage at the collector load resistor is a high negative value. Again, a positive swing of the input signal results in an amplified negative swing at the output.

In the common collector circuit, an in-phase condition between the input signal and the output signal prevails. For the P-N-P transistor connected in this fashion, a negative swing of the input signal produces a strong current of holes from emitter to base and from base to collector. The point at which these holes enter the load resistor is positive, leaving the output end of the resistor negative. A similar analysis using electrons instead of holes shows that the same situation is true of the N-P-N transistor.

From the foregoing explanations of P-N-P and N-P-N transistors in their different connections, two points stand out. One is that, regardless of the type of transistor used, the circuits give the same results—at least as far as the relative phases of output and input signals are concerned—if they are similarly connected. The second is that in the common emitter circuit, the phase of the output signal is *inverted* with respect to the input signal; in both the other circuits, the phase of the input signal is preserved at the output. This latter is an important point. In audio circuits, the phase of the signal does not much matter when the signal is applied to the receiver speaker to be transformed into sound. As long as the audio signal is in all other respects faithful to the sound

originally generating it, the speaker output will be equally faithful to the original sound. But in video circuits, the phase of the signal is extremely important (Chapter 14). As time goes on, TV receivers become increasingly transistorized; phase inversion effects of transistors are consequently worth the television engineer's attention.

Transistor Amplifiers

While no harm will be done if the output signal of an audio amplifier is out of phase with the input signal, a definite departure from the wave *shape* of the output signal compared with the input will cause distortion (Chapter 4).

In that chapter, it was pointed out that overdriving can cause distortion in a triode vacuum tube amplifier. The same is true of the transistor audio amplifier. With a normal signal at the transistor amplifier input, the circuit works effectively. But if, in any circuit, the input signal is allowed to swing to peaks greater than the forward base-emitter bias voltage, the output signal will suffer distortion in some part of its cycle. We can see how this works in the case of the usual type of transistor connection—the common emitter type—used for audio amplification.

If the transistor involved is a P-N-P, the base of the transistor is biased negative with respect to the emitter. When the input signal is in its negative swing, the base-emitter voltage is increased in the forward direction. As long as this increase in voltage is within the capabilities of the transistor, the corresponding swing of the output voltage will not be distorted. On the positive swing of the input signal, however, the net voltage between base and emitter is reduced. If the positive swing exceeds the base-emitter bias, the net effect is to give the base a positive *reverse* bias. No hole current can flow from emitter to base during this portion of the input signal cycle, and no current can flow through the collector load resistor. The result is distortion in the output signal. This situation of an excessive positive swing of the input signal corresponds to that described in Chapter 4, in which the grid of a vacuum tube triode becomes positive, and by so doing causes distortion of the output signal.

An excessive negative swing of the input signal in this same transistor situation can also cause trouble. The high forward emitter-base voltage thus produced pushes a strong hole current from emitter to base and into the collector. The consequent large positive potential at the point at which current enters the load may drive the transistor into its saturation region, in which the collector becomes so highly positive that the base-collector voltage is in an abnormal forward direction when it should actually be reversed. When this happens, the collector voltage changes only slightly regardless of the collector current. The transistor is just as prone to saturation and the distortion resulting from saturation as the vacuum tube triode.

Classifying Transistor Amplifiers

Many such comparisons can be made between the transistor and the vacuum tube triode. Although the two are based on widely differing principles, they behave in just about the same way. The emitter in the transistor sprays current carriers—holes or electrons—just as the cathode in the vacuum tube sprays electrons; the collector absorbs the current carriers just as the plate absorbs electrons; and the base is interposed between emitter and collector just as the grid is interposed between cathode and plate.

It follows that the transistor in its amplification function can be classified as A, AB, B, and C in the same manner as the vacuum tube amplifier. In the Class A amplifier, a full cycle of collector current flows for a full cycle of input voltage. This implies that the emitter-base voltage will not be permitted to swing past the normal forward bias and that the voltage across the collector load will be such as to keep the collector-base voltage in the normal reverse direction. With the normal bias voltages applied at all times, normal current flows through the collector circuit at all times. As in the vacuum tube Class A amplifier, the outstanding asset of the Class A transistor amplifier is minimum distortion. Its liability is poor efficiency.

The efficiency of the amplifier can be increased by giving the emitter-base diode a zero or even a slightly reversed bias. No collector current can then flow as long as no input signal is applied to the base. But if a signal is given to the base of a P-N-P transistor connected in common-emitter fashion, only the negative half of the input cycle will produce a corresponding voltage swing

at the output; the positive half cannot be reproduced because the emitter-base voltage is in reverse during that half-cycle. Thus the signal undergoes severe distortion in the loss, at the output, of one half of the wave. This is the result of Class B amplifier operation, in which the amplifying device is biased at cutoff. The definition of Class B operation for the transistor is thus practically the same as for the vacuum tube.

The Class AB situation also reflects a close parallel between transistor and vacuum tube. Here there is a forward bias between emitter and base, but the bias is not so large as to exceed the input signal swing. For most but not all of the input cycle, therefore, there is a corresponding signal at the collector.

Finally, Class C is that mode of amplifier operation in which the emitter-base bias is fairly large in the reverse direction. Only a small portion of the input signal is negative enough—in the P-N-P transistor connected in the common-emitter manner—to drive the emitter-base voltage in the forward direction, and only that small portion of the signal is reproduced at the amplifier's output. Here again the parallel between transistor and vacuum tube is preserved.

The Transistor Tetrode

While analogies between the transistor and the vacuum tube are useful, they can be pushed too far. At least one example is the transistor tetrode. Unlike the vacuum tube tetrode, which has four active elements, the transistor tetrode has the same three elements as the transistor types discussed above. The justification for the "tetrode" title—the word means "four-electrode"—is the fact that a fourth connecting wire is added to the three terminals the usual transistor possesses.

The new connection is made to the base, but at its opposite side. In the normal operation of the tetrode, this second base terminal is given a d-c voltage opposed in polarity to the bias voltage of the other base connection; for example, the voltage applied to the second base terminal of the P-N-P transistor is positive since the original base terminal for that transistor is biased negatively. The following paragraph demonstrates the superiority of the P-N-P tetrode over the ordinary three-terminal arrangement.

Let us assume, to begin with, that no voltage is applied to the second base terminal. In normal P-N-P fashion, holes from the emitter P region diffuse throughout the base. But if a positive voltage is applied to the second base terminal, the holes are repelled away from the area to which this terminal is connected and are forced to move through the base region along a very narrow corridor close to the original base contact. As a result, the activity between emitter and base, and between base and collector, is restricted to much smaller

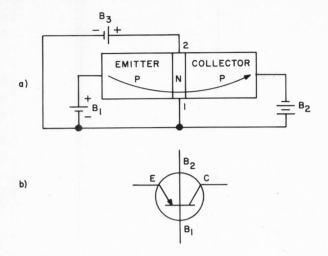

Fig. 18.9. *The P-N-P Tetrode:* **The action of the tetrode is illustrated in (a). Holes flowing from emitter to collector through the base region are repelled into a narrow corridor at the bottom of the region by the electric field of the second base terminal (2). B_1 and B_2 are the normal biasing batteries of emitter and collector; B_3 is the bias voltage for base terminal 2. The schematic drawing of the P-N-P tetrode is shown in (b). E is the emitter, C the collector, and B_1 and B_2 the first and second base terminals.**

areas of the junctions between the three sections. In this last sentence can be detected the advantage of the four-terminal over the three-terminal transistor: since the effective areas between the three sections are shrunken, the capacitance between them is diminished. The tetrode can therefore operate at much higher frequencies without the threat of regenerative oscillation caused by capacitive coupling between output and input. This, as a glance back at Chapter 5 will show, was precisely the reason for the development of the vacuum tube tetrode.

Semiconductors vs. Vacuum Tubes

From what we have seen of semiconductors, they can duplicate practically every feat of which the vacuum tube is capable. This in itself would not be much of an argument for the former; but the semiconductor possesses so many other virtues that it is only a question of time until it thrusts the tube into the limbo of forgotten electronic components.

First and foremost, the semiconductor has no heater and needs none. The problem of carrying away the heat developed in electronic gear is considerably less important in transistorized equipment.

Packaging, too, is simplified. The transistor in the pocket-sized receivers so many teenagers carry around with them is about as big as the teenager's fingertip. In military electronic equipments such as the proximity

fuze and the sidewinder—shells which detonate automatically when they near an enemy aircraft—the required diodes and amplifiers can be crammed into the limited space available. The elaborate electronic measuring instruments which make up the payloads of our space-exploring rockets use semiconductors for the same reason.

Again, the space engineer prefers semiconductors because they are sturdier than vacuum tubes; the rocket payload is subject to tremendous mechanical strains from vibration and acceleration of the powerful engines. The weight of the payload is another consideration; the development of the tiny transistor has encouraged manufacturers of resistors, capacitors, and other electronic components to minimize their products in proportion, and a few pounds of equipment can work just as well—if not better—than the much weightier apparatus of just a few years ago.

GLOSSARY

Acceptor ion. An atom in a doped semiconductor crystal which accepts an electron or gives up a hole.

Base. The middle section of a transistor.

Collector. The transistor terminal which collects charge carriers.

Donor ion. An atom in a doped semiconductor crystal which gives up an electron.

Doping. The process of adding alien elements to a semiconductor crystal to supply it with charge carriers—electrons or holes.

Emitter. The transistor terminal which emits charge carriers.

Forward bias. A voltage applied to a P-N crystal such that the positive terminal of the voltage is applied to the P section and the negative to the N section.

Hole. A freely moving positive charge in a doped semiconductor crystal.

Junction. The interface between an N and P section.

N-P-N. A transistor composed of two N-type crystals separated by a P-type.

N-type. A semiconductor crystal doped to provide excess electrons.

P-N-P. A transistor composed of two P-type crystals separated by an N-type.

P-type. A semiconductor crystal doped to provide excess holes.

Reverse bias. A voltage applied to a P-N crystal such that the positive terminal of the voltage is applied to the N section and the negative to the P section.

Semiconductor. A material which partially conducts an electric current.

Transistor. A three-element semiconductor device consisting of emitter, base, and collector.

Transistor tetrode. A transistor in which an extra terminal is supplied to the base.

Zener. A semiconductor diode which, under reverse bias, is capable of conducting heavy currents.

Chapter Nineteen

COMPUTERS

EVER SINCE Adam was banished from the Garden of Eden under the heavy curse of having to earn his bread by the sweat of his brow, his descendants have earnestly devoted themselves to the problem of how to dodge work. Now, electronics may not provide the final solution to this overriding problem, but it can go a long way toward solving the smaller tactical puzzles in the grand strategy. And it has gone a long way by giving us the computer.

Unlike most other electronic devices discussed in this book, the computer does not depend on any interchange of signals through space. No receivers or transmitters are involved, although the computer may be part of a system in which they play a part. The computer's only purpose is to solve problems of one kind or another on the basis of information fed to it. Usually, it employs electron tubes or semiconductors in making its calculations; and since it is often difficult to divide its character into purely electronic and purely mechanical facets, the whole comes into the province of the electronic engineer.

There are two kinds of computers, broadly speaking, which engage the electronic engineer's attention. The first is the analog type, a device in which a quantity is expressed in the form of an electrical voltage or a mechanical rotation; the quantity, that is to say, is converted into its electrical or mechanical analog. The second is the digital type, in which the computation is made in discrete units. It is by no means a coincidence that the word "digit" means both finger and number; if ancient man used his fingers and toes as units in his simple calculations, modern man uses unit electrical pulses for his more intricate mathematical efforts.

While so complex a subject as computers cannot be adequately covered in a single chapter—or even a single volume—a fairly clear idea of the components and basic principles of both types can be conveyed. We begin with the analog computer.

Synchro Motors and Generators

We have already been introduced to some of the components used in analog computers. Back in Chapter 6, the synchro motor was mentioned as a device whose shaft goes through an output rotation under the influence of an input signal, and the synchro generator as a device which produces an output signal when its shaft is given an input rotation. It is obvious from these definitions that each instrument is the reverse of the other. Despite that, however, their essential construction is much the same. Each consists of a stator with three coils connected electrically in the form of a capital Y, and a single rotor coil mechanically joined to the shaft. Connected to the rotor coil is a source of a-c voltage, usually about 26 volts, with a frequency of either 60 or 400 cps. It is important for the accuracy of the computer that this *excitation* voltage, as it is called, be maintained as close as possible to its proper voltage and frequency.

If the device is a generator, its output signal will be conducted out along three wires, one of which is connected to each leg of the Y. The voltage at each of these wires depends on how the rotor coil is oriented with respect to the particular stator coil to which the wire is connected. For example, if the shaft is set so that the rotor coil is parallel to one of the coils in the

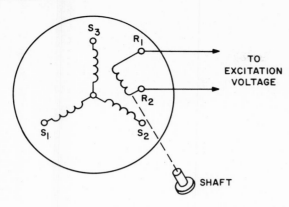

Fig. 19.1. *Synchro Motor or Generator:* **In the synchro motor, a voltage is applied to each of the three stator terminals (S_1, S_2, S_3) and the excited rotor coil (R_1, R_2) turns the shaft to a particular angle. In the synchro generator, the voltages at S_1, S_2, and S_3 are the result of the angle to which the rotor is turned. In analog computer schematics, electrical connections are shown in solid lines, mechanical connections in dashed lines.**

Y, a situation of close coupling will exist between the two coils; in that case, the stator coil will share most of the magnetic field inside the rotor, and the voltage across the stator will be a maximum. The situation is reversed when the rotor is at right angles to a particular stator coil; then the linkage between the two is a minimum, and the voltage induced in the stator is a minimum. Thus, in the synchro generator, the voltage at each of the three legs of the Y at any moment is a measure of the angle to which the shaft of the generator happens to be turned.

The synchro motor action begins when signal voltages are applied to each of the Y stator coil terminals. Then a magnetic field is created in each stator coil, and each exerts a force on the rotor's own magnetic field of excitation. The position the rotor finally attains is the resultant of these three forces. As long as the voltages applied to the three stator leads remain fixed, the shaft of the synchro motor will remain in this equilibrium position. A change in those voltages will drive the rotor into finding and settling at a new angle.

The Synchro Control Transformer

The synchro motor is a transducer; it simply converts the three-cornered electrical energy applied to it into the mechanical energy of a rotating shaft. It is also something of a slave since its activity is controlled from a distant source. But if a slight change is made in it, it can become more than a mere slave by perform-

ing the simple arithmetical process of subtraction. The change consists in removing the excitation voltage from the rotor coil.

When that change is made, the rotor coil becomes the source of an output voltage. The input voltage is still the three-terminal voltage applied to the Y-shaped stator coils, and the rotor coil is close enough to those coils to have a voltage induced in it. However, the magnitude of that voltage depends on the orientation of the rotor with respect to the stator coils; and since the rotor is mechanically joined to the shaft, the output voltage depends on the rotation applied to the shaft. In effect, this instrument is a transformer, with the three stator coils as its primaries, and the rotor as a secondary. A device of this sort, having three Y-connected primaries and a rotating secondary controlled by a shaft, is called a *synchro control transformer*.

In a typical application of the synchro control transformer, its three electrical input signals come from a synchro generator. From the description of the synchro generator, given earlier, it is apparent that the signal input to the control transformer depends on the angle of rotation of this generator's shaft. Thus the signal output of the control transformer rotor depends in part on the shaft rotation of the generator. As we have just found, that output depends also on the angle of rotation of the control transformer shaft. Now, there is a

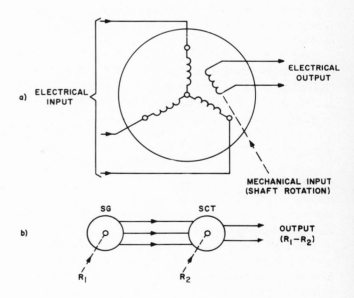

Fig. 19.2. *The Synchro Control Transformer:* **The schematic of the transformer is shown in (a). In (b), the method of connection of the synchro generator (SG) to the synchro control transformer (SCT) is shown. The electrical output of the SCT is proportional to the difference between the angle of rotation of the synchro generator shaft (R_1) and the angle of rotation of the synchro control transformer shaft (R_2).**

position of the control transformer rotor such that its output is a minimum—practically zero. That null voltage occurs when the angle of rotation of the generator shaft is equal to the angle of rotation of the control transformer shaft. Thus the output of the control transformer is a measure of the difference between the angles to which the two shafts are turned; obviously, if both angles are equal, the difference between them is zero.

The Servomechanism

The ability of the SCT—the synchro control transformer—to detect the difference between two shaft rotation angles suggests that it might be used as an error detector, just as the discriminator circuit is used as an error detector in the automatic frequency control system (Chapter 11). The blocks of the afc system form a closed loop, a fact responsible for the system's error-defeating tendencies. Similar closed loops in the analog computer can help reduce its errors. Where the afc arrangement is strictly electronic, however, the computer's are electromechanical. A closed loop of the latter type, made up of components which are both electrical and mechanical, is known as a *servomechanism,* or servo for short. It would be no exaggeration to say that the servo is one of the most important inventions of modern times, for it is not only basic to the computer, but is a vital ingredient in automation, the blessing which may yet save humanity from Adam's curse.

If the servo were an open loop system, it would consist simply of an input electrical signal, a vacuum tube or transistor amplifier, and a motor. Such an arrangement has the advantage of driving a mechanical

arrangement with much greater power than the unaided synchro motor. Its disadvantage, however, is serious: there is no guarantee of the system's accuracy. But if this open-loop were converted to a closed loop by doubling it back on itself, so to speak, the system could correct its errors as does the afc circuit.

In the normal operation of the closed-loop servo, a three-terminal signal, usually obtained from a synchro generator, is fed to the input of the synchro control transformer. That signal represents the angle of rotation of the synchro generator shaft. Now, if the shaft of the loop motor is geared back to the shaft of the synchro control transformer, the output of the SCT becomes an error signal representing the difference between the input signal to the servo and the motor shaft rotation. This error signal is put through the servo amplifier and brought back to the motor; the motor shaft position is then corrected.

If the servo loop were simply a closed circle going nowhere, there would be no point in having it in the first place. The motor shaft, however, also drives some other device in addition to driving the SCT shaft for error correction. We shall see what that device, in an analog computer, might be. But it should be understood that the shaft of the servo loop motor does not rotate continuously as does the shaft of an electric fan motor, for example. It turns only to the point at which the error voltage put out by the SCT is zero. At that point, the angle of rotation of the motor shaft is equivalent to the angle represented by the signal put into the servo.

The Servo Amplifier

The purpose of the servo amplifier is, of course, to strengthen the error signal to the level at which it can properly drive the motor. The heavier the load the servo motor must drive, the heavier the motor should be; and the heavier the motor, the greater the power supplied by the amplifier. At least one practical application of these principles is the servo that drives a radar antenna when the radar set is in the tracking mode (Chapter 15). Antennas are frequently heavy, requiring strong motors to rotate them quickly and easily to the proper position. If the motor positioning the antenna must be a powerful one, the amplifier feeding it must be capable of supplying that power.

When the input signal to the servo changes, the motor shaft rotates to a new position at which the SCT error signal will again be zero. Hence the servo we have discussed is often called a *follow-up,* because its action follows the change in signal. This action is a necessary one in analog computers, since the result obtained from the computation must follow changes in the given quantities. In seeking its new equilibrium po-

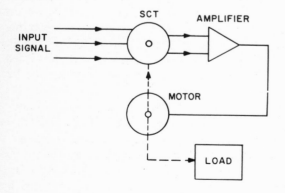

Fig. 19.3. *The Servo Loop:* The error in the system is detected by the SCT in the form of an electrical signal which is amplified and fed to a motor. The mechanical feed back from motor to SCT corrects the error. Generally, amplifiers are represented in servo schematic drawings as triangles pointing in the direction of signal transfer.

sition, the motor should not show a tendency to hunt —that is, first overshoot and then fall short of the resting point it should attain, like a swinging pendulum before it settles down. This is one fault that a well-designed amplifier can help cure. The amplifier should be stable; and one way of building stability into a servo amplifier is to equip it with a degenerative feedback circuit (Chapter 12). Like many other electronic devices nowadays, the servo amplifier is often transistorized, lending it the advantages of compactness and longer life.

The Mechanical Differential

Simple mathematical operations like addition and subtraction are not the only ones analog computers are called on to perform, but they are often part of a complex overall operation. A computer, for example, may have the job of guiding an aircraft automatically to some predetermined point. To do the job adequately, it must have at least one piece of information—the speed of the aircraft with respect to ground. The aircraft is traveling through swiftly moving currents of air. If it is met with strong headwinds in the course of its flight, its speed relative to the ground is reduced by the opposing force of the wind. It may, on the other hand, be helped along by a tailwind and attain a ground speed equal to the sum of its airspeed and the velocity of the tailwind. The first possibility involves an arithmetical process on the part of the computer, in which the headwind velocity is subtracted from the ship's airspeed; the second involves a summing process combining the two velocities.

If the airspeed and wind velocity information in a

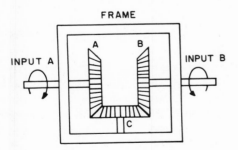

FRAME

INPUT A   INPUT B

A   B

C

Fig. 19.4. *Mechanical Differential:* The shafts of the two input gears A and B pierce the frame but are not anchored to it. The shaft of the intermediate gear C is free to rotate but is held to the frame. If the two input shafts are rotated in the direction shown, the frame will rotate through an angle equal to the difference between the two input angles of rotation. If input A is opposite to the given direction, the angle of rotation of the frame is proportional to the sum of the two inputs.

particular section of the computer is provided in the form of two shaft rotations, the sum or difference between them can be calculated by a *mechanical differential.* The two input shafts of the device penetrate the differential frame, but rotate independently of it. The intermediate gear linking the two input gears is part of the frame but is capable of rotating around its own axis. Now, let us assume that the two input shafts are turned in the direction indicated on the accompanying diagram, but that A is rotated through a larger angle than B. Since these two rotations oppose each other through the intermediate gear, the net effect of the arrangement is to hold shaft B fast while A rotates in its original direction through an angle equivalent to the difference between the two input angles. If the shaft of B is held fast and the shaft of C is fixed in the frame, then the rotation of A must drag the frame with it through the same angle. Thus the upper part of the frame in the diagram emerges from the plane of the page while the lower part rotates into it. The output of the system is therefore the angle of rotation of the frame, equal to the difference between the two input rotations.

A similar analysis shows how the differential calculates a sum. In this case, one of the two input gears, A or B, rotates in the direction opposite to that shown in the drawing, and the two rotations aid each other through the intermediate gear. The frame then has no choice but to turn through an angle equal to the sum of the two input rotations.

The portion of the computer in which this type of analog calculation takes place would have to have two channels to begin with: one for the aircraft's airspeed, the other for the wind velocity. The value of the airspeed might be set in by hand through a crank marked off in units of so many miles per hour. Geared to the crank is the shaft of a synchro generator, the output of which is then an electrical signal representing the airspeed of the craft. This signal is, in turn, applied to a closed-loop servo which not only corrects itself but also positions one of the input shafts of the mechanical differential.

A channel of similar design takes care of the wind velocity. This might begin with a wind velocity sensor, a device which may itself be an analog computer since wind velocity depends on air pressure, the altitude of the aircraft, the density of the air outside the aircraft, and other factors. These are properly weighed by the sensor, and the result given in the form of a shaft rotation. A synchro generator converts the shaft rotation into a corresponding electrical signal, and the latter is the stimulus for a closed servo loop. The motor in this loop controls the second input shaft of the mechanical differential.

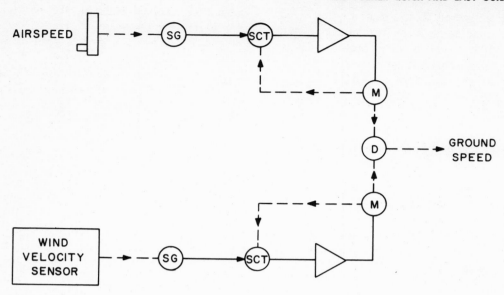

Fig. 19.5. *Ground Speed Computer:* The airspeed is cranked into the computer. Since the crank is geared to the shaft of the synchro generator (SG) the output of the generator is an electrical signal representing the airspeed. This signal controls a follow-up servo. The motor shaft of the servo is geared to one input shaft of a mechanical differential (D). The wind velocity sensor feeds its information into the second differential input shaft. Hence the rotation of the differential frame is proportional to the ground speed of the aircraft.

The final process in at least this portion of the whole computer takes place in the differential. As a result of the two shaft angles given to the differential, its frame assumes an output rotatory angle equal to the sum or difference of the input angles depending on how the wind is moving with respect to the aircraft. A gear is attached to the frame to rotate with the frame, and through this gear the ground speed information calculated by the differential is communicated to some other part of the computer where that information is required. If the section for which the information is destined is so far removed from the differential that a complex system of gears and shafts would be needed to transport it, the differential frame gear need only be engaged to the rotor of a synchro generator to have the information carried over a three-wire cable as an electrical signal.

Synchro Differential Generator

The mechanical differential requires two inputs in mechanical form. But suppose one of these inputs takes an electrical form; must the engineer in charge of the design be so frustrated that he has to junk his original design and begin all over again? Certainly not. He simply uses a *synchro differential generator* instead of a mechanical differential.

The synchro differential generator—which may be abbreviated SDG—performs the same computation as the mechanical differentiator, the subtraction or addition of two input quantities. Only one of these inputs need be mechanical; the other is supplied electrically by a three-wire cable. The output of the SDG is electrical, and is also a three-terminal system. From these facts plus the knowledge of what synchros in general are like, we may gather that the SDG has three stator coils arranged in the familiar Y formation, and three Y-connected rotor coils controlled by a shaft. The three-terminal input signal is connected to the stator coils, while the mechanical input is a shaft rotation geared to the SDG shaft. No separate excitation is required since the input signal furnishes the stator coils with a magnetic field. As the shaft of the SDG is rotated, the coupling between stator and rotor coils varies, and the output signal is varied accordingly. Thus the three-terminal output signal depends both on the strength of the signal supplied and on the angle through which the shaft is turned.

In a rather simpler way, the SDG might be applied to this same problem of computing the ground speed. As before, the airspeed can be cranked into a synchro generator, with the output of the latter device connected through a three-line cable to the stator coil terminals of the SDG. The motor of the wind velocity follow-up servo could then be geared to the shaft of the SDG, thus providing the latter with its mechanical input. Since the signal input to the SDG is proportional to the airspeed and the mechanical input is proportional to the wind velocity, the resultant output of the synchro differential generator is a measure of the aircraft ground speed.

Synchro Differential Motor

The companion device to the synchro differential generator is the *synchro differential motor*. In this component, addition or subtraction can also be carried out, with two electrical inputs and a mechanical output. The construction of the SDM is similar to that of the SDG; the rotor consists of three Y-connected coils while the stator is similarly equipped. One input signal is applied along a three-wire cable to the stator coils and the second input connected by the same means to the rotor terminals. As long as the two input signals are kept unchanged, the force resulting from the inter-action of the fields in both sets of coils is fixed, and the shaft is kept at the angle it has assumed. Thus the synchro differential motor, like the synchro motor, does not rotate continuously, but adopts an equilibrium shaft position which is the resultant of the two signals applied to it.

Multiplication and Division

There are times, in an analog computer, when the calculation involved calls for the multiplication of a quantity by a constant factor—by 10, say. This is very easily done by using a step-up transformer, a device which was explained in Chapter 2. The transformer consists merely of two coil windings around a common iron core. If one of these windings has ten times the number of turns of the other, an input voltage applied to the smaller winding will emerge across the terminals of the larger with ten times the magnitude.

The same transformer can be used as a constant divider. An input signal, representing the quantity to be divided, is applied to the larger winding. The voltage then obtained from the terminals of the smaller is one-tenth the input. In both cases, the voltage used must be a-c. But a-c voltages of 60 or 400 cps are common currency in. analog computers. As a matter of fact, all the electrical signals discussed in this chapter thus far are of that type.

Another method of division is practiced electro-mechanically through the use of the potentiometer, which is simply a variable resistor. If an a-c voltage is connected across the terminals of a uniform resistance wire—a wire with constant resistance throughout its length—then various fractions of this input voltage can be tapped off by sliding the tap on the wire to various points. If the tap is set to the mid-point of the wire, for example, the voltage between the tap and one end of the wire is one-half the input voltage. Thus a division by two is made. Division by three can be made simply by sliding the tap to one-third the length of the wire. And so on. If the tap is controlled by a servo motor,

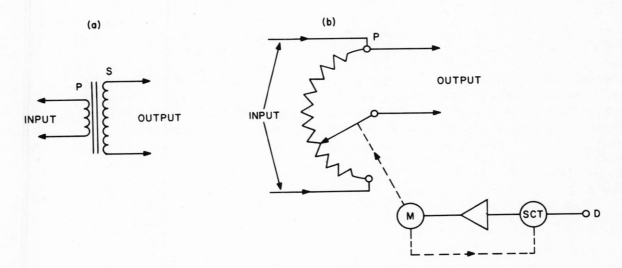

Fig. 19.6. *Multiplication and Division:* **Multiplication by a constant factor is made by the transformer in (a). The output voltage is a multiple of the input by a number equal to the ratio of secondary to primary turns. Division is shown in (b). Here the output voltage is that fraction of the input voltage equal to the ratio of the portion of resistance element between the tap and the endpoint (P) to the total length of resistance element. The position of the tap is controlled by the servo motor (M) which, in turn, is controlled by the driving signal D.**

it can be positioned automatically, and with excellent precision. Such a controlled potentiometer is a device frequently used in analog computers.

The Digital Computer

What we have seen of analog computer components tends to underline at least one important difference between analog and digital systems. The electrical and mechanical representations of the quantities the analog computer handles usually vary smoothly: the motor of a follow-up servo does not rotate in quick jumps but in continuous fashion; the output of a servo-controlled potentiometer rises or falls gradually as the wiper slides over the resistance element. The digital computer, however, generally works in discrete jumps, each jump representing a number. And since the digital computer is essentially an electronic device, the numbers it deals with are usually represented by pulses.

But the counting system the digital computer uses is not the one ordinary mortals are accustomed to. For all its complexity and in spite of the staggering problems it can solve, the computer is essentially simple-minded. It recognizes only two digits, 0 and 1, and handles practically all its operations in those two digits alone. Thus the unit electrical circuits in the digital computer are devices which are either shut off completely to represent zero, or are turned on completely to represent one. A method of counting in which only two such digits are recognized is known as a *binary* system.

How the Binary System Works

Learning the peculiarities of the binary system is a little like returning to the first grade for a refresher course in infantile arithmetic. In those days of our past, we were told that 1 plus 1 made 2. Adding another 1 increased the total to 3. An increase of another unit made a grand total of 4; and so on up to 9. But when another unit was added to 9, an astonishing thing happened: the 9 suddenly changed to zero, and a 1 "carried" before the zero thus: 10.

As adults, we can understand the significance of that system. The customary method of counting is *decimal*;

Fig. 19.7.   Binary Signal for the Letter "A": In many computers, the first letter of the alphabet is symbolized by the binary number 1010100. The corresponding pulse signal, consisting of seven bits, is shown.

that is, a system based on 10. In reading any number —say, 234—we recognize the digit at the extreme right as representing units, the digit immediately to the left of it, tens, and the digit to the left of that, hundreds. Since a unit is ten divided by ten, and a hundred is ten times ten, we understand that each of the figures in 234 are in one way or another related to this foundation number of 10. Strangely enough, however, there is no single digit to represent the number "ten."

A similar state of affairs exists in the binary system. That system is based on the number 2, but the digit 2 never appears in binary computation. In the binary method, as in any other method of counting, we start with 0—nothing. Adding a unit to that gives us 1, which is reasonable enough. But, if we add yet another 1 to this quantity, the same amazing transformation encountered in the decimal system takes place: the 1 turns into 0, and a 1 is carried to the left of the 0. We thus find that $1+1=10$. How do we read this result? We certainly cannot read it as "ten" simply because 1 and 1 cannot possibly be ten. The 0 indicates to us that there are no units; the 1 to the left of it indicates that there is 1 two. Hence the number is read as 2.

But let us go a bit further with this bizarre but fascinating system. We add another 1 to our 10. Since this addition represents the insertion of another unit, we increase the 0 by one. Thus, $10+1=11$. This is simple enough, but when we add still another 1, remarkable changes again take place. The 1 at the right of the 11 cannot go up to 2 since there is no 2. It must therefore go back to 0, and a 1 should be carried over to the digit just to the left of it, which is 1. This latter digit, given the "carried" 1, must also revert to 0, leaving a 1 to be carried just to the left of this 0. We consequently have: $11+1=100$.

Now, how do we read this number "100" in the binary system? The 0 at the right signifies no units. The 0 to the left of it signifies no two's. But the 1 at the extreme left of the figure represents one two-times-two, or four. What we have done in this paragraph and the one before it was add $1+1+1+1$. In the binary system, this is 100 although in the decimal system it happens to be 4.

It is all really very simple even if it does make the head swim a bit. For comfort, let us go back to the decimal system, which we all understand, and to our sample number 234. The digit to the right is units— four, to be exact. The digit just to the left of that represents tens, which is only reasonable since the basis of the system is ten. We have three of those, or thirty. The digit to the left of the 3 represents ten-times-tens or hundreds, and we have two of those, or two hundred. Consequently, our number reads two hundred thirty four. We can extend this method to read any number in the decimal system: the digit to the extreme right of the number represents units; the digit to the left of that represents tens; the digit to the left of that represents ten-times-tens; the digit to the left of that represents ten-times-ten-times-tens (thousands); and so on.

Now, applying the same method to the binary system, but remembering that the system is based on *two*, how do we read a binary number like 110011? Suppose we take this problem in steps, designating each step by a letter rather than a number to minimize confusion:

(a) The digit to the extreme right represents units, and we have one of those, or a total of one.

(b) The digit next left represents two's, and we have one of those, or two. This, added to the one of step (a), gives a total of three.

(c) The digit next left is in the position of two-times-two, or four; but there are none of those. We therefore still have the total of three.

(d) The digit next left occupies the two-times-two-times-two position, but since the digit is a 0 it will amount to nothing and add nothing to the total.

(e) The digit next left occupies the two-times-two-times-two-times-two position, which has the value of sixteen. The digit is a 1, and 1 times sixteen is sixteen. This, added to our previous total of three, gives nineteen.

(f) The final digit is also 1, in the position of two multiplied by itself five times, or thirty-two. Thirty-two multiplied by 1 is still thirty-two; adding it to our previous total of nineteen gives the grand total of fifty-one. We have now arrived at the solution of the problem we set ourselves: the binary number 110011 is equal to the decimal number 51.

Binary Points

The numbers the digital computer handles are not always integers; they may be fractions, corresponding to digits to the right of the decimal point in numbers of the decimal system. The decimal point which marks the separation between integers and fractions has its counterpart in the *binary point*.

Here again it must be borne in mind that the binary system is based on the number 2 as distinct from the decimal system's basis of 10. If the digit just to the right of the binary point in a given binary number is 1, then its equivalent decimal value is ½; if the second digit to the right of the binary point is also 1, its decimal value is ¼—that is, one divided by two-times-two. Still a third 1 to the right of the binary point will have the decimal value of ⅛, or one divided by two-times-two-times-two. And so on. We can see that the correspondence here to the decimal system is quite close: the digit just to the right of a decimal point is

expressed in tenths; the digit next right is expressed in hundredths, or one divided by ten-times-ten, and so on.

Bits

Toward the beginning of this discussion of the binary system, the point was made that the 0 can symbolize a circuit switched off, and the 1 a circuit switched on. Now, the terms "off" and "on" are, to some extent, points of information. If these can be described by digits, then so can other data. A digit or a group of digits may represent a particular operation of the machine; more, they may even represent the electrical signal which initiates that operation. They may, in fact, symbolize anything important to the work involved. Many computers are set up for printing letters of the alphabet, for billing and other purposes, as well as figures. For such machines there is a method of coding in which each letter is equivalent to a set of digits— usually seven of them—in twenty-six different combinations.

Since the digital computer is primarily an electrical device, all these digital combinations are transformed into electrical signals to permit the circuits in the system to perform the necessary computing operations. These signals consist of whole strings of pulses. True to the on-off scheme, the 1 digit manifests itself as a square-pulse peak while the 0 appears as the valley between pulses. Each of these signal forms is known as a *bit*, a word manufactured from the first two and the final letters of "binary digit." The digital number 1101, for example, whose equivalent in everyday decimal is 13, shows up electrically as two pulses rather close together, followed by a wide gap—to represent the 0 or "off" condition—and then by another pulse. Thus the signal is worth, if the reader will pardon the pun, four bits. The whole train of pulses is known as a *word*. This term has its unfortunate aspects since the train may be the electrical signal for a letter of the alphabet, as has been mentioned, which would make a word the representative of a letter.

Boolean Algebra

About a hundred years ago, an English mathematician named George Boole was struck by the parallel between logic and mathematics, and proceeded to work out a system in which logical statements could be symbolized by mathematical formulas. For example, the simple sentence "I am a man" can easily be translated into the formula I=M. Boole could not possibly have foreseen the impact his system of algebra would have on the twentieth century world, but it has been enormous. For the mathematical tool he developed has proved to be a powerful one in the science of computers. If the arguments of logic can be telescoped into symbols, and symbols into electrical pulses easily handled and easily combined, then the computer can become a thinking machine.

The digital computers built nowadays are predominantly transistorized. In accord with the spirit of the times, therefore, we shall look into some of these logic circuits in their semiconductor forms, a process the preceding chapter has prepared us for.

AND Circuits

The three fundamental logic circuits of the digital computer are given names that, at first glance, seem rather peculiar: AND, OR, and NOT. These are common terms in speech and are equally common elements of logic; hence they are applicable to computers.

A computer, let us say, is given three instructions to be simultaneously performed. The instructions are inserted into the machine in binary form: 1101, say, represents the first, 0101 the second, and 1110 the third. Having been converted to their corresponding pulse signals, the instruction words 1101, 0101, 1110, will then be put into a special circuit to combine them into a four-bit word representing the three operations involved. This special circuit is known as the AND circuit; justly so, because its output represents instructions 1101 AND 0101 AND 1110.

The AND circuit produces a pulse output only when a pulse is simultaneously present at each of its inputs; the absence of just one input pulse is enough to nullify

the action of the circuit. In a sense, the AND circuit works like a legislative council that can pass laws only on unanimous votes. One "nyet" is sufficient to keep an act from the statute books. Since a 1 is represented electrically by a pulse, only two of the first digits on the extreme left of the four-bit words 1101, 0101, 1110, are pulses. Hence, for this bit, the AND output must be a 0. The second digit in each word is 1, however; on this unanimous vote, the AND circuit emits an output pulse. There is no agreement on the third bits, and again no agreement on the fourth. The output of the AND circuit corresponding to the four-bit inputs, therefore, is 0100. Note that the AND circuit is *not* a circuit for simple addition. The sum of 1101, 0101, 1110—actually 100000 in binary—cannot possibly be 0100.

In the diode AND circuit, current will flow through that diode to which a negative or zero voltage—corresponding to 0—is applied. As we found in the preceding chapter, current will flow in the semiconductor diode when the diode is forward biased; that is, when the voltage applied to the P terminal is more positive than the voltage applied to the N. A current flowing through one or more diodes will pass through the diode involved to the positive power supply terminal, thus bypassing the load resistor—R_L in the accompanying diagram. The load resistor is then short-circuited, in effect, and no voltage appears across it. However, if positive pulses are simultaneously applied to the N terminals of the diodes, no bypassing current can flow, and the positive voltage of the power supply appears at the output in the form of a pulse.

OR Circuits

Again, the computer may be offered a choice of one or more instructions to be fulfilled. In this last sentence, the word OR is the clue to the nature of the circuit involved. An OR circuit operates by putting out a 1 pulse when any or all of the input pulses are positive. It so happens that, in the sample words 1101, 0101, 1110 we have chosen, at least one of the first, second, third, or fourth bits is a 1. If these words were put into an OR circuit, the output would consist of four consecutive 1's—four positive pulses. But if any one set of bits were all 0's, there would be no output for that set.

When the pulses of the word sources in the schematic of the OR circuit are 0's—zero or negative voltage—the P terminals are at the same or a more negative potential than the N terminals. No current can then flow through the circuit, and no output voltage will appear across the load resistor. But this is only true if the "nyets" are unanimous. If one or more of the bits

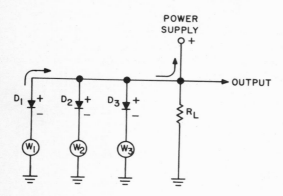

Fig. 19.8. *AND Circuit:* As long as any bit of the word inputs (W_1, W_2, W_3) is negative, corresponding to 0, current will flow through one or more of the diodes (D_1, D_2, D_3) to short-circuit the load resistor (R_L). Only when simultaneous positive pulses are applied to the diodes by W_1 and W_2 and W_3 will a positive pulse appear at the output. The P terminals of the semiconductor diodes are designated by plus signs and the N terminals by minus signs. Electronic current flow, if it occurs, takes place in the direction of the arrows.

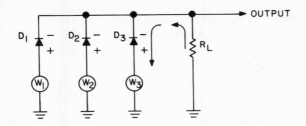

Fig. 19.9. *OR Circuit:* Current can flow through one or more of the diodes only when a positive pulse is applied to the diodes involved. The arrows show direction of electronic current flow, W_1, W_2, W_3 are the word voltage sources, D_1, D_2, D_3 are semiconductor diodes, and R_L is the load resistor.

applied simultaneously to the diodes are positive pulses, however, a forward bias is placed across the crystals getting the pulses, and current flows through the load resistor in such direction as to produce a positive pulse output. In this circuit, as always, the terminal of a resistor in which electronic current enters is negative with respect to the opposite terminal. Hence the "hot" side of the output is positive with respect to ground.

NOT Circuits

The last of the three basic logic circuits is the NOT. This circuit simply negates everything put into it, like a Supreme Court justice who dissents from the majority opinion in every case. A "yes" vote put into it becomes a "no" at its output; conversely, a "no" input comes out as a "yes." In terms of binaural digits, in which a 1 is comparable to "yes" and a 0 to a "no," an instruction, statement, or other information in the binary form of 1101, say, will come out of the NOT circuit as 0010.

In electrical terms, the NOT circuit is simply an arrangement which inverts the pulses put into it. The circuit has a single input—as distinct from AND and OR, which may have two, three, or more inputs—and a single output. Thus a signal of three initial pulse bits followed by a negative or zero bit emerges from the NOT circuit as three initial zero bits followed by a positive bit, corresponding to the example given in the preceding paragraph.

The cue word in this description of the NOT circuit is "invert." Any circuit capable of inverting the input signal so that positive pulses become negative, and vice versa, is capable of working as a NOT circuit. We have seen, in the course of this book, that vacuum tube amplifiers of ordinary design can carry out this type of inversion; some of the transistor circuits of the preceding chapter work in similar fashion. Any of these will do as NOT circuits.

Memory

There is at least one strong parallel between the computer and the human brain. Both store the facts with which they work in memory systems. But while the mechanism of human memory is still a complex enigma, no corresponding mystery surrounds the storage system in the digital computer.

Perhaps the most familiar type of storage device is the punched card, an oblong of ordinary stiff paper perforated at strategic points with small rectangular holes. The positions and distributions of the holes, arranged according to a predetermined scheme, reflect the information the card contains. That information may be anything from the highlights in the history of one man's life—a personnel record, for example—to pertinent data on a bank check. The computer is a sorting device which automatically divides the cards into groups, with each group deposited in a separate pigeonhole, depending on the positions of the perforations and on the standards the sorting process uses. These standards the operator sets into the machine. In this way the personnel department of a large corporation can select that member of its staff with a unique combination of skills simply by running all the cards in its files through a sorting machine set to choose those skills. Sorters now manufactured can dispose of the cards at as fast a rate as 2000 per minute.

Another common memory device is the magnetic drum, a rotating cylinder which is given its stored information by impressing a magnetic field on various points of its surface. For these different points the field is in one direction or its opposite, depending on whether it represents the binary 1 or 0. A close relative is the magnetic tape, which is not much different from the variety the hi-fi fan treasures for his tape recordings (Chapter 13). The tape in the digital computer however, is usually given a magnetic field of constant strength in one direction or the other rather than a smoothly varying field corresponding to an audio signal.

In the line of magnetic memory devices is the ferrite core. This is a tiny transformer-like affair in which a primary and second-coil is wound around a ferrite ring. The field in the core can be changed easily and quickly from one direction to the other if any change in the bit it memorizes is necessary.

In addition to these magnetic components, there are electric memory systems in which the polarity of an electrically charged point corresponds to the 1 or 0 bit, and the charged points are distributed according to a logically dictated pattern. These systems usually take the form of an evacuated tube with much the same setup as the television camera tube of Chapter 6. The charges are stored on the target, and the information they contain is drawn from them by a scanning beam deflected across and down the target by horizontal and vertical deflection systems. Thanks to the rapidity with which the scanning beam can be swept over the target, the stored information is available to the computer in a matter of microseconds.

The Future

We have reserved this and the preceding chapters for the last because their subjects—semiconductors and computers—are perhaps the two most explosively dynamic forces in modern electronics. The extent of the semiconductor revolution in components—the tools of the electronics engineer—has hardly been realized. As for computers, analog and digital, there seems to be no end to the miracles these are capable of achieving. Their potential and the potentialities of electronics in general are enormous.

GLOSSARY

Analog computer. A calculating device in which quantities are represented by shaft rotations or voltages.

AND circuit. A logic circuit of digital computers which produces a positive output pulse only when all input signals are positively pulsed.

Binary point. The dot in a binary number which corresponds to the decimal point in the decimal system.

Binary system. A system of counting based on 2.

Bit. A binary digit, 0 or 1.

Boolean algebra. A method of expressing logic in the form of mathematical symbols.

Decimal system. The common system of counting based on 10.

Digital computer. A calculating device using discrete numbers.

Excitation. The operating a-c voltage fed to synchro motors and generators.

Ferrite. An iron compound capable of being magnetized.

Follow-up servo. A servomechanism which follows changes in the input signal.

Integer. A whole number.

Mechanical differential. A mechanical device in analog computers which provides an output mechanical rotation equal to the sum or difference of two input rotations.

NOT circuit. A logic circuit of digital computers which inverts an input pulse signal.

Null. A zero or minimum voltage.

OR circuit. A logic circuit of digital computers which produces a positive pulse if any one or more positive pulses are present in the input signals.

Potentiometer. A three-terminal variable resistor.

Synchro control transformer. A shafted device with one rotor and three stator coils in which the a-c voltage developed across the rotor is equal to the difference between an input signal and an input shaft rotation.

Synchro differential generator. A shafted device with three rotor and three stator coils which produces a three-terminal output signal equal to the sum or difference of an input signal and an input shaft rotation.

Synchro differential motor. A shafted device with three rotor and three stator coils which produces a shaft rotation equal to the sum or difference of two input signals.

Word. A group of bits.

ELECTRONICS DICTIONARY

"A" voltage. The voltage applied to the terminals of a tube heater.

A-c bias. An ultrasonic signal which reduces distortion in tape recorders.

Accelerating anode. An electrode given a high positive potential to speed up the moving electrons in the beam of a writing tube.

Acceptor ion. An atom in a doped semiconductor crystal which accepts an electron or gives up a hole.

Acoustical feedback. The return of sound from the loud-speakers to the microphone in public address systems.

Acoustics. The science of sound.

Afc. Automatic frequency control; a system involving a discriminator and reactance modulator for controlling the frequency of an oscillator.

Agc. Automatic gain control; an electronic system in radar and the visual section of television receivers which controls the amplification of forward end tubes.

Aileron. The hinged flap in either wing of an aircraft.

Air core transformer. A transformer of two or more windings around a hollow non-magnetic core.

Altimeter. A device which measures the altitude of an aircraft.

Ammeter. An instrument for measuring electric current.

Amplitude. The peak of an a-c current or voltage wave.

Amplitude distortion. Distortion in which the peaks of a signal are altered.

Amplitude modulation. A system of radio transmission in which the amplitude of a carrier is varied in accordance with a meaningful signal.

Analog computer. A calculating device in which quantities are represented by shaft rotations or voltages.

AND circuit. A logic circuit of digital computers which produces a positive output voltage only when all input signals are positively pulsed.

Antenna. A metal structure or wire which picks up or transmits electromagnetic energy through space.

Antenna horn. An enlarged opening of a waveguide at the focus of a radar reflector.

Antenna loop. A flat coil of wire which serves both as antenna and as part of the input resonant circuit of a receiver.

Arcing. Sparking across a narrow gap between conductors.

Armstrong oscillator. An oscillator in which feedback is achieved through coupled plate and grid circuit coils.

A-scope. A radar scope giving target range information.

Aspect ratio. The 4:3 ratio of picture width to height in television.

Atom. Smallest unit of a chemical element.

Autopilot. An automatic piloting system for aircraft.

Avc. Automatic volume control; an electronic system in radio receivers which controls the amplification of forward end tubes.

Azimuth. The circle of the compass marked off in 360 degrees, with the zero mark at north.

"B" voltage. A positive d-c voltage applied to the plate of a tube through the plate load.

Baffle. A large board on which a speaker is mounted.

Band width. The frequencies emitted by a transmitter and picked up by a receiver; any range of frequencies.

Base. The middle section of a transistor; the arrangement of prongs at the bottom of a tube.

Bass. The low frequency tones in sound.

Bass reflex enclosure. A speaker enclosure so designed that the base tones are reinforced.

Beam power tube. A power amplifier in which the electron stream is concentrated to form a virtual suppressor.

Beat frequency. The difference frequency between two heterodyned signals.

Bfo. Beat frequency oscillator; the oscillator in a CW receiver which heterodynes with the i-f signal to produce an audio note.

Bias. A negative d-c voltage applied to the control grid of a tube through the grid load.

Binary point. The dot in a binary number which corresponds to the decimal point in the decimal system.

Binary system. A system of counting based on 2.

Binaural. Two-eared; same as *stereophonic.*

Bit. A binary digit, 0 or 1.

Black level. The cutoff voltage on the TV kinescope grid.

Blacker-than-black. A voltage more negative than the black level.

Blanking. Cutting off the electron beam in a writing tube.

Blanking pulse. The negative pulse that cuts off the kinescope electron beam.

Bleeder resistor. The resistor connected between the positive and negative terminals of a power supply.

Blip. The pulse on a radar screen representing the object tracked.

Blocking capacitor. A fixed condenser which simultaneously blocks the d-c voltage at the plate of one tube from the grid of the next, and transfers the output a-c signal of the first tube to the grid of the second.

Blocking oscillator. A relaxation oscillator used in sync circuits of radar and television equipment.

Boolean algebra. A method of expressing logic in the form of mathematical symbols.

Brightness. The overall lighting of a televised scene; the luminance level.

Bug. A high-speed telegraph key.

Button. The capsule in a carbon microphone which contains the carbon particles.

Bypass capacitor. A condenser which routes a-c current around another component.

"C" voltage. A former term for bias voltage.

Camera tube. The tube in a television camera which converts the light and dark elements of a picture into the picture signal.

Capacitor. An electronic component consisting of two metal plates separated by a nonconductor.

Capstan. A rotating device in the tape recorder which assists the movement of the tape.

Carbon microphone. A microphone in which the variation in resistance of carbon particles produces the audio signal.

Cardioid. The heart-shaped directivity pattern of a loop and sensing antenna.

Carrier. A high frequency signal on which a meaningful signal is impressed.

Cartridge. The electrical device in the phonograph pickup head.

Cascade. A succession of amplifying stages.

Cathode. The element in a vacuum tube with emits electrons.

Cathode biasing. A method of obtaining bias by the insertion of a resistor shunted by a capacitor in the cathode circuit of a tube.

Cathode follower. An electronic circuit used for matching the output of one piece of electronic equipment with the input of another; in general, a circuit in which the input signal is applied to the control grid of the tube and the output signal taken off the cathode resistor.

Cathode ray tube. Same as *writing tube;* often abbreviated crt.

Cavity resonator. The metal chamber in a uhf oscillator which determines the frequency of oscillation.

Chaff. Strips of aluminum foil used as camouflage against tracking radar.

Chassis. The metal base on which most electronic equipment is built.

Choke. An electrical component consisting of a coil of wire wound around an air or iron core.

Chrominance signal. The combined luminance and color signals in color TV.

Class A. Operation of an amplifier tube in which plate current flows for a complete cycle of input control grid voltage.

Class AB. Operation of an amplifier tube in which plate current flows for more than half but less than the full cycle of input grid voltage.

Class B. Operation of an amplifier tube in which plate current flows for approximately half the cycle of input grid voltage.

Class C. Operation of an amplifier tube in which plate current flows for less than half the cycle of input voltage.

Clutter. False blips on a radar A-scope.

Cold cathode gas tube. A gas-filled tube in which the cathode is not heated.

Collector. The transistor terminal which collects charge carriers.

Color-killer. A tube in the color TV receiver which prevents the appearance of color on the picture tube screen during black-and-white telecast reception.

Colpitts oscillator. An oscillator in which two resonant circuit capacitors are used, with a tap between the two capacitors.

Combination set. A receiver combining AM, FM, and phonograph; some of these receivers also include television and a tape recorder.

Comparator. The control tube of a horizontal afc circuit.

Component. A part—resistor, capacitor, tube, choke, etc.—in an electronic circuit.

Composite video signal. The video signal of TV, consisting of picture signal, blanking pulses, and sync pulses.

Condenser. Same as *capacitor.*

Contrast. The comparative values of light and shade in the televised scene.

Convergence coils. The yoke just back of the deflection yoke on a three-gun color TV picture tube; the coils which focus the three beams on mask holes.

Converter. A single stage combining the functions of local oscillator and first detector.

Coupling capacitor. A capacitor used between circuits to allow a-c signal voltage to pass from one circuit to another while blocking the passage of d-c; often used as a synonym for *blocking capacitor.*

Cps. Cycles per second.

Crossover frequency. The point of division between separated frequency bands of the crossover network.

Crossover network. The device between audio amplifier output and speaker system which divides the high from the low frequencies.

Crystal cartridge. A phonograph cartridge containing Rochelle salt crystals.

Crystal microphone. A microphone containing Rochelle salt crystals.

Current. The flow of charge carriers through a circuit.

Cursor. An electronic device for measuring range; used in radar.

Cutoff. The condition in a tube in which the grid is so negative as to halt the flow of electrons to the plate.

Cutting head. The device holding the stylus in recording on discs.

CW. Continuous wave; the method of dot-and-dash transmissions.

Cycle. A complete positive and negative alternation of a-c voltage.

Damper. A diode in the flyback power supply which prevents ringing.

Db. Decibel; the unit in which the intensity of sound is measured.

D.c. amplifier. Direct coupled amplifier; an amplifier in which the coupling between the plate of one stage and the grid of the succeeding stage is made through a conductor rather than a capacitor.

Decelerating ring. A metallic ring on the inner wall of an image orthicon, used to slow down electrons in the scanning beam before they reach the target.

Decimal system. The common system of counting based on 10.

Deflection coils. Coils of wire in which the magnetic field used to swing the electron beam in writing tubes is generated.

Deflection yoke. The ring around the neck of a writing

tube which contains the deflection coils.

Degenerative feedback. A type of feedback in which the returned output signal is opposite in phase to the input signal.

Detector. In general, a circuit which extracts the meaningful signal from the carrier. (See also *second detector.*)

Detent. The mechanism in a TV tuner which holds the tuner to a particular channel.

D-f signal. The 30 cps signal of a military direction finder.

Diamond stylus. A diamond-tipped record player needle.

Diaphragm. A vibrating device.

Dielectric. The nonconducting element in a capacitor.

Differentiator. In general, a resistor-condenser circuit which converts a pulse into a large positive and a large negative voltage spike.

Digital computer. A calculating device using discrete numbers.

Diode. A vacuum tube or semiconductor with two active elements.

Dipole. A doublet antenna often used in vhf and uhf systems.

Direct FM. The system of FM transmission in which the audio modulates the frequency of the master oscillator through a reactance modulator.

Directivity pattern. A geometrical representation of the output strength in various directions of a transmitter antenna; also used in reference to the sensitivity of a receiver antenna.

Discriminator. A balanced, duo-diode detector circuit which converts frequency deviations into a variable d-c or audio signal.

Dish. The reflector of a radar antenna.

Distortion. Variation in the output signal of an amplifier as compared with the input signal.

Distributed capacitance. The virtual capacitance existing between adjacent loops in a coil.

Donor ion. An atom in a doped semiconductor crystal which gives up an electron.

Doping. The process of adding alien elements to a semiconductor crystal to supply it with charge carriers—electrons or holes.

Doppler radar. A type of radar used for the detection of rapidly moving objects.

Double-ended amplifier. A two-tube amplifier with a symmetrical circuit arrangement.

Doubler. A frequency multiplier which multiplies the frequency of an input signal by two.

Doublet. Same as *dipole.*

Duo-diode. A vacuum tube containing a double diode.

Duplexer. The device in a radar unit which cuts the receiver off from the antenna while the transmitter is in operation.

Duty cycle. The ratio of pulse width to the period between pulses in radar equipment.

Dynamic cartridge. A cartridge in which the stylus moves a coil of wire through a permanent magnetic field.

Dynamic microphone. A microphone in which the diaphragm moves a coil of wire through a permanent

magnetic field.

ECM. Electronic countermeasures; electronic equipment for jamming enemy radar.

Electrode. A metal body capable of having an electric charge.

Electrolytic. A type of capacitor with permanent polarity markings.

Electromagnetic deflection. Swerving the beam in writing tubes by means of a magnetic field; i.e., by means of deflection coils.

Electromagnetic wave. A wave of radio, light, or heat.

Electron. A subatomic particle of negative charge.

Electron gun. The device in a writing beam which generates the electron beam.

Electron image. The pattern of electrons emitted by the image orthicon photocathode which corresponds to the light and shade in the object before the television camera.

Electron multiplier. A tube with several successive plates which multiplies electrons incident on the plates through secondary emission.

Electrostatic deflection. Swerving the beam in writing tubes by means of an electrostatic field; i.e. by means of deflection plates.

Electrostatic shield. A metal mesh used to screen one device from the electric field of another.

Elevator. The horizontal hinged flap in the tail assembly of an aircraft.

Emitter. The transistor terminal which emits charge carriers.

Enclosure. A cabinet containing speakers.

Equalizer. An elaborate tone control system designed to compensate for frequency distortion in phonograph records.

Erase head. The device in a tape recorder which removes the recorded sound from a used tape.

Excitation. The operating a-c voltage fed to synchro motors and generators.

Feedback. The transfer of energy from the output of a circuit back to its input.

Ferrite. An iron compound capable of being magnetized.

Filament. The hot wire in a vacuum tube.

Filter. In general, a circuit which removes an undesired signal.

Final. The last amplifying stage of a transmitter.

Fine tuning capacitor. In general, a small variable capacitor for delicate tuning of a resonant circuit.

Firing. The heavy flow of electrons from cathode to plate in a gas tube.

Firing potential. The potential applied to the plate of a gas diode or the grid of a thyratron at which firing occurs.

First detector. The heterodyne detector in a superheterodyne.

Fix. The position, in latitude and longitude, of a ship.

Fluorescent screen. The coating on the inner wall of the face of a writing tube.

Flutter. A rapid wavering in pitch of a played-back phonograph or tape recording.

Flux. The lines of force of a magnetic field.

Flyback power supply. The high voltage circuit in a television set.

Flywheel effect. The effect of a resonant circuit in which an input electrical impulse of less than one cycle produces a complete output cycle.

FM multiplex. A system of stereophonic broadcasting using frequency modulation.

Focusing coil. The coil in a writing tube which guides the electrons in the beam.

Follow-up servo. A servomechanism which follows changes in the input signal.

Forward bias. A voltage applied to a P-N crystal such that the positive terminal of the voltage is applied to the P section and the negative to the N section.

Frequency. The number of cycles per second of an a-c wave.

Frequency deviation. The swing of an FM carrier away from its resting frequency.

Frequency distortion. A type of distortion in which certain frequencies are lost or discriminated against.

Frequency divider. A circuit which reduces the frequency of an oscillator.

Frequency modulation. A system of radio transmission in which the frequency of a carrier is varied in accordance with a meaningful signal.

Frequency multiplier. A circuit which multiplies the frequency of an input signal by a whole number.

Front end. The stages between antenna and i-f amplifier in a superheterodyne.

Full-wave power supply. A power supply using two diodes which draw current during both the positive and negative half-cycles of the input a-c voltage.

Fundamental. The basic frequency of a vibrating object emitting sound.

Ganging. Mounting the rotor plates of two or more tuning capacitors on a common shaft; also applies to simultaneously operated switches.

Gas tube. An electron tube into which a chemically inactive gas has been injected.

Gating pulse. A pulse which permits the operation of a circuit.

Glide path. The downward path followed by an aircraft in landing.

Glide path localizer. The transmitter, in the ILS, which sets the glide path for the homing aircraft.

Grass. The visible evidence of electrical noise in an A-scope display.

Grid. A thin wire mesh between cathode and plate in a triode.

Grid bypass. A small fixed condenser which bypasses the signal away from the grid leak.

Grid leak. A grid resistor through which d-c grid current flows.

Grid leak detector. A detector which depends on the flow of grid current for its operation.

Grid modulation. A system of modulation in an AM transmitter in which the modulating audio is applied to the grid circuit of an r-f amplifier.

Grille cloth. The cloth covering the mouth of the speaker in a baffle or cabinet.

Ground wave. The earth-bound wave from a low frequency transmitter antenna.

Gyroscope. A steadying device consisting of a rapidly rotating disc pivoted in a frame; same as *gyro*.

Half-wave power supply. A power supply using a single diode which draws current during one phase of the input alternating voltage.

Harmonic. A frequency equal to a whole-number multiple of a fundamental.

Hartley oscillator. An oscillator circuit in which the coil of the resonant circuit is tapped.

Headphones. Head telephone receivers; a headset.

Heater. The filament in a vacuum tube.

Height control. The TV receiver hand control which varies the height of the picture.

Heising modulation. A system of modulation in an AM transmitter in which the modulating audio is applied to the plate circuit of an r-f amplifier.

Heterodyning. Mixing two signals in a detector to obtain the beat frequency.

Hi-fi. High fidelity.

High fidelity. A system which reproduces sound with a minimum of distortion.

High voltage cage. The metal guard around the tubes and circuits of the flyback power supply in a TV receiver.

Hill-and-dale. A method of disc recording in which the stylus moves up and down.

Hold controls. A pair of TV receiver hand controls which help synchronize the picture horizontally and vertically.

Hole. A freely moving positive charge in a doped semiconductor crystal.

Horizontal afc. The automatic frequency control in the horizontal sync circuit of a TV receiver.

Horizontal control tube. The comparator stage of the horizontal afc system.

Horizontal oscillator. The relaxation oscillator in the TV receiver's horizontal sync circuit.

Horizontal output stage. The power amplifier stage in the TV receiver's horizontal sync circuits.

Horizontally-deflecting coils. The deflecting coils of a writing tube which exert a sidewise force on the writing beam.

Horizontally deflecting plates. The deflecting plates in a writing tube which exert a sidewise force on the writing beam.

Hyperbola. A curve drawn between two fixed points such that the differences between the distances from any point on the curve to the two fixed points is the same.

Idler. The supply reel in a tape recorder.

I-f. Intermediate frequency; the signal in a superheterodyne which appears at the output of the first detector.

I-f alignment. The process of tuning the resonant circuits in the i-f strip to their proper frequencies.

I-f strip. The intermediate frequency amplifier stages in a superheterodyne.

I-f trimmer. A small variable capacitor in an i-f amplifier resonant circuit of an AM broadcast band receiver.

IFF. Identification, friend or foe; a method of challenge through radar.

ILS. Instrument landing system; a navigational device for aircraft.

Image interference. A failing peculiar to superheterodynes in which two stations separated by a frequency equal to twice the i-f of the receiver may be simultaneously received.

Image orthicon. A highly sensitive television camera tube.

Inductance. The electrical property of a coil of wire.

Insulation. A nonconducting material.

Integer. A whole number.

Integrator. A resistor-condenser circuit at the input to the vertical oscillator in a TV receiver.

Intelligence. The meaningful signal impressed on a carrier wave.

Intercarrier signal. The 4.5 mc signal in a TV receiver.

Interelectrode capacitance. The effective capacitance between electrodes in a vacuum tube.

Interlock switch. An automatic safety circuit-breaker which cuts off the power when the high voltage cage in a TV receiver is opened.

Intermediate power amplifier. An r-f amplifier just ahead of the final power amplifier in a transmitter.

International code. The system used in radio telegraphy in which a group of dots and dashes stands for a letter of the alphabet.

Ion. An atom with an electric charge.

Ion trap. A permanent magnet clamped to the neck of a kinescope which prevents ions from striking the kinescope screen.

Ionosphere. The charged layer in the upper reaches of the earth's atmosphere.

Ips. Inches per second; the speed of tape movement in a recorder.

Junction. The interface between an N and P section in a semiconductor.

Kilocycle. One thousand cycles; abbreviated kc.

Kinescope. The writing tube in a television receiver which converts the picture signal into light.

Klystron. A uhf oscillator tube containing its own cavity resonator, which depends on the bunching of electrons for its operation.

Land. The flat surface between adjacent grooves in a phonograph record.

Leading edge. The initial rise of a square pulse.

Lighthouse tube. A uhf triode resembling a miniature lighthouse.

Limiter. An overdriven amplifier which, in the FM receiver, eliminates electrical noise from the i-f carrier.

Linearity controls. The TV receiver hand controls which help correct distortion in the picture.

Line of sight. As far as the eye can see; the range of very high frequency signals.

Load. A component developing a useful voltage.

Local oscillator. The front end oscillator in a superheterodyne.

Loran. Abbreviation for "long range navigation"; a hyperbolic system.

LP. Long-playing; a phonograph disc, finely cut, which is recorded and played back at a 33⅓ rpm speed.

Luminance signal. The signal controlling light values in the color TV receiver.

"Magic eye" tube. A vacuum tube, used as tuning indicator, which is controlled by avc voltage.

Magnetostriction. The expansion and contraction in length of the iron core of a coil through which an a-c current is passed.

Magnetron. A uhf diode oscillator containing its own cavity resonator in which electrons are whirled in a circular path by a magnetic field.

Main bang. The burst of r-f emitted by a radar antenna.

Marker pips. The pulses produced by a cursor oscillator.

Mask. The device in the three-gun color TV picture tube which helps restrict each beam to the phosphor dot of its own color.

Master oscillator. The carrier-generating stage of a transmitter.

Mechanical differential. A mechanical device in analog computers which provides an output mechanical rotation equal to the sum or difference of two input rotations.

Megacycle. One million cycles; abbreviated mc.

Mercury vapor tube. A tube containing a small pool of mercury.

Microphone. A device which converts sound into an audio signal.

Microsecond. A millionth of a second; a time interval often used in electronics.

Midrange speaker. A loudspeaker which best reproduces sounds in the medium audible range.

Miniature tube. A small glass tube generally used in receivers.

Modulator. The stage in a transmitter which varies the wave shape of the master oscillator output.

Molecule. A group of atoms.

Monaural. One-eared; a single-channeled sound system.

Monitor. A TV receiver in the control room of a TV transmitting studio.

Monitoring. Checking a newly made recording by listening to its playback.

MOPA. Master oscillator-power amplifier; a two-stage CW transmitter.

Multivibrator. A relaxation oscillator used in the sync circuits of a television receiver.

Negative feedback. Same as *degenerative feedback.*

Negative frequency deviation. A drop of the FM carrier below the resting frequency.

NOT circuit. A logic circuit of digital computers which inverts an input pulse signal.

N-P-N. A transistor composed of two N-type crystals separated by a P-type.

N-type. A semiconductor crystal doped to provide excess electrons.

Nucleus. The center of an atom.

Null. A zero or minimum voltage.

Octal tube. A tube with a standard eight-pin base.

One-shot multivibrator. A multivibrator which goes through only one cycle when triggered.

Oscillator. A circuit which emits electromagnetic waves.

Oscillograph. A test instrument using a writing tube which shows the wave shape of an input voltage.

Oscilloscope. Same as *oscillograph.*

Overcutting. Erratic cutting of a master disc in which adjacent grooves intersect.

Overdriving. Applying an excessive signal to an amplifier tube.

Output transformer. A step-down, iron core transformer between the output tube and the speaker voice coil in a receiver.

Oxide. A chemical coating usually applied to the electron-producing element in an electronic tube.

PA. Public address; an amplifying system for large audiences.

Pentagrid converter. A converter tube with five grids.

Pentode. A tube containing five active elements.

Persistence. The length of time in which the fluorescent screen of a writing tube holds the written image.

Phase inverter. An amplifier which supplies a positive and negative half-cycle of output for every half-cycle of input voltage.

Phase modulation. An indirect method of FM transmission in which the phase of the carrier is changed in accordance with the audio signal.

Phasemeter. A device which measures the phase of an a-c signal.

Phosphor dots. Elements in the screen of the color TV picture tube which glow in the three primary colors.

Photocathode. The electrode in the image orthicon which emits the electron image when struck by light from the televised object.

Photocell. A vacuum tube which converts light into electrical energy.

Pickup arm. The pivoted arm, in a phonograph, which holds the cartridge and playback needle.

Picture carrier. The television carrier modulated by the video signal.

Piezoelectric crystal. A crystal which converts mechanical pressure into an electrical signal or converts a signal into pressure.

Pitch axis. The straight line joining the wing tips of an aircraft.

Plate. The metal element in a vacuum tube which collects the electron stream.

Plate modulation. Same as *Heising modulation.*

Plumbing. The term applied to waveguides and cavities in uhf equipment.

PM speaker. A speaker in which the constant magnetic field is supplied by a permament magnet.

P-N-P. A transistor composed of two P-type crystals separated by an N-type.

Port. A hole cut in the front of a bass reflex enclosure to permit air inside the enclosure to circulate to the front.

Positive frequency deviation. A change in the FM carrier to a frequency higher than its resting frequency.

Potential. The degree of electrification of a body.

Potentiometer. A three-terminal variable resistor.

Powdered iron core. A coil or transformer core containing powdered iron.

Power amplifier. A tube or circuit designed to amplify both voltage and current.

Power supply. An electronic circuit which converts an input a-c voltage into an output d-c voltage.

PPI. Plan position indicator; a type of radar scope on which the map of the area surrounding the radar antenna is plotted.

Preamplifier. A one- or two-stage amplifier required to strengthen the output of a weak electrical device to the point where it can drive a main amplifier.

Precession. The rotation of a gyro around its output axis as the result of an applied torque about its input axis.

Prf. Pulse repetition frequency; the number of pulses made by the radar transmitter per second.

Prf switch. The switch in the radar set which governs the pulse rate frequency.

Primary. The input winding of a transformer.

Primary colors. The basic tints of color television: red, green, blue.

P-type. A semiconductor crystal doped to provide excess holes.

Pulsating d-c. An electric current which flows in a single direction and varies in intensity.

Pulse. A voltage which rises and falls abruptly.

Pulse generator. The circuit in a TV transmitter which generates the basic timing pulses for blanking and sync.

Pulse width. The time duration, in microseconds, of the pulse.

Push-pull amplifier. A double-ended amplifier often used as the power output stage in an audio amplifier system.

Quartz crystal. A piezoelectric crystal which regulates an oscillator frequency.

Radar. A means of determining the direction and range of an object through the use of electromagnetic waves.

Radar beacon. A radio transmitter which automatically responds to a transmitted pulse.

Radio direction finder. A radio receiver with a special antenna capable of locating the direction of a transmitter; a navigation device.

Raster. The bright white glow which covers the television screen when no signal is received.

Ratio detector. The duo-diode detector used in most modern FM receivers.

Reactance modulator. A circuit capable of acting as a variable capacitor. A second variety of reactance modulator acts as a variable inductance or coil.

Rear end. The receiver circuits following the detector.

Recording head. The device, in tape or disc equipment, which contains the electrical recording device.

Reflector. The dish or similar device which in radar equipment reflects the main bang outward from the horn or reflects the echo bursts into the horn.

Regenerative feedback. A type of feedback in which the returned output signal is in phase with the input signal.

Relaxation oscillator. An oscillator whose output steadily rises and then quickly drops.

Reluctance. The opposition, in a magnetic circuit, to flux.

Remote cutoff pentode. A type of pentode in which an unusually high negative grid voltage is required to drive the tube into cutoff.

Reproducing head. The playback head in a tape recorder.

Resistor. A component which opposes the flow of a-c and d-c current.

Resonance. Sympathetic electrical vibration of a circuit to a signal.

Resonant circuit. A circuit in resonance.

Resting frequency. The frequency of the unmodulated FM carrier.

Reverse bias. A voltage applied to a P-N crystal such that the positive terminal of the voltage is applied to the N section and the negative to the P section.

R-f. Radio frequency; the frequency of a received carrier signal.

RIAA. An equalizer for the playback of modern phonograph records.

Ribbon lead-in. The two-conductor wire interconnecting the dipole antenna and the front end of the TV receiver.

Ribbon microphone. A high fidelity microphone in which the vibration of a thin metal ribbon in a magnetic field generates the audio signal.

Riding gain. The process, in making a recording, of varying the volume control of the amplifier to keep the amplitude of the audio signal at a reasonable level.

Rise time. The time, in microseconds, taken by a pulse to rise from zero to its maximum level.

Rpm. Revolutions per minute.

Rumble. A bassy, growling sound heard in a playback on a poor phonograph turntable.

Runway localizer. The transmitter, in the ILS, which sets the runway path for the homing aircraft.

Sapphire stylus. A sapphire-tipped record-player needle.

Saturation. The condition in a tube or semiconductor in which maximum current flows.

Schematic. A drawing using conventional symbols which shows the connection of components in a circuit.

Scope. Common term for a writing tube.

Screen. The electrode just beyond the control grid in a tetrode or pentode.

Sea return. Interference on the scope of a sea-going radar set caused by reflections from water waves.

Search mode. The operation of a radar set scouting for enemy craft.

Secondary. The output winding of a transformer.

Secondary emission. Electrons knocked out of a metal by incident primary electrons.

Second detector. The detector in the superheterodyne which extracts the audio signal from the modulated i-f carrier.

Selectivity. The ability of a receiver to choose a particular carrier.

Semiconductor. A material which partially conducts an electric current.

Sensing antenna. A vertical conductor which, together with the loop antenna, forms the cardioid.

Sequence switch. The stage in an active sonar system which controls transmitted and received signals.

Servomechanism. A self-correcting device which converts an electrical signal into a mechanical shaft rotation.

Sharp cutoff tube. An amplifier which provides high amplification but is prone to overloading.

Shielding. A method of preventing interaction between circuits by surrounding the circuits with metal plates.

Shoran. Abbreviation for "short range navigation," a triangulation navigational device.

Short waves. International AM broadcasting in the frequency vicinity of 20–30 mc.

Side band. The range of frequencies above and below the unmodulated carrier put out by a transmitter.

Side frequency. A single frequency in the side band.

Sine wave. A perfectly formed electromagnetic wave with no harmonics.

Single-ended amplifier. A single-stage amplifier using one tube.

Sky wave. A radio wave which travels through space rather than along the ground.

Slave. A piece of electronic gear under the control of signals from a master equipment.

Slug tuning. Tuning a resonant circuit by varying the powdered iron core of the coil.

Snow. The flaky appearance of a television picture indicating high noise level.

Sonar. Abbreviation for "sound navigation and range"; an instrument for undersea navigation and detection.

Sonic. Relating to sound.

Sound carrier. The television carrier modulated by the audio signal.

Sound strip. The stages in a TV receiver concerned with the sound program.

Speaker. A device which converts audio into sound; short for "loudspeaker."

Speaker diaphragm. The vibrating element of a speaker.

Stabilizing capacitor. The large capacitor which steadies the operation of the ratio detector.

Stabilizing resistor. An unbypassed resistor in the cathode circuit of an i-f amplifier tube which helps keep the tube from being overloaded.

Stagger tuning. A method used in TV and radar receivers of broadening the i-f band, in which the resonant circuits of the i-f strip are tuned to various points in the i-f band width.

Static. Natural or man-made noises of electrical origin.

Station selector. The receiver device which chooses a particular carrier.

Step-down transformer. A component consisting of two coupled coils in which the output voltage is less than the input voltage.

Step-up transformer. A component consisting of two coupled coils in which the output voltage is greater than the input voltage.

Stereophonic. Giving the illusion of three-dimensional sound.

Strobe. Short for "stroboscope," a device containing a rapidly blinking light.

Stylus. The cutting needle which, in the recording process, etches the grooves of a record master; also used for the playback needle of a phonograph.

Sunspots. Electrical disturbances in the sun which affect the ionosphere and so affect radio communication.

Superheterodyne. A receiver in which carrier frequencies at the forward end are reduced through heterodyning.

Suppressor. The grid between screen and plate in the pentode.

SW-BC switch. The switch on some AM receivers which set the receiver for either standard broadcast or short wave reception.

Sweep circuits. The circuits in equipment containing a writing tube which guide the movement of the beam in the tube.

Synchro control transformer. A shafted device with one rotor and three stator coils in which the a-c voltage developed across the rotor is equal to the difference between an input signal and an input shaft rotation.

Synchro differential generator. A shafted device with three rotor stator coils which produces a three-terminal output signal equal to the sum or difference of an input signal and an input shaft rotation.

Synchro differential motor. A shafted device with three rotor and three stator coils which produces a shaft rotation equal to the sum or difference of two input signals.

Synchro generator. A shafted electronic component which emits a low frequency a-c signal proportional to the angle of rotation of its shaft.

Synchro motor. The reverse of a synchro generator; this device converts a 60 or 400 cycle per second signal into a proportional rotation of its shaft.

Sync. Short for "synchronism" or "synchronization."

Sync circuits. The circuits in radar and television which control the movements of the scope beam.

Sync clipper. The stage in the TV receiver sync circuits which removes sync pulses from the video signal; same as *sync separator.*

Sync pulse. An electrical pulse transmitted to a slave circuit by the master equipment to operate the slave in synchronism with the master.

Sync separator. Same as *sync clipper.*

Take-up reel. The motor-driven reel in the tape recorder on which the tape winds.

Tank circuit. A resonant circuit of coil and capacitor.

Tape. A strip of nonconducting material with a coating of iron oxide used for magnetic recording.

Tape recorder. A device used for magnetic recording.

Target. The surface struck by the electron beam in a writing tube.

Target screen. The fine screen near the image orthicon target which takes up secondary electrons emitted by the target.

Telemetering. The exchange of guidance and other informational signals between earth stations and satellites or guided missiles.

Tertiary. The third winding of the transformer interlinking the last i-f stage with the ratio detector in an FM receiver.

Test tape. A tape of alternating black and white squares used for testing the speed of travel of tape in a recorder.

Tetrode. A tube containing four active elements.

Thyratron. A triode gas tube.

Tickler coil. The plate circuit coil in the Armstrong oscillator.

Timer. The stages in the radar transmitter which control the synchronization function.

Tone control. A circuit for setting the bass or treble response of an amplifier to the listener's satisfaction.

Torque. A force exerted on a rigid body which results in the rotation of that body around one of its axes.

T-r. Transmit-receiver; the switch in the radar duplexer.

Tracking. The adjustment of a superheterodyne front end to insure the uniformity of the receiver's i-f over the whole range of the dial.

Tracking mode. The operation of a radar set following the progress of an enemy ship.

Trailing edge. The drop in voltage at the end of a pulse.

Transducer. In general, a device which converts one kind of energy into another.

Transformer. A component made up of two or more coils wound around the same core.

Transistor. A three-element semiconductor device consisting of emitter, base, and collector.

Transistor tetrode. A transistor in which an extra terminal is supplied to the base.

Transmitter. Equipment for radiating electromagnetic waves.

Transponder. Same as *radar beacon.*

Trap, 4.5 mc. A coil-condenser circuit resonant to 4.5 mc which separates sound and sight signals in the TV receiver.

Treble. The high frequency tones in sound.

Trf. Tuned radio frequency; a radio receiver in which the forward end consists only of tuned radio frequency amplifier stages.

Trio. Neighboring red, blue, and green phosphor dots in the screen of the color TV picture tube.

Triode. A tube containing three active elements.

Tripler. A circuit which multiplies the frequency of an input signal by three.

Tuner. A radio receiver without an audio amplifier; also

the tuning system in a receiver.

Turnstile antenna. The antenna, consisting of crossed dipoles, of a TV or FM transmitter.

Turntable. The rotating metal base disc of a phonograph.

Tweeter. A small speaker which best reproduces treble tones.

Uhf. Ultra-high frequency; the frequencies, roughly, in the 100 to 10,000 mc range.

Ultrasonic. Of a frequency higher than the audible range.

Variable capacitor. A capacitor consisting of two inter-meshing sets of metal plates.

Variable-mu tube. Same as *remote cutoff pentode.*

Variable reluctance cartridge. A phonograph pickup cartridge in which the varying reluctance in a magnetic circuit produces the audio signal.

Vertical blanking pulse. The pulse which cuts off the kinescope scanning beam when a field is completed.

Vertical oscillator. The relaxation oscillator in the vertical sync circuit of the TV receiver.

Vertical output stage. The power amplifier stage in the TV receiver's vertical sync circuit.

Vertical sync pulses. The series of pulses which controls the TV receiver's vertical and horizontal oscillators.

Vertically-deflecting coils. The deflecting coils of a writing tube which exert an up and down force on the writing beam.

Vertically-deflecting plates. The deflecting plates in a writing tube which exert an up and down force on the writing beam.

Vestigial side band filter. The filter in a TV transmitter which cuts a two mc portion from the band width of the transmitted picture carrier.

Vestigial side band transmission. Transmission of the TV signal in which a portion of the lower side band is cut off.

Vhf. Very high frequency; the frequencies, roughly, in the 10 to 100 mc range.

Video carrier. Same as *picture carrier.*

Video signal. An electrical signal corresponding to light.

Voice coil. The coil of few turns around the cylindrical extension of the PM speaker cone.

Voltage. Electromotive force; the electrical force required to push current through a circuit.

Voltage regulation. The ability of a power supply to keep its output d-c voltage steady though drawing varying currents.

VOR. Very high frequency omnidirectional radio range; a device to aid aircraft in locating their home base.

Waveguides. Hollow metal tubes used to interconnect points in uhf equipment.

Wave length. The distance (usually given in meters or centimeters) between the peaks of two consecutive waves in a wave train.

Width control. The TV receiver hand control which varies the width of the picture.

Woofer. A large speaker which best reproduces bass tones.

Word. A group of bits.

Wow. The slow variation of tonal pitch in a poor recording.

Writing tube. A special type of vacuum tube in which an electron beam automatically writes or scans information on a target.

Yaw axis. A vertical line through the fuselage of an aircraft, and perpendicular to the plane of the pitch and roll axes.

Zener. A semiconductor diode which, under reverse bias, is capable of conducting heavy currents.